Voyages to Saturn

Voyager 2 looked at the underside of Saturn's rings as it sped away from the planet.

NASA SP–451

Voyages to Saturn

David Morrison

NASA Scientific and Technical Information Branch 1982
National Aeronautics and Space Administration
Washington, DC

For sale by the Superintendent of Documents
U.S. Government Printing Office, Washington, D.C. 20402
Library of Congress Catalog Card Number 81-600073

Foreword

The Voyager spacecraft were outstanding successes in their serial flybys of Saturn—returning far more new information than had been collected in three centuries of Earth observation. It would be well to remember that these are risky ventures, involving intricate mechanisms dispatched hundreds of millions of miles to perform subtle and delicate measurements, traversing immense distances of cold, dark, airless space, and surviving unexplored fields of particles and magnetic force.

That we can confidently plan and execute such ventures is testimony to the power of high technology well and artfully employed. It indicates that the academic community, the Federal Government, and American industry can work together in these landmark enterprises with a comity (and mutual advantage) not always found in ordinary associations.

December 1981

James M. Beggs
Administrator
National Aeronautics and Space Administration

Acknowledgment

The author is grateful to the many members of the Voyager Project team, the Jet Propulsion Laboratory Public Information Office, and the NASA Scientific and Technical Information Branch who offered assistance and encouragement in the preparation and publication of this book, and to a number of colleagues who provided helpful comments on parts of the manuscript. Among many too numerous to name individually, I particularly wish to thank M.H. Acuna, J.K. Alexander, G.A. Briggs, S.A. Collins, L.E. Edwards, J. Koch, A.L. Lane, J. Loudon, E.D. Miner, N.F. Ness, F.L. Scarf, L. Soderblom, B.A. Smith, E.C. Stone, J.L. Ward, and J.J. Van der Woude.

Contents

The Ringed Planet

Of all the wandering stars called planets by ancient peoples, Saturn is the faintest and moves most slowly against the stellar tapestry. As long as 2500 years ago, people recognized that Saturn marked the outer limits of the visible solar system. In spite of its great distance from Earth, Saturn has come to symbolize all the planets. Its beautiful rings, discovered in the seventeenth century, give it a unique majesty, and no one who has seen Saturn through a moderately large telescope is likely to forget the experience. Even after faint rings were discovered around Jupiter and Uranus in the 1970s, Saturn retained its special place in our imaginations as *the* ringed planet.

Saturn is the second largest planet, with a diameter of 120 000 kilometers; only Jupiter is larger. Nearly 800 Earths could fit inside Saturn, yet its mass is only about 100 times that of Earth, indicating that Saturn has a much lower density. In fact, Saturn is the only planet with a density of less than 1 gram per cubic centimeter: Saturn would float in water! Saturn has such a low density because it is a gas planet with a huge atmosphere of hydrogen and helium. Of course,

the ancient peoples who first saw it as a bright star and followed its slow motion against the background of fixed stars did not think of Saturn as a place at all.

Naked-Eye Observations

The earliest systematic recorded observations of Saturn and the other planets were made in the first millennium B.C. in the Mesopotamian empires of Assyria and Babylon. Later, during the Hellenistic period, observers and theorists in Greece, Asia Minor, and North Africa developed several elaborate cosmological theories to describe and explain the motions of the planets, including the suggestion that the planets circled the Sun rather than the Earth (the heliocentric theory). These Greek scholars made remarkable progress in describing and predicting the apparent motion of the Sun and planets. However, at the same time the people of the ancient world began to associate the planets with events on Earth and with the gods who were believed to influence human life. The planet Saturn came to be identified with the ancient Greek god Cronus, the father of Zeus. The Romans, who named the planet Saturn, associated it with their god of sowing, and at the time of the winter solstice they held a great festival, the Saturnalia, in his honor. The Greco-Roman astrological systems associated Saturn with age, poverty, and deformity, and asserted that the planet's position in the sky at the time of a person's birth could affect his personality and influence his life. Today there are no Cronus- and Saturn-worshippers, but strangely the 2000-year-old ideas of astrology persist.

From the fall of the Roman Empire to the time of Copernicus, little progress in astronomy was made in the European world. Only in the Islamic nations stretching from Central Asia to Spain and in the Imperial Courts of China were observations of the planets made and astronomical theories debated. In the sixteenth century European astronomy reasserted itself: In Poland Nicolaus Copernicus developed the theory of heliocentric planetary motion; the Danish astronomer Tycho Brahe systematically recorded accurate observations of the planets; and Johannes Kepler, a German, discovered the mathematical laws of planetary motion. Then, in the first decade of the seventeenth century, Galileo Galilei, in Italy, used the newly invented telescope to observe the skies, and the modern science of astronomy was born.

Galileo, Huygens, and Cassini

In July 1610 at Padua, Galileo first observed Saturn with his telescope. What he saw mystified him, for Saturn appeared to have appendages or companions on either side. In a letter to the Grand Duke of Tuscany, Galileo wrote, ''The fact is that the planet Saturn is not one alone but is composed of three, which almost touch one another and never move nor change with respect to one another. They are arranged in a line parallel to the zodiac, and the middle one is about three times the size of the lateral ones.'' At first Galileo thought that these companions might be large satellites similar to the satellites of Jupiter he had discovered a few months before. However, since the companions did not move or change in brightness, Galileo knew that this phenomenon was unlike any he had encountered in his observations of the other planets.

Two years later the situation became even more confused when Galileo found he could no longer see the two companions of Saturn. This result so shocked him that he questioned whether his telescopic observations were providing a true picture of the heavens. In December 1612 he wrote, ''I do not know what to say in a case so surprising, so unlooked for, and so novel. The shortness of the time, the unexpected nature of the event, the weakness of my understanding, and the fear of being mistaken have greatly confounded me.'' The next year, however, Galileo again saw the two companions, and soon other observers detected the appendages on either side of Saturn. For nearly 40 years this strange aspect of the planet was seen and recorded by astronomers without any reasonable explanation being offered.

In 1655 the Dutch observer and instrument maker Christian Huygens, just 26 years old, found the solution to the puzzle of the appendages of Saturn. With an improved telescope he was able to see that the appendages were part of a continuous bright ring of material surrounding

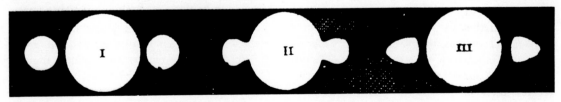

Early telescopic drawings of Saturn made before the true nature of the rings was understood. These drawings were made I by Galileo (1610), II by Scheiner (1614), and III by Riccio (1641). From Systema Saturnium, *1659.*

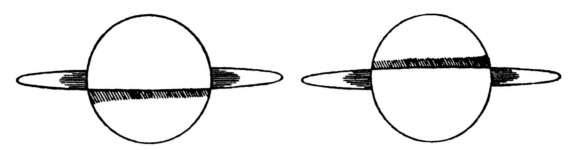

Saturn as seen by Christian Huygens in 1655 and 1656. Huygens was the first to recognize that the ring was a continuous band separated from the planet. (Left) The south side of the rings. (Right) The north side of the rings. From Systema Saturnium.

the planet. He described his discovery in a Latin anagram that may be translated, "It is surrounded by a thin, flat ring, nowhere touching and inclined to the ecliptic." Huygens recognized that the variation in the appearance of Saturn was caused by variations in the apparent tilt of the ring. The rotational pole of Saturn is inclined 27 degrees to the orbital plane. Since the rings gird the planet in its equatorial plane, they too are inclined 27 degrees. From the Earth, the rings appear open when Saturn is in the part of its orbit corresponding to summer or winter, that is, when the poles are tipped toward the Sun and Earth. But as Saturn approaches the equinoxes of its orbit, the rings appear slimmer and are more difficult to see. Huygens realized that the disappearance of the appendages noted by Galileo in 1612 occurred when the Earth was in the plane of the rings, an event that occurred approximately every 15 years. Huygens also discovered the largest satellite of Saturn, Titan, which he found to revolve around the planet in the same plane as the ring with a period of about 2 weeks.

Titan was the sixth planetary satellite to be discovered, following the four Galilean satellites of Jupiter and Earth's Moon. (We use the term "satellite" rather than "moon" for a body that orbits a planet to avoid confusion with the Moon, our own satellite.) Titan, larger than the planet Mercury, is a substantial world in its own right. We now know that its diameter and mass are close to that of Jupiter's largest satellite, Ganymede. Titan was the first satellite of Saturn to be discovered because it is the largest. One difference be-

tween the Saturnian and Jovian satellite systems is the fact that Titan is so much larger than its neighbors, whereas four of Jupiter's satellites are planet-sized worlds.

The next great seventeenth century observer of Saturn was an Italian, Jean Dominique Cassini, who moved to France at the invitation of King Louis XIV to supervise the new Paris Observatory, becoming its first director and a naturalized French citizen. In 1671 Cassini discovered a second satellite of Saturn, Iapetus, and a year later a third, Rhea. Iapetus could be seen clearly when it was on one side of Saturn, but on the opposite part of its orbit it was invisible. Cassini correctly deduced the cause of this strange phenomenon: Iapetus always keeps the same face toward Saturn and is much less reflective on its leading hemisphere than on its trailing hemisphere.

The first hint of structure within the supposedly solid ring of Saturn was found by Cassini in 1675 in the form of an apparent division about two-thirds of the way out in the ring. This gap is now known as the Cassini Division. The ring outside the gap is called the A Ring, and the brighter ring inside is the B Ring.

In 1684 Cassini discovered two more satellites of Saturn, now known as Dione and Tethys. The mythological satellite names were suggested at the beginning of the nineteenth century. Cassini wished to name the four satellites he had discovered after his patron, King Louis XIV, just as Galileo had wanted to name the four large satellites of Jupiter for the Medici family of Florence. In the mythological nomenclature that eventually prevailed, all the satellites of Saturn are named for the Titans and the Giants, the children of Cronus.

The Mystery of the Rings

Most astronomers of the seventeenth and eighteenth centuries believed that the rings of Saturn were solid bands of material, although Cassini had suggested that they were formed of a swarm of small satellites in orbit around the planet. In 1785 the French mathematician Pierre Simon de Laplace calculated that a solid ring would be disrupted by gravitational tides from Saturn. Laplace suggested that the two broad visible rings must each consist of many narrower solid rings separated by small gaps, similar to the large Cassini Division, but too small to be seen with existing telescopes. In spite of its artificiality Laplace's theory was widely accepted for about half a century.

The greatest observer of the late eighteenth century was the Englishman William Herschel, discoverer of the planet Uranus. In 1789 Herschel discovered two more inner satellites of Saturn, Enceladus and Mimas, bringing the total to seven. Herschel was one of the first to emphasize the extreme thinness of the Saturn ring system, estimating that the rings must be no more than about 500 kilometers thick.

The fully open rings of Saturn as drawn by J. D. Cassini in 1676. This is the first representation of the Cassini Division between the outer A Ring and the brighter B Ring.

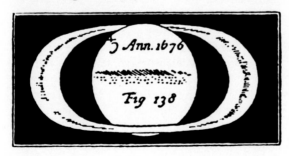

Herschel studied the planet Saturn as well as its rings and satellites. He described faint, dusky bands on the disk. From the changes in these bands he concluded that, as in the case of Jupiter, they were atmospheric features and not markings on a solid surface. He also computed a rotational period for Saturn of 10 hours, 16 minutes, a remarkably accurate result considering the absence of clearly defined spots whose motion could be timed. The absence of discrete cloud features (such as the Great Red Spot or the white ovals on Jupiter) continued to frustrate observers of Saturn throughout the nineteenth century, making it impossible to determine an accurate rotation period for the planet.

In 1850 a new inner ring of Saturn was discovered independently in America and in England. The American observers were William C. Bond and George P. Bond of Harvard Observatory; the Englishman was an amateur astronomer, the Reverend William Rutter Dawes. They observed a faint, dusky ring extending inward from the B Ring about halfway to the apparent surface of Saturn. The most remarkable aspect of the new ring was that it was largely transparent, and the disk of Saturn could clearly be seen through it. This discovery did not seem consistent with the theory that the rings were solid.

Until the middle of the nineteenth century, astronomers had no idea how such a strange phenomenon as the rings of Saturn might have originated. In 1848 the French mathematician Edouard Roche calculated that if a satellite were brought too close to a large planet, it would be disrupted by tidal forces into a great many smaller bodies. The distance at which such a disruption would take place corresponded approximately to the position of the rings. Roche suggested that the rings of Saturn had originated from the destruction of a satellite and that they were made up of the millions of fragments of this catastrophic event.

The question of the solidity of the rings was finally settled in 1857 in response to a prize offered by the University of Cambridge for an essay on the following problem: "To determine the extent

Ring Gaps and Resonances

For more than a century, ever since astronomers first recognized that the rings of Saturn were composed of billions of individual moonlets in orbit around the planet, scientists have sought an explanation for the sharp boundaries of the rings and for the Cassini Division between the A and B Rings. Why should the individual orbits of so many tiny particles line up to produce these apparently sharp edges? The most common explanation involves the theory of satellite ring resonances. In effect, it postulates that the ring particles are held in specific orbits by the gravitational pull of the major satellites of Saturn.

The resonance theory states the following: If two particles are at different distances from Saturn, they will travel at different speeds and complete one circuit of the planet in different times. Suppose that the particles are spaced such that the inner particle completes two trips around Saturn in exactly the same length of time that the outer particle, or satellite, makes one trip. Then, once in each two orbits for the inner one, or once in each orbit for the outer, they will line up and feel each other's gravitational pull. If the orbital periods are not exact multiples of each other, the gravitational pulls will be in one direction one time, another direction another time, and the effects will average out. But when the periods are simple multiples of each other, the pulls occur each time in the same direction in the same part of the orbit. If the inner particle is one of the ring particles and the outer one a major satellite, the inner particle tends to have its eccentricity increased; that is, its orbit becomes less circular and it has a greater chance of bumping into one of its neighbors. Thus it is postulated that a ring particle at a distance from Saturn that corresponds to a simple resonance with a satellite will be more likely to suffer collisions and ultimately be either broken up or moved into another orbit.

The Cassini Division is located at a distance from Saturn at which two satellite resonances exist. A particle moving in the Cassini Division has a period exactly one-half as long as that of Mimas and one-third as long as that of Enceladus. It was suggested many years ago that the Cassini Division was probably caused by the resonant gravitational interactions of its particles with Mimas and Enceladus. Another resonance might produce the boundary between the B and C Rings, which corresponds to a period just one-third that of Mimas. Unfortunately, no simple resonance can be correlated with the sharp outer boundary of the A Ring. Also, no obvious resonance appeared to account for the briefly glimpsed Division within the A Ring.

More complicated gravitational resonances might also affect the orbits of the ring particles. Some of these depend on the small eccentricities in the orbit of the satellite rather than on a simple fractional relationship between the periods.

In general, the idea that satellite resonances defined the boundaries of the rings was accepted by astronomers until 1977, when the ring system of the planet Uranus was discovered. The rings of Uranus are very different from those of Saturn: they appear black, being composed of very dark particles rather than the bright, icy snowballs of the Saturn rings. But more startling, the rings of Uranus are not broad, flat planes of material; they are thin and ribbon-like, no more than a few tens of kilometers across. Whereas the Saturn system might be described as rings with a few gaps, the Uranus system is gaps with only a few rings. Clearly, some new explanation was required for the rings of Uranus. One suggestion was that there were embedded within the rings many small, invisible satellites that were large enough to provide a gravitational herding effect, keeping the particles in the rings from wandering too far out of their orbits. In 1979 the situation was complicated even further by the discovery of the fairly narrow ring surrounding Jupiter and by the Pioneer Saturn discovery outside the A Ring of the thin F Ring, whose dimensions were more like those of the ribbon rings of Uranus than the more familiar broad rings of Saturn.

It was with great anticipation that dynamicists awaited the first detailed Voyager photographs of the rings of Saturn. Would new gaps be seen, and, if so, would these correspond to satellite resonances? Or would small satellites be discovered, either embedded within the rings or orbiting on their edges, as had been suggested in the case of Uranus? Less confident that they understood the rings of Saturn since the discovery of the very different ring systems of Jupiter and Uranus, astronomers were prepared for surprises from the Voyager 1 encounter. As described in the final chapter, the Voyager results appear to confirm the importance of resonances for some of the major gaps, but the fantastic structure in the rings revealed in the new photographs clearly demands other explanations as well.

to which the stability and appearance of Saturn's rings would be consistent with alternative opinions about their nature, whether they are rigid or fluid, or made up of masses of matter not mutually coherent.'' The prize was won by the young Scottish physicist James Clerk Maxwell, who developed a mathematical argument to show that even a very thin solid ring was unstable and would be torn apart by gravitational forces. Thus the possibility that the rings might be solid was finally rejected. Maxwell also showed that the rings could not be fluid and concluded that the only reasonable hypothesis was that the rings consisted of a vast multitude of small satellites too small to be seen individually, but collectively giving the appearance of a continuous ring. Each tiny satellite would follow its own orbit around Saturn, with the inner ones moving faster than those farther out (the opposite of a solid ring, for which the outer rim would move faster than the inner). In 1895 James E. Keeler, at the Allegheny Observatory in Pittsburgh, Pennsylvania, used a photographic spectroscope to measure directly the rotation speeds at different parts of the rings, demonstrating the effect predicted by Maxwell. Keeler found velocities of rotation varying from 20 kilometers per second at the inner edge of Ring B to just under 16 kilometers per second at the outer edge of Ring A.

Two more small satellites of Saturn were discovered during the nineteenth century. In 1848 George Bond in the United States and William Lassell, an English amateur astronomer, discovered Hyperion circling Saturn in a rather eccentric orbit between Titan and Iapetus. The ninth satellite, Phoebe, was discovered in 1898 by William Pickering, working at Harvard Observatory's southern hemisphere observing station in Peru. Phoebe is the outermost known satellite of Saturn, orbiting with a retrograde motion 13 million kilometers from the planet. Both Hyperion and Phoebe are smaller than the other known satellites, and Phoebe is suspected to be a captured asteroid.

Early in the twentieth century the fact that the rings could not be seen in even the largest telescopes on the day the Earth passed through the ring plane led to better estimates of the thickness of the rings. These analyses showed that the rings could not be more than 15 kilometers thick, suggesting that the total volume of particles in the rings was small compared to that of even a single large satellite.

One of the last great visual observers of Saturn was the French astronomer Bernard Lyot. His drawings, made from observations with the 61-centimeter aperture telescope at the Pic-du-Midi Observatory high in the French Pyrenees, showed considerable structure in the rings. Particularly prominent was a gap near the outer edge of the A Ring, often called the Keeler or Encke Division (see note on page 55). This Division is one of the most difficult features to see on the rings, requiring an extremely steady image and a sharp eye. Because of the inevitable atmospheric blurring that takes place during a photographic exposure, the Division has never been captured on film. Lyot also reported additional ring structure, including a division between the B Ring and the fainter C Ring. However, at this time there were very few astronomers in the world specializing in the study of the planets.

The New Astrophysics

During the first half of the twentieth century, most astronomers turned their attention primarily to investigations of stars and galaxies. The construction of large new telescopes, improvements in photographic and spectrographic instruments, and especially the application of physical laws to astronomical problems generated the new field of astrophysics. For the first time scientists could formulate reliable theories on the chemical composition of stars, the interior nuclear processes that provided their energy, their clustering into giant island universes, and the large-scale expansion of the universe. Amid the many triumphs of astrophysics, only a few astronomers attempted to apply the new instruments and techniques to study the planets and their rings and satellites.

One of the first products of the astrophysical study of the outer planets was the spectroscopic

The finest pre-Voyager representation of the rings of Saturn was made by Bernard Lyot from visual observations obtained in 1943 with the 61-centimeter refractor at the Pic-du-Midi Observatory. Considerable structure is shown in both the A and B Rings. Note the Division near the outer edge of the A Ring; it was never photographed from Earth but is clearly seen in the Voyager photographs. From The Planet Saturn *by A.F.O'D. Alexander. Used by permission of Dover Publications, Inc.*

discovery on Saturn in 1932 of the gases methane and ammonia, which are the simplest compounds of carbon and nitrogen with hydrogen. The presence of dark absorption lines in the spectra of the outer planets had been known for some time, but their identification with these simple molecules was primarily the work of Rupert Wildt of Yale University. Noting the low densities of the outer planets and the presence of methane and ammonia, Wildt developed a hypothesis for the structure of Jupiter and Saturn that has formed the basis for modern thinking about the giant planets. Wildt proposed that these planets, because of their large size and the great distance from the Sun at which they formed, had been able to retain the cosmically abundant gases hydrogen and helium, as well as the heavier elements more common on Earth. He suggested that Saturn must have an Earth-like rocky and metallic core surrounded by a thick layer of ices of water, ammonia, and methane, surmounted in turn by a hydrogen-rich atmosphere. Thus Saturn, as well as Jupiter, Uranus, and Neptune, were hypothesized to be great gas bags consisting largely of atmosphere, with perhaps no solid surface beneath the thousands of kilometers of dense gas and shifting clouds.

In the winter of 1943-1944, a startling new discovery about Saturn's largest satellite, Titan, was made by the Dutch-American astronomer Gerard P. Kuiper, observing with the 2.1-meter telescope of the McDonald Observatory in Texas. Kuiper obtained photographic spectra in the infrared as well as the visible wavelengths of light. The spectra showed the characteristic absorption bands of methane on Titan, clearly indicating that this satellite possessed an atmosphere, something no other satellite was known to have. Kuiper also measured the size of Titan, a difficult task because of its great distance from Earth, and found that it was apparently the largest satellite in the solar system.

As astronomical instrumentation improved, so did the ability of astronomers to define the thickness of Saturn's rings from data obtained when the rings were seen nearly edge-on. In 1966 observers around the world coordinated their efforts to obtain an excellent record of the changing brightness of the rings, hour by hour, around the time of ring plane crossing. Subsequent analysis of these data by Soviet astronomer M. S. Bobrov set an upper limit for the thickness of the rings of only 3 kilometers. Bobrov also calculated that the particles within the rings were distributed in such a way that their typical separation was about 10 times their diameter.

During the 1966 ring plane crossing, observers took advantage of the faintness of the rings and the absence of light scattered from them to search close to Saturn for indications of faint satellites or other rings. At least two new satellites were discovered near the outer edge of Ring A—the

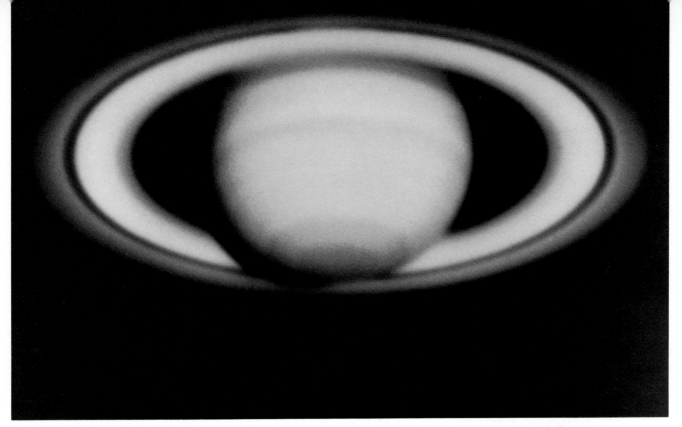

One of the best photographs of Saturn and its rings ever taken from Earth. The rings are fully open in this photo from the early 1970s, taken with the 1.5-meter telescope of the Catalina Observatory of the University of Arizona. The resolution is about 2000 kilometers—sufficient to show the Cassini Division clearly but not to reveal the narrower Keeler Division. Photo courtesy of the University of Arizona.

first by French astronomer Audouin Dollfus, the second by University of Arizona astronomers Stephen Larson and John Fountain. One of these two satellites was informally given the name Janus and is often listed as a tenth satellite of Saturn. However, the observations extended over only a few weeks, and did not permit determination of the exact orbit for either satellite; thus the final naming was deferred 15 years until another ring plane crossing would permit further observation. As it happened, the year of the next ring plane crossing (1980) was the year in which the Voyager 1 spacecraft made its flyby of Saturn, providing many additional opportunities to observe the two small satellites.

A new, outer ring was discovered photographically during the 1966 ring plane crossing. W. A. Feibelman at the Allegheny Observatory took a single, 30-minute exposure in which Saturn and the known rings were completely overexposed. Far from the planet a faint new ring was visible, only about a millionth as bright as the A, B, or C rings. The new ring extended out 400 000

kilometers from Saturn; its inner edge was lost in the glare of the overexposed image of the planet. The ring was also photographed at about the same time at the University of Arizona. In 1969 still another faint ring, interior to the C Ring, was photographed by Pierre Guérin at the Pic-du-Midi Observatory. This ring was designated Ring D, and the faint outer ring was called Ring E. (The rings were named in the order of their discovery, not in the order of their relative positions.)

The Rebirth of Planetary Astronomy

Reflecting the entrance of many young astronomers into the field of planetary studies, as well as stimulation provided by the launching of planetary space probes by the United States and the USSR, a renaissance in planetary science took place during the 1970s. Suddenly there was renewed interest in all the planets.

In 1970 infrared observations of the rings of Saturn made by Kuiper and his colleagues at the

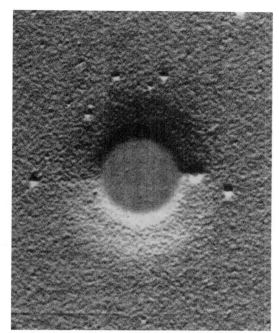

Discovery photograph of the faint E Ring of Saturn, obtained during the 1966 ring plane crossing. The planet Saturn and its A, B, and C Rings are completely overexposed in this 30-minute exposure from the Allegheny Observatory. The E Ring is seen as a line extending beyond the overexposed central image in these two versions of the original photo, specially processed by the JPL Image Processing Lab to reveal faint linear features. Photo courtesy of W. A. Feibelman, NASA Goddard Space Flight Center.

University of Arizona with a new NASA-supported telescope provided the first key to understanding the composition of the ring particles. As interpreted by Carl B. Pilcher and his colleagues at the Massachusetts Institute of Technology, the spectra showed that the particles in the rings were composed of plain water ice with, at most, a small contamination by darker rocky material. In 1971 the first measurement of the temperature of the ring particles was made from infrared observations—it was a frigid – 190° C. At the same time, several attempts to detect similar thermal emissions from the rings at longer radio wavelengths indicated much lower apparent temperatures. The ring particles may really have been at – 190° C, but it seemed that they were not very good emitters of radio radiation, suggesting that most of the particles were relatively small, no more than 1 meter in diameter.

Particles of submeter size are neither good emitters nor good reflectors of radio-wave energy; they do not interact readily with microwaves. Thus it was with considerable surprise that the

first attempt to measure the radar reflectivity of Saturn, by Richard Goldstein of the Cal Tech Jet Propulsion Laboratory, in 1973, yielded a strong return signal from the rings. A great deal of theoretical analysis was required to explain the peculiar ability of small particles to react so strongly with radar waves. Eventually it was concluded by James B. Pollock of the NASA-Ames Research Center and other theorists that the only way to produce simultaneously the effects obtained from radio and radar waves was for the rings to be made up of small particles composed of nearly pure water ice. The typical diameter of one of these particles was perhaps 10 or 20 centimeters—a rather large snowball. Thus, by the mid-1970s, it was widely agreed that the ring particles not only had icy surfaces, but were composed entirely of ice.

Titan became the subject of a great deal of excitement in 1972 when infrared temperature measurements showed this satellite to be surprisingly warm, as much as 60° C hotter than would be expected for a body in equilibrium with the

The Kuiper Airborne Observatory (KAO), a unique infrared astronomical facility operated by NASA. Flying at altitudes above most of the terrestrial atmosphere, the KAO permits studies to be made in parts of the spectrum that are inaccessible to ground-based telescopes. Observations from the KAO's 1-meter telescope were important in establishing that Saturn has an internal heat source and in probing the upper atmosphere of Titan.

sunlight falling on it at that distance from the Sun. Apparently at least some parts of the atmosphere of Titan were relatively hot. At about the same time, optical polarization measurements of Titan made by Joseph Veverka of Cornell University indicated that the light we see coming from the satellite is not reflected from a solid surface but from an opaque layer of clouds in the atmosphere.

Suddenly it seemed possible that the atmosphere of Titan, known since Kuiper's discovery of methane in 1944, might be significantly more massive than had been suspected. Several astronomers went so far as to suggest that the high infrared temperatures of Titan were the result of a massive greenhouse effect in its atmosphere, similar to the greenhouse effect that so drastically heats the surface of Venus. The possible combination of a warm surface with the presence of organic compounds such as methane was of great interest to exobiologists. Here was an object that might, even today, be mimicking the conditions under which life arose on Earth. Titan, it was argued, might hold vital clues to the early chemical and biological evolution of the solar system. These ideas received further support

when infrared spectra of the atmosphere showed emissions by a number of simple hydrocarbons such as ethane and acetylene. Here was just the kind of organic soup believed to be required for the origin of life.

A number of models were developed by theorists to illustrate the range of surface conditions that might exist on Titan. (Each model is essentially a self-consistent quantitative description that does not violate any of the constraints imposed by observations, such as the measured infrared temperatures.) One extreme was represented by the cold surface models, originally suggested by Robert E. Danielson of Princeton University. In these models, the only gas in the atmosphere was methane, the clouds were near the surface or perhaps not present at all, and the atmosphere had a surface pressure of only 20 millibars, or 2 percent of the sea-level pressure on Earth. At the other extreme were massive atmosphere models that postulated a deep but unseen atmosphere below the opaque clouds. In some models the atmosphere contained hydrogen and ammonia as well as methane, and a greenhouse effect raised the surface temperature high enough to permit cold "oceans" of ammonia-water solutions. Another version, developed by Donald M. Hunten of the University of Arizona, postulated nitrogen as the primary atmospheric constituent. Hunten suggested that the clouds were condensed methane at a temperature of about − 200° C. Above the main cloud deck, sunlight was absorbed by a thin haze or smog, heating the thin upper atmosphere to produce the high temperatures. Below the clouds the temperature and pressure increased with depth. The bottom of the clouds was at a pressure of about 1 bar and a temperature of about − 175° C, but in Hunten's model the atmosphere itself could be much deeper, possibly 100 kilometers, which would lead to a surface temperature of − 75° C and a pressure of 21 bars!

An important constraint on these models was provided in 1979 when John Caldwell of the State University of New York and his colleagues used the newly completed Very Large Array (VLA) radio telescope in New Mexico to penetrate the clouds of Titan and measured a surface temperature of about − 190° C. This value appeared to preclude the models with the most massive atmospheres and the highest surface pressures, but a wide range of possibilities remained, including models in which the atmosphere of Titan was greater than that of Earth—a remarkable prospect for a "mere" satellite.

The smaller satellites of Saturn were also the focus of considerable study during the 1970s. In 1975 groups of astronomers led by David Morrison and Dale Cruikshank of the University of Hawaii and Uwe Fink of the University of Arizona used infrared observations to identify water ice or frost as the primary surface constituent on Rhea,

The very large array (VLA) radio telescope of the National Radio Astronomy Observatory, located near Socorro, New Mexico. The individual receivers, working together as a single giant radio telescope, can produce images of the radio sky with resolutions that rival optical astronomy. John Caldwell and his colleagues used the VLA in 1979 to measure the surface temperature of Titan at − 190° C, a value that excluded the possibility that a massive greenhouse effect was generating a warm surface beneath the clouds of the satellite. Photo courtesy of the National Radio Astronomy Observatory and the National Science Foundation.

Mauna Kea Observatory of the University of Hawaii, one of the leading optical observatories where modern astrophysical studies of the planets are being carried out. Astronomers have used facilities located atop the 4200-meter extinct volcano to study the surface compositions of the satellites of Saturn, the temperatures of satellites and rings, and the composition and structure of the atmospheres of Saturn and Titan. Photo courtesy of the University of Hawaii.

The 64-meter radar telescope of the JPL Goldstone Tracking Station in California's Mohave Desert. Normally used for tracking and communication with spacecraft, this facility can also be operated as a radio or a radar telescope. Richard Goldstein and his colleagues used this telescope in 1973 to make the first radar detection of Saturn's rings, which proved to be remarkably efficient reflectors of microwaves.

Dione, Tethys, Enceladus, and the bright (trailing) hemisphere of Iapetus. Several indirect techniques also provided moderately good values for the size and mass of some of these satellites which suggested that they had low densities—perhaps as low as 1.0 gram per cubic centimeter—and a bulk composition dominated by ice.

Peculiar Iapetus naturally attracted the attention of observers, who concluded that the dark leading hemisphere had a reflectivity of less than 10 percent, that the bright surface material extended over the poles, and that the boundaries between the light and dark hemispheres were very sharp and were aligned closely with the motion of the satellite; that is, the dark side faced precisely forward in the orbit, the bright side precisely backward. No convincing explanations were suggested for the unique contrasts between the two hemispheres of this satellite.

Although somewhat smaller and less dense than Jupiter, Saturn was expected to possess an atmosphere similar to the Jovian one. Both planets were presumed to have predominantly hydrogen and helium atmospheres, with traces of methane, ammonia, and water, and an upper cloud deck of frozen ammonia cirrus. But telescopic images showed that the two planets did not look alike. Saturn presented a frustratingly bland countenance, unlike Jupiter's contrasting belts and zones, its many light and dark cloud features, and its Great Red Spot. NASA supported an extensive effort to photograph Saturn and the other planets from the best observatory sites, but years of effort yielded almost no evidence of discrete atmospheric features on Saturn. It seemed enveloped in a uniform shroud of haze, and even its rotation period remained uncertain by ten minutes or so.

In 1969 astronomers using infrared techniques discovered that Jupiter was warmer than it would be if it were in equilibrium with the incident sunlight, indicating that the planet had a substantial internal heat source. At the same time, observations suggested that Saturn might also have an internal heat source. But the observations of Saturn were harder to interpret because of the thermal radiation from the rings. To determine whether Saturn had an internal heat source, it was necessary to correct for the emission of the rings. The ring correction could be made theoretically, by calculating how much radiation should be coming from the rings, or empirically, by waiting until the rings were nearly edge-on (in 1979 and 1980) and therefore not contributing observable energy. By the late 1970s, both approaches had been used, and astronomers were convinced that Saturn really did have an internal heat source comparable to that of Jupiter. Theorists suggested that the main energy source in both planets was the escape of deep interior heat generated more

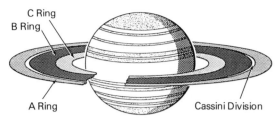

Prespacecraft nomenclature for Saturn and its rings. Only three rings are shown: the A Ring, B Ring, and C Ring, with the Cassini Division separating the A and B Rings.

than four billion years ago when the planet first formed, but it was also proposed that Saturn might have an additional energy source from the gravitational separation of hydrogen and helium in its core. However, a more accurate value for the total heat budget was needed to test these ideas.

Jupiter and Saturn were also compared in regard to their magnetic fields. The magnetic field of Jupiter and the charged atomic particles trapped in it had been discovered from measurements of the radio-wave radiation emitted in the planet's magnetosphere. Did Saturn have a similar magnetosphere? Presumably, even if it did, the charged particles in the inner magnetosphere would be absorbed by collisions with the rings, and the radio emitting areas would be correspondingly reduced. The radio emissions might also be shifted to very long wavelengths, which could not penetrate the ionosphere of the Earth. Searches by ground-based radio telescopes were unsuccessful, but in 1975 a few long-wave radio bursts from the direction of Saturn were detected by the IMP-6 Earth satellite. These observations suggested that Saturn had a magnetosphere, but better understanding would require direct measurements by spacecraft-borne instruments.

By the mid-1970s, the Pioneer 10 and 11 spacecraft had reached Jupiter, and Pioneer 11 was targeted to continue to Saturn, to arrive in 1979. The Voyager 1 and 2 spacecraft, with Saturn their primary target, were scheduled for launch in 1977. Thus, even while a strong program of ground-based investigation of the Saturn system continued, increasing attention was directed to the first spacecraft observations of the ringed planet and its retinue of satellites.

Pioneer to Saturn

The space age dawned in 1957 with the launch of Sputnik 1, the first artificial satellite, followed within five years by many more spacecraft, including a flyby of Venus by the first interplanetary spacecraft, Mariner 2. Additional United States Mariner missions to the planets followed, with exploratory visits to Mars in 1964 and 1969, returns to Venus in 1965 and 1974, a first reconnaissance of Mercury in 1974, and an extremely successful Mars orbiter in 1971. In the same period the USSR sent a dozen spacecraft to Mars and Venus and successfully landed instrumented probes on the surface of Venus. These missions, in addition to the extensive exploration of the Moon carried out in preparation for the Apollo landings, provided a revolutionary new perspective on our sister worlds in the inner solar system. But what of the giant gas planets, separated by immense distances, floating in the deep cold of the outer solar system? Could we reach them too? By the late 1960s, NASA scientists and engineers were determined to try.

Several barriers stood in the way of a successful exploration of the outer solar system. The most difficult to overcome was the vast distance which necessitated larger rockets and much more reliable, automatic spacecraft that could spend years unattended in space and still provide flawless operation as they reached a remote world. Other barriers included the difficulties of communicating over such vast distances and the lack of a satisfactory solar power source so far from the Sun. It was clear that a new generation of spacecraft employing fundamental advances in electronics, power sources, communications, and reliability would be required to reach to Jupiter, Saturn, and beyond.

Jupiter, the nearest of the giant planets, was a logical first target; Saturn and more distant planets at first seemed beyond our reach. Then, in the late 1960s, scientists began to find solutions that opened up the more distant reaches of the solar system. In any gravitational encounter between two bodies—a planet and a spacecraft, for instance—one will lose energy and the other will gain it. Why not aim a spacecraft to fly past Jupiter in just the right way to gain speed and receive a boost toward the next target, Saturn? In this way, the launch vehicle requirements and travel times to distant objects were greatly reduced. A launch at the time of the appropriate planetary configuration and careful navigation would ensure that the gravitational boost would be just right to provide the correct trajectory to the second target.

In the late 1970s, all the outer planets would lie in a rough alignment, inspiring mission planners to link several gravity-assisted encounters, so that a single spacecraft could explore three or four planets, gaining energy from each encounter to speed it on to its next target. This concept of a series of multiplanet flights was named the Outer Planets Grand Tour, and NASA hoped to initiate the missions for launch between 1977 and 1979.

The essential first step in the Grand Tour was a flyby of Jupiter. In addition to the distance, which was much greater than had been dealt with in previous planetary missions, a spacecraft to Jupiter would encounter two other potentially serious problems: the asteroid belt and the Jovian magnetosphere. The asteroids are small planets that orbit the Sun between Mars and Jupiter; it was feared that this region of space might contain so much debris that a lethal impact would be likely for any spacecraft bound for the outer solar system. The Jovian magnetosphere, like that of Earth, contains energetic electrons, protons, and heavy ions trapped in the planet's magnetic field; calculations of the resulting radiation suggested that the delicate electronic parts of a spacecraft might be "cooked." The first step in any program of exploration beyond Mars was to assess these potential dangers. The Pioneer Project was created to carry out this pathfinding task.

The Pioneer Mission

The Pioneer Jupiter Mission began in 1969. Its objectives were to explore the interplanetary medium beyond Mars, to assess the hazards of the asteroid belt, and to explore the magnetosphere of Jupiter. At that time, no one imagined that Pioneer would also provide our first visit to Saturn, nearly twice as far from Earth as Jupiter.

The Pioneer Project was assigned by NASA to its Ames Research Center near San Francisco, with

The Pioneer missions were controlled from NASA's Ames Research Center near Palo Alto, California. In addition to its work on the Pioneer spacecraft, Ames has led in the NASA development of direct entry probes for the atmospheres of Venus and Jupiter and carries out major life sciences research. Ames is also one of the most important NASA centers for aeronautical research and development.

Charles F. Hall as Project Manager and magnetospheric physicist John H. Wolfe as Project Scientist. The spacecraft, designed for simplicity and reliability, was based on a series of successful Earth-orbiting probes. Unlike the Mariner spacecraft used for investigation of the inner planets, the Pioneers rotated several times per minute around an axis pointed toward Earth. In addition to providing stability, this arrangement ensured that the disk-shaped communications antenna remained aligned toward Earth. It was ideal for particles and fields instruments—those designed to measure the magnetic fields and charged particles in the immediate vicinity of the spacecraft. The spinning design allowed these instruments to point successively in many directions, so that they could accurately characterize the trajectories of the charged particles, moving with the magnetic fields in space. A spinning spacecraft does not, however, provide a good base for optical instruments, which must remain pointed toward a

The two Pioneer spacecraft were designed and fabricated by TRW Systems Group at their Redondo Beach, California, facility. Each weighed about 260 kilograms and carried a set of sophisticated instruments for the scientific investigation of Jupiter and Saturn and of interplanetary space. Data systems on board controlled the instrumentation, received and processed commands, and transmitted information across the vast distance to Earth.

distant target. Pioneer carried three optical instruments, but these were of secondary importance.

Each Pioneer spacecraft—designated after launch as Pioneers 10 and 11—had a mass of 258 kilograms and was about the size of a large kitchen range. Since sunlight would be so weak in the outer solar system, the spacecraft carried their own specially developed power sources—radioisotope thermoelectric generators (RTGs) that provided 140 watts of power. The launch vehicle was

an Atlas-Centaur rocket equipped with an additional solid-propellant third stage. This powerful combination could accelerate the spacecraft to a speed of more than 50 000 kilometers per hour, the highest speed ever reached by an interplanetary spacecraft.

Control and communication over distances of nearly a billion kilometers constituted major challenges for the Pioneer Jupiter team. The light travel time imposed an inevitable lag between events at the spacecraft and receipt of a radio signal on Earth. It was decided, however, not to undertake the difficult task of designing an autonomous spacecraft (as the later Voyagers would be), but to learn to operate with ground control in spite of the round-trip time lag of 90 minutes for Jupiter and nearly three hours for Saturn.

The same radio link that transmitted instructions from Earth-based controllers also carried the data from the spacecraft instruments back to the waiting scientists. The transmitter power was only 8 watts. The incredibly weak signals received on Earth were picked up by the giant 64-meter-diameter antennas of three NASA Deep Space Tracking Stations in California, Australia, and Spain, and were relayed from there to Ames Research Center. The weaker the signal, the more slowly the data must be transmitted to ensure the necessary data quality. From Jupiter, Pioneer transmitted at 2048 data bits per second, while from Saturn the rate was partly 512 and partly 1024 bits per second.

Equipment for eleven scientific investigations was carried on Pioneer, providing a 25-kilogram payload of instruments. These instruments were chosen competitively from proposals submitted to NASA in 1969 by scientists from universities, industry, NASA laboratories, and from abroad. Seven of the instruments selected measured particles and fields, two investigated meteoroidal debris near the spacecraft, three carried out remote sensing observations of Jupiter and its environment, and two made use of the spacecraft itself to carry out scientific investigations.

Less than three years after the start of the Pioneer Project, the first spacecraft was ready for launch from the Kennedy Space Center at Cape

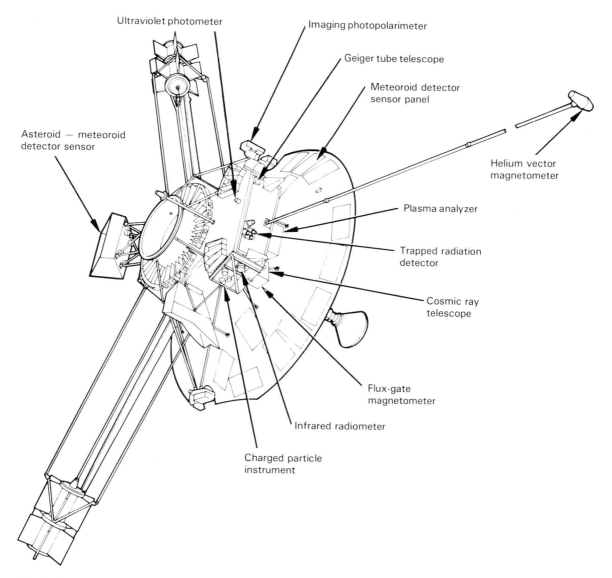

Ultraviolet photometer

Imaging photopolarimeter

Geiger tube telescope

Meteoroid detector
sensor panel

Asteroid — meteoroid
detector sensor

Helium vector
magnetometer

Plasma analyzer

Trapped radiation
detector

Cosmic ray
telescope

Flux-gate
magnetometer

Infrared radiometer

Charged particle
instrument

Twelve instruments were carried on board the Pioneer Saturn spacecraft. Seven of these were designed to measure particles and fields, two recorded small particles, and three were remote sensing instruments designed to study Jupiter, Saturn, and their rings and satellites.

Canaveral, Florida. Pioneer 10 began its historic journey toward Jupiter on March 2, 1972. The second spacecraft was to wait more than a year before launch, so that the results from Pioneer 10 could be used in the selection of a trajectory for Pioneer 11's Jupiter flyby. This interval between the launches of the two spacecraft was to play a crucial role in the ultimate decision to send the se-

cond spacecraft on to Saturn. Pioneer 11 was finally launched on April 5, 1973, to begin its billion-kilometer, two-year flight to Jupiter.

Encounters With Jupiter

In July 1972 Pioneer 10 entered the asteroid belt, the first major supposed barrier to outer

17

solar system exploration. To the relief of all, no danger in the small debris was detected, and the spacecraft emerged unscathed in February 1973. A year later, Pioneer 11 made an equally uneventful transit of the asteroid belt. The pathway to the outer solar system was open! The Pioneers were halfway to their goals, but there remained the major challenge of the potentially lethal magnetosphere of Jupiter.

On November 26, 1973, Pioneer 10 began its encounter with the giant planet. At a distance of 8.5 million kilometers—109 Jupiter radii (R_J)—the spacecraft sensed an abrupt change in its environment. It had reached the bow shock, the region where the supersonic solar wind of outward-flowing charged particles is suddenly slowed to subsonic speed by the impending barrier of the Jovian magnetosphere. The next day, at 96 R_J, Pioneer 10 crossed the magnetopause—the boundary of the magnetosphere—and began to measure directly the planet's magnetic field and trapped particles.

During the last days of November, as the spacecraft penetrated nearer and nearer the planet, the level of trapped radiation increased. A week after first entering the magnetosphere, Pioneer 10 was plunging directly into the maelstrom of the intense inner radiation belts. Several instruments saturated and their measurements went off scale. The intense blast of x-rays and gamma rays induced by collisions with energetic charged particles resulted in false computer commands, as the electronics teetered near the edge of breakdown. But no major failures occurred, and on December 3, at a distance of just 130 000 kilometers from the cloud tops, Pioneer 10 passed its closest approach to Jupiter and began its return toward calmer waters. The little spacecraft had passed its most severe test with flying colors, laying the foundation on which all subsequent missions to Jupiter would be built.

At the same time that the particles and fields instruments on Pioneer 10 were analyzing the magnetosphere, the three optical instruments were observing Jupiter and its satellites. The photopolarimeter, operating as a line-scan camera, built up photographs of the planet showing individual features as small as 500 kilometers

across and providing new insight into the complex motions of the Jovian atmosphere. An infrared instrument measured the thermal output of Jupiter, verifying that the planet had an internal heat source of some 10^{17} watts (a hundred billion megawatts) in addition to the energy provided by absorbed sunlight. This instrument also measured helium in Jupiter's atmosphere. The ultraviolet photometer mapped glows, presumably arising from hydrogen gas, coming from Jupiter and from a large region near its innermost large satellite, Io. Analysis of the spacecraft trajectory provided information on the fluid interior of Jupiter, and the magnetometer data mapped out the planet's magnetic field.

The trajectory of Pioneer 10 was chosen not only to measure the intense inner radiation belts but also to probe the atmospheres of Jupiter and Io. As seen from Earth, the spacecraft passed behind, or was occulted by, each object. The changes induced in the radio signal as a result of passing through the ionosphere or neutral atmosphere provided a powerful means of deducing the structure of the atmosphere. One result of the Pioneer 10 occultation experiment was the discovery of an unexpected tenuous atmosphere surrounding Io. After its flyby of Jupiter, Pioneer 10 continued outward, the first spacecraft to explore the space beyond Jupiter and, ultimately, the first to leave the solar system entirely.

Pioneer 11 approached Jupiter just a year after Pioneer 10. In the meantime, the Pioneer 10 data on the magnetosphere had been analyzed, and project officials felt confident that they could select a new and in many ways more demanding trajectory for Pioneer 11. It had been calculated that, if Pioneer 11 flew close enough to Jupiter, its orbit could be bent back on itself; in this way the spacecraft could be redirected toward Saturn, on nearly the other side of the solar system. This was not an ideal way to reach Saturn—indeed, the alignment could hardly have been worse—but it allowed the possibility that Pioneer 11 would be the first spacecraft to reach the ringed planet. In spite of the risks, the Pioneer engineers and scientists had confidence that their sturdy craft could meet this challenge, which greatly exceeded the original objectives of the Pioneer program.

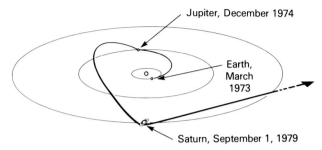

The trajectory of Pioneer Saturn required a two-billion-kilometer trip across the solar system. Following its launch in 1973, this spacecraft traveled outward to Jupiter, arriving late in 1974. Following a retrograde flyby of Jupiter, the spacecraft traveled nearly across the solar system to its historic encounter with Saturn in 1979. After the Saturn encounter, the Pioneer spacecraft continued to move outward, ultimately to escape entirely from the Sun's gravity.

Because Saturn was on the other side of the Sun from Jupiter, it was necessary to use the gravity of Jupiter to slow the Pioneer 11 spacecraft so that it would drop back toward the Sun. To accomplish this, the spacecraft was targeted to swing around Jupiter in a retrograde sense, from front to back. The large change in energy necessitated a very close flyby—closer than that of the first Pioneer. To penetrate so deeply into the radiation belts without overtaxing the spacecraft, the mission directors chose a path that cut across the Jovian equatorial plane at a high angle. Since most of the magnetospheric energetic particles were near the equator, this oblique trajectory actually produced a smaller total radiation dose, even though the peak intensity exceeded that experienced by Pioneer 10. This high-inclination orbit also provided a glimpse of the polar regions of Jupiter and a sampling of the magnetospheric structure at high latitudes.

On November 26, 1974, Pioneer 11 crossed the Jovian bow shock. Closest approach to Jupiter, on December 2, was only 43 000 kilometers above the cloud tops. Ironically, the most serious threat to the success of the encounter developed not in space, but on Earth, where a strike by diesel generator operators at the Australian tracking sta-

tion almost caused the loss of six hours of unique data near closest approach. Like its predecessor, Pioneer 11 suffered radiation-induced problems during the hours of strongest exposure, but none of these resulted in permanent damage to the spacecraft or its scientific instruments.

The Pioneer 11 pictures of Jupiter were even more detailed than those of Pioneer 10. Studies of the Jovian polar areas provided new data on regions of the planet poorly seen from either the Earth or the later Voyager encounters, and a great deal was learned about the complex physics of the magnetosphere. Following the successful completion of its Jupiter investigations, Pioneer 11 was renamed Pioneer Saturn by NASA, and the Pioneer Project was formally extended to include a Saturn encounter five years later, in 1979.

Targeting at Saturn

From 1974 to 1979 Pioneer Saturn continued its particles and fields measurements of interplanetary space. The sling-shot effect of Jupiter's gravity had slowed it and lifted it out of the ecliptic plane into a region of the solar system never before studied by a space probe. By early 1976, when the spacecraft was about halfway along its trajectory between the two giant planets, it was more than 150 million kilometers (1 astronomical unit) north of the Sun. From this unique perspective, Pioneer discovered properties of the solar magnetic field that could not be detected from the plane of the planets.

During the long flight, problems developed with two of the Pioneer science instruments. Not long after the Jupiter encounter, occasional spurious electronic command signals began to appear, which, after several months of detective work, were attributed to problems in the circuits of one of the meteoroid-detection instruments. Since the damage could not be repaired, it was necessary to turn off the instrument. A more serious problem was the loss of the plasma detector. As part of the test sequence that eventually identified the source of the spurious commands, the plasma instrument was switched off and left in that mode for several days, allowing it to cool—by too much, as it turned out. When the

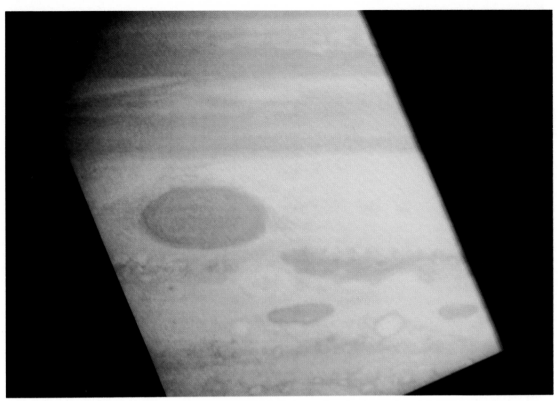

One of the best Pioneer images of Jupiter was obtained at a range of 545 000 kilometers by Pioneer 11. Structure within the Great Red Spot and the surrounding belts and zones can be seen. There was less turbulent cloud activity around the Spot at the times of the Pioneer flybys than was seen five years later by the Voyager cameras.

command to restart was sent, the plasma instrument did not respond. Further efforts to restore this important fields and particles detector were made, but to no effect.

The Jupiter flyby had aimed Pioneer in the general direction of Saturn, but several times during the long years of flight across the solar system it was necessary to use the onboard rocket to make small trajectory corrections. The nominal aimpoint was to one side of the planet and rings. By the end of 1977 it was necessary to decide exactly what sort of flyby would be the most scientifically productive. Several options were considered, including a plunge directly through the Cassini Division, but in the end two targeting choices came to the forefront, each with its own rationale and advocates.

The "inside" option provided the closest possible flyby of Saturn, and hence the greatest penetration of the magnetosphere. The aimpoint would be about midway between the inner edge of the C Ring and the cloud tops. The problem

with this trajectory was the danger of the ring plane crossing which would occur within the faint D Ring. Various estimates of the expected particle density in the D Ring suggested a low probability of spacecraft survival.

The greatest danger to the spacecraft would come from ring particles in the size range from about a millimeter to a centimeter—a grain of sand to a pea. At about 30 kilometers per second, the speed at which a collision with the spacecraft would take place, these particles would blast clear through the spacecraft structure; even one such impact could be lethal. Much smaller particles could not penetrate the skin of the spacecraft; if they were much larger they would be so widely spaced that there probably would not be any hits at all. Unfortunately, no one knew the typical size of the particles in the D Ring, so estimates of the chances of spacecraft survival ranged from less than 1 percent to greater than 99 percent.

The "outside" targeting option for Pioneer was at a point well outside the visible rings, at a distance of 2.9 Saturn radii (R_S) from the center of the planet. In addition to being considered much safer, this location was desirable because it was exactly the distance from Saturn at which Voyager 2 would have to cross the rings in 1981 if it were to continue to Uranus.

The question of which option would produce the most useful scientific results was complex. Either trajectory could tell something about the density of ring particles if it resulted in a catastrophic death of the spacecraft, but that seemed a high price to pay. The inside option could yield the most exciting results, but the advantage would be lost if an untimely end at ring plane crossing terminated the mission. After considerable debate, the twelve Pioneer Saturn Principal Investigators voted 11 to 1 for the inside option, arguing for the importance of this unique opportunity to make measurements close to the planet. There was a kind of bravura spirit that imbued this group who had been working together for more than a decade: If little Pioneer had survived so far against all the odds, why not go for broke? It just might make it through the D Ring, and, if not, at least the mission would end on a dramatic note.

Other considerations, however, favored the more conservative course. The primary scientific arguments for the outside option were based on the importance of the survival of the spacecraft, so that it could complete its investigations of Saturn and Titan (which would be missed entirely if the spacecraft were lost on ring plane crossing) and continue to measure interplanetary space beyond Saturn. In addition, Voyager Project officials argued for the importance of Pioneer's pathfinding role. They were worried about targeting Voyager 2 so close to the rings, and they felt that if any spacecraft were to be risked on this venture, it should be the Pioneer, already beyond its nominal lifetime, and not the more capable Voyager in the midst of its mission.

The final targeting decision was made in May 1978 by Tom Young, then the Director of Planetary Programs at NASA Headquarters. Overruling the recommendation of the Pioneer Principal Investigators, he selected the outside option as likely to provide a greater total scientific return from both Pioneer and Voyager. Thus Pioneer became, in a sense, the pathfinder to Uranus as well as to Jupiter and Saturn.

The final burn of the small rockets that adjusted the trajectory was made in July 1978. The target date for encounter was set for September 1, 1979; without this change in the flight path, the encounter would have taken place several days later, when radio interference from the Sun, nearby in the sky at this time of year, would have created problems for the spacecraft telemetry signal. The exact time of day was selected to permit redundant Earth coverage by the Deep Space Network stations in Australia and Spain during the most critical part of the encounter.

Early in 1979 Pioneer was well north of the ecliptic but descending rapidly toward Saturn, still more than 200 million kilometers away. At this part of Saturn's orbit, the rings were only slightly inclined to the Sun; a year later, they would appear exactly edge-on. The sunlight provided oblique illumination (at a 2 degree angle at encounter) of the southern face of the rings, while the spacecraft saw the northern face at an inclination of 6 degrees—a unique (if somewhat confusing) perspective that added considerably to the importance of the Pioneer images.

In the meantime, another fortunate event took place: the resurrection of the plasma instrument, which had been inoperative since April 1975. During October and November 1977, a special series of commands had been sent to Pioneer to try to overcome the damaged electronic switching circuits that were believed to be the source of the failure—the remote equivalent of kicking a recalcitrant machine. On December 3, 1977, the plasma instrument responded and returned to normal operation, ready to do its part in the first exploration of the magnetosphere of Saturn.

Encounter With Saturn

As the Pioneer spacecraft neared Saturn in August 1979, the primary scientific interest focused on the magnetic field and associated magnetosphere of the planet. Although there was some evidence of long-wave radio bursts detected near

Earth, the very existence of a magnetosphere was open to doubt. The question was not whether Saturn had a magnetic field—most investigators felt sure it did—but whether this field trapped many charged atomic particles. It seemed certain that charged particles entering the inner magnetosphere would collide with the rings and be eliminated. There might be interesting consequences of such collisions, such as the production of a tenuous atmosphere of water vapor from the icy material of the rings. If the faint but wide E Ring were real, the collisional sweeping up of magnetospheric particles could extend over most of the magnetosphere.

Another mystery concerned the interaction of Titan with the magnetosphere of Saturn. Here might be the unique situation of a satellite with a large atmosphere orbiting within a magnetosphere; atoms escaping from the atmosphere could possibly constitute a major source of charged particles, like the sulfur dioxide molecules from volcanoes on the Jovian satellite Io. Investigators wondered how strong the magnetic field was, and how large the magnetosphere might be. If it did not extend to the orbit of Titan, the situation would be very different. Theorists had developed a variety of alternative models for the magnetosphere of Saturn depending on whether Titan was inside or outside.

The Jovian magnetosphere had extended to about 100 R_J during the Pioneer encounters, but it had been compressed to only about 50 R_J during the Voyager encounters, which took place in a period of high solar wind pressure. Before Pioneer, the best guess was that Saturn's magnetosphere might be about half as large—perhaps in the range of 25–50 R_S. The radius of the orbit of Titan is 20 R_S. If the larger value were the true one, the Pioneer spacecraft would reach the bow shock on August 30, two days before encounter. Scientists anxiously watched the data from the particles and fields instruments all night and into the morning of August 31. As additional experimentors and members of the press arrived, everyone asked if there had been any sign of the bow shock. Could it be that Saturn had no magnetic field? Or was it simply that the high

pressure of the solar wind had compressed the magnetosphere more than had been expected?

Finally, at 7 a.m. on August 31, the first indication of the bow shock, at a distance of 24 R_S from the planet, was received at Ames. An hour and a half later, the shock, pushed inward by an increase in the solar pressure, passed the spacecraft, and Pioneer was again in interplanetary space. Not until a little after noon did it catch up with the bow shock. Finally, at about 5 p.m., Pioneer crossed the magnetopause—only 17 R_S from Saturn.

To the surprise of most scientists, Titan was outside the magnetosphere—or rather it would have been, had it been in the sunward facing part of its orbit. Subsequent calculations indicated, however, that this was an unusual case, caused by the very high level of activity on the Sun. Normally Titan would be inside the magnetosphere, and exceptions probably take place only occasionally, even during the peak years of the solar activity cycle.

During the last two or three days of August, while most of the investigators were preoccupied by the wait for the magnetosphere, the imaging polarimeter had begun to produce pictures of Saturn that exceeded in resolution any ever obtained from Earth. To the disappointment of experts on planetary atmospheres, however, the disk of Saturn revealed almost no detail. Clearly Saturn was very different from Jupiter; it lacked the striking alternation of dark belts and bright zones and the swirling, colorful storm systems that were so prominent on Jupiter.

The images of the rings proved more interesting. As seen by Pioneer, they were almost unrecognizable to astronomers accustomed to the usual view of the sunlit face. The Pioneer pictures, taken in light that diffused through to the unilluminated side, were almost a negative, with the normally brightest areas, such as the B Ring, appearing dark because of their opacity to transmitted light. The brightest parts of the rings as seen by Pioneer were the C Ring and the Cassini Division, both apparently containing just enough particles to transmit and scatter the sunlight back toward the spacecraft. Thus what was bright for

Pioneer were lightly populated parts of the rings. However, the areas that appeared dark were ambiguous—they could be regions that were opaque because of high particle density or regions that contained no particles at all to scatter the light. For example, the Pioneer investigators saw a dimmer region in the midst of the bright Cassini Division and thought it was an empty area; later it

Pioneer Saturn discovered a new ring—the F Ring—just a few thousand kilometers beyond the outer edge of the A Ring. This image obtained by the Pioneer photopolarimeter also shows a new satellite, provisionally called 1979S1. A few hours later the spacecraft nearly collided with the same satellite as it skimmed below the rings. It was later determined that 1979S1 was one of the two co-orbital satellites of Saturn first seen in 1966.

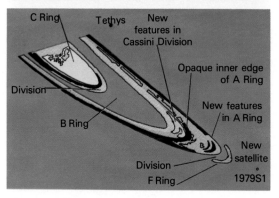

turned out that this dimming was the effect of more particles in the middle of the Division, not fewer.

Perhaps the most exciting Pioneer image was obtained just after midnight on September 1, at a range from the planet of about 1 million kilometers, providing a resolution of about 1000 kilometers. This picture revealed a narrow new ring, called the F Ring, about 3000 kilometers beyond the outer edge of the A Ring. The F Ring was not resolved in the Pioneer pictures; it could have been any width up to about 1000 kilometers. The narrowness of this ring set it off from the other Saturn rings and was reminiscent of the Jupiter ring discovered by Voyager, or perhaps the still narrower rings of Uranus.

The same picture that revealed the F Ring also showed a new satellite inside the orbit of Mimas. Both S-10 (sometimes called Janus) and S-11 had been seen in this region in 1966, but it was not clear at first whether the Pioneer object was one of these, or if so, which one. Thus it was given the provisional designation 1979S1, for the first new Saturn satellite discovered in 1979.

As Pioneer plunged closer and closer to Saturn, the ultraviolet and infrared instruments observed the planet and the space around it. Saturn showed up strongly in the long-wave ultraviolet channel, sensitive to a broad range of wavelengths that included the brightest line (Lyman α) of atomic hydrogen. A more diffuse glow was seen from a large region that included the orbit of Titan, and there was further evidence of emission from the region of the B Ring, possibly an indication of a tenuous atmosphere of water vapor and hydrogen. Thermal infrared emission from Saturn provided a first measurement of helium in the atmosphere and a value for the global temperature: −180° C. This temperature, although low by most standards, was substantially higher than would be expected from the effect of sunlight alone; it yielded a value for the internal heat source of Saturn that was relatively higher than that for Jupiter. Saturn, radiating more than twice as much heat as it received from the Sun, apparently had an additional internal energy source not acting on Jupiter.

The critical crossing of the ring plane was expected at a spacecraft time of about 9:02 a.m. on September 1, 1979. At that moment, collisions with ring particles, even 38 000 kilometers beyond the visible edge of the A Ring, might destroy the spacecraft, but it would not be until 86 minutes later (10:28 a.m.) that the radio waves would reach Earth and the scientists and engineers waiting at Mission Control would know the truth. As the "moment of truth" approached, a hushed silence fell over the watchers. The countdown to expected ring plane crossing was broadcast across the nation on public radio and television, as well as throughout the sprawling Ames Research Center. At 10:28 the radio signal continued to be received. Another slow minute was ticked off in case the original time estimate had been in error. Still the data flowed back from Pioneer and were received at the Deep Space Network station in the Mohave Desert and relayed to Ames. Finally, Project Manager Charlie Hall said he thought we had made it. There were scattered cheers and many sighs of relief. A few rueful comments were also made about not having tried for the target point inside the rings. But there was little time for either celebration or regrets, since Pioneer was now on the most crucial leg of its journey, exploring space near Saturn that would probably not be visited by spacecraft again in this century. The closest approach to Saturn, just 21 000 kilometers above the clouds, would take place in 29 minutes. The speed of Pioneer at this time would reach 114 000 kilometers per hour.

Near Collision With a Satellite

The Pioneer spacecraft, swinging under the rings to its closest approach to Saturn at a distance of 1.35 R_S, would traverse the part of the magnetosphere that was "shadowed" by the rings. Electrons and protons spiraling in Saturn's magnetic field should be depleted where the ring particles were densely packed or at the position corresponding to the orbit of a satellite. Thus a profile of the radiation belts should reveal the profile of solid material—rings or satellites—with a high level of sensitivity. James van Allen of the University of Iowa, the discoverer of the Earth's radiation belts, dubbed this technique "particle

beam astronomy." It was anticipated that a definitive search could be made for small satellites or faint rings near the outer edge of the visible ring system.

Between the orbits of Rhea (8.8 R_S) and Dione (6.3 R_S), the maximum intensity of low-energy magnetospheric electrons was detected. As Pioneer crossed the orbit of Dione, a sharp dip in intensity was recorded. But the electron counts recovered only slightly, then continued to drop rapidly as the spacecraft neared the orbit of Tethys at 4.9 R_S. Values remained low on both sides of Enceladus, perhaps indicating absorption by the diffuse E Ring. There was a small maximum outside the orbit of Mimas (3.1 R_S), and then a rise to a maximum at 2.7 R_S, very close to the supposed orbit of S-10 (Janus). A maximum was inconsistent with the presence of a satellite, indicating that the nominal orbit for this inner satellite was in error.

Additional structure was detected in the charged particles, including the indication of the F Ring. At 2.292 R_S, the edge of the A Ring, the counts of charged particles of all energies dropped to zero. In the magnetic shadow of the rings, Pioneer found itself in the most radiation-free environment it had experienced since it sat in its shroud on top of an Atlas-Centaur rocket at Cape Canaveral six years before. On the outbound journey, the same signatures of the rings and satellites were seen in the charged particle measurements. But in the midst of this orderly mapping out of the Saturn radiation belts, Pioneer was to have an adventure.

A few minutes after the ring plane crossing at 2.82 R_S, as the spacecraft traversed the region between the orbit of Mimas and the F Ring, it nearly collided with a large object! The evidence appeared, not in the imaging data, but in the records from the particles and fields detectors. At 2.53 R_S, the counting rates on several energetic particle detectors suddenly and dramatically dropped for about 8 seconds, accompanied by alterations in the magnetic field. Apparently the spacecraft had passed right through the magnetic wake of a satellite. From the duration of the dropout, scientists estimated the diameter of the unknown object at about 200 kilometers and the

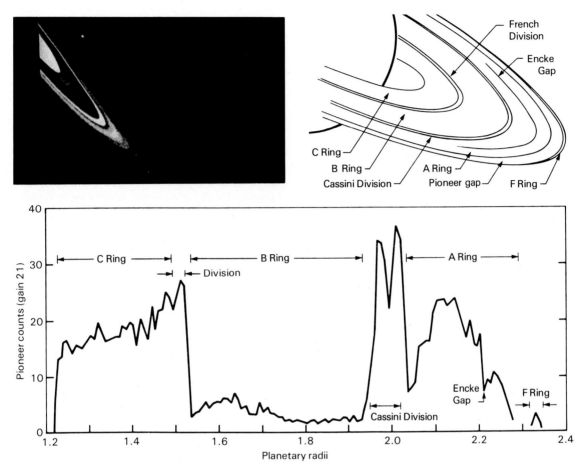

The Pioneer spacecraft was able to view the unilluminated side of the rings, providing a unique vantage point for their study. Seen from this angle, the brightest parts of the rings are those with a small number of particles, enough to scatter the sunlight but not so many as to make the rings appear opaque. The brightest region is the Cassini Division, with the C Ring only slightly dimmer. The least brightness corresponds to the opaque B Ring as well as to true gaps between the rings. The trace shows the brightness of the unilluminated side of the rings plotted against distance from Saturn, with an effective resolution of about 1000 kilometers.

miss distance at less than several thousand kilometers. At this time the spacecraft was only about 2000 kilometers below the ring plane, where the unknown object was almost certainly orbiting. The new satellite, at 2.53 R_S, was called 1979S2. The chances of such a near collision were extraordinarily small, but once again the Pioneer luck had resulted in a major and quite unexpected discovery.

New satellite 1979S1, photographed by the Pioneer imaging system the previous day, was also

at a distance from Saturn of 2.53 R_S, corresponding to an orbital period of 17 hours. A little "back of the envelope" arithmetic showed that this satellite would have made just one circuit of Saturn in the interval since it was first seen and would have been in about the right position to be intercepted by the spacecraft as it flew beneath the rings. Thus, almost certainly, satellite 1979S1 was the same as 1979S2: a new satellite of Saturn between Mimas and the F Ring, about 200 kilometers in diameter, with an orbital radius of 2.53 R_S.

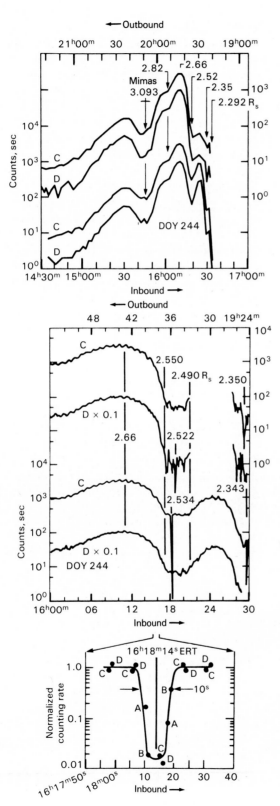

This new satellite was certainly real—so real it had almost brought Pioneer to a premature end—but apparently Janus was not. At least, the orbit indicated for Janus from the 1966 observations (with a radius of 2.65 R_S) was wrong. Many scientists guessed that the new satellite, which was bright enough that it should have been visible when the rings were edge-on in 1966, probably accounted for some and perhaps most of the earlier observations, but that errors had been made in deducing the orbit. New ground-based observations during the 1980 ring plane crossing would be required to resolve the ambiguity of the existing data.

The Surprising Magnetic Field of Saturn

Before the Pioneer encounter with Saturn, intrinsic magnetic fields had been discovered and analyzed on three planets: Earth, Mercury, and Jupiter. Pioneer found Saturn to be a fourth planetary magnet, intermediate in strength between Jupiter and Earth. Saturn's field was dipolar, with the north and south magnetic poles reversed (as are Jupiter's) compared to those of Earth. Saturn's magnetic field was found to be 500 times stronger than Earth's but 35 times weaker than

The particles and fields instruments on Pioneer Saturn were used to search for unknown satellites and rings by measuring the absorption of energetic charged particles. The top figure shows the profiles of charged particle intensities as the spacecraft moved toward and away from Saturn. Drops in the counting rates show the absorption by Mimas and several other possible rings or satellites closer to the planet. Also shown is a very sharp drop in particle count at 2.52 R_S. The middle figure shows the absorption in greater detail. The lower figure shows the eight-second absorption of 1979S2. Scientists concluded that this peculiar effect must have been the result of Pioneer Saturn's passage through the magnetic wake of an unknown satellite, apparently missing collision by no more than a few thousand kilometers. This feature was later determined to be 1979S1, the satellite discovered by photography on the previous day.

Jupiter's. These values refer to the total magnetic moment; at the surface of Saturn, which is much farther from the source than is the surface of Earth, the two fields have similar magnitude.

The most unexpected aspect of the magnetic field of Saturn was its close alignment with the rotational axis of the planet. The magnetic fields of Earth, Jupiter, and the Sun are tilted by about 10 degrees, and theorists had postulated that this difference between the magnetic and rotational axes was an important element of the internal dynamo process that generated the magnetic field. The discovery that Saturn's magnetic axis lines up almost exactly with the rotational axis necessitates a basic reexamination of the theory of planetary magnetism.

The magnetosphere of Saturn was unusually compressed during the Pioneer encounter, but even under normal conditions it would be substantially smaller than Jupiter's. In addition, the population of energetic particles—primarily electrons and protons—was found to be much smaller than in the Jovian radiation belts, primarily as a result of particle absorption by the satellites and rings. The belts are comparable in intensity to those of the Earth, but occupy a volume several thousand times larger than our own magnetosphere. Because of the alignment between the magnetic and rotation axes, the charged particles at Saturn do not experience the rotational wobble that characterizes the radiation belts of Jupiter and Earth.

Following its closest approach to Saturn on September 1, Pioneer Saturn retraced the route outward, continuing to skim just a few thousand kilometers beneath the rings. The view from the spacecraft would have been truly spectacular, but it was impossible to capture with the Pioneer imaging system. As seen from Earth, the spacecraft passed behind Saturn, and the radio occultation provided the first probe of the atmospheric structure of the planet, including the discovery of a rather thin ionosphere. A second ring plane crossing, at 2.78 R_S, took place two hours after closest

Looking toward Saturn, Pioneer photographed the dark side of the rings and the shadow of the rings against the planet. The edge of the disk can be clearly seen through the Cassini Division and the C Ring. The Keeler Gap can also be seen faintly silhouetted against the planet.

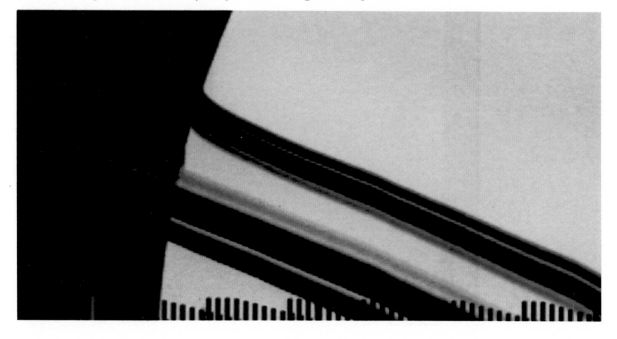

approach, without any indication of damage to the spacecraft.

On the outbound leg of its journey, Pioneer looked back at a crescent Saturn. Again it was on the opposite side of the rings from the solar illumination, so the C Ring and the Cassini Division appeared brightest. Just one day after the Saturn encounter, Pioneer crossed the orbit of Titan and made a few distant observations of that planet-sized satellite at a range of 363 000 kilometers. Not until the early morning hours of September 3 did it again reach the edge of the magnetosphere. Between September 3 and September 8 there were five magnetopause crossings and nine bow shock crossings before the spacecraft emerged permanently into the interplanetary medium. Meanwhile, the increasing proximity in the sky of Saturn and the Sun produced radio interference, and for several days in mid-September contact with Pioneer was lost completely. By October, however, all was back to normal, with the spacecraft now beyond the orbit of Saturn, measuring the solar wind.

Pioneer Saturn became the second spacecraft to escape solar gravity completely and to leave the solar system and penetrate interstellar space. It is continuing to explore new regions, exiting from the solar system in a direction approximately opposite to that of its twin, Pioneer 10. As the first spacecraft to reach Saturn, Pioneer earned worldwide acclaim, and it formed the centerpiece for a *Newsweek* cover story on planetary exploration. As NASA's Tom Young, then Deputy Director of Ames, said "We welcome Saturn into our books of knowledge with a lot of pride that we did it. We can report to Voyager: 'Come on through, the rings are clear.'"

1980 Earth Observations of Saturn's Rings and Inner Satellites

A little more than a year passed between the Pioneer encounter with Saturn and the arrival of the more sophisticated Voyager spacecraft. This interval was of particular interest to astronomers, because it included the time at which the rings appear edge-on as seen from Earth. For the first time since 1966 it was possible to search for new

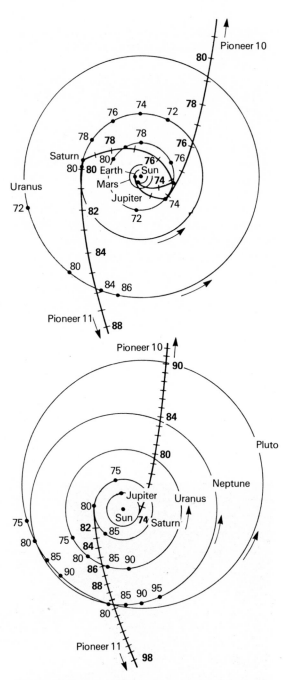

The two Pioneer spacecraft were the first human artifacts to escape entirely from the solar system. Pioneer 10 began the outbound leg of its journey in 1973 following its flyby of Jupiter. The second Pioneer, after flying past Saturn in late 1979, continued outward in a direction almost opposite to that of its twin. By 1990 both spacecraft will be near the orbit of Pluto.

In 1980 the rings of Saturn were turned edge-on to the Earth, providing an opportunity to search for otherwise invisible small satellites near the rings. Here are shown a series of photographs taken at the University of Arizona with a CCD camera at the 1.5-meter telescope of the Catalina Observatory. Several new objects are pointed out, labeled with their provisional designations. These designations (such as 1979S3) would be used until definite orbits for each new object could be determined. During the ring plane crossing, extensive observations were made of the two co-orbital satellites (S-10 and S-11), and the small satellite Dione B (or S-12) was seen for the first time. Photo courtesy of Bradford Smith, University of Arizona.

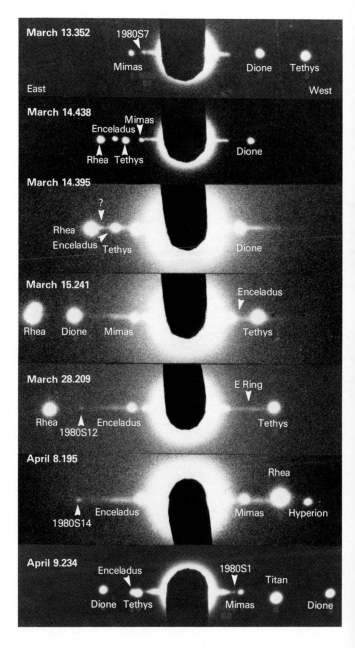

inner satellites and faint rings, taking advantage of the virtual absence of the bright rings as they dwindled to an almost invisible line in even the largest telescopes. Also, it was anticipated that the ambiguities concerning S-10, S-11, and the satellite discovered by Pioneer could be resolved.

The main focus of activity at many observatories around the world was the photographic search for faint inner satellites near the edge of the rings. In the United States, at Lowell Observatory and at the University of Arizona, this project was greatly enhanced by the introduction of a special new imaging detector, the charge coupled device (CCD), developed by NASA for the cameras on the Space Telescope. Other programs were carried out at the Pic-du-Midi Observatory in France, the Jet Propulsion Laboratory's Table Mountain Observatory, McDonald Observatory of the University of Texas, and Mauna Kea Observatory of the University of Hawaii.

The first reported sighting of a new satellite was made in Texas on December 9, 1979, but it could not be followed up to calculate an orbit. The next discovery was object 1980S1, first detected by Bradford Smith and his colleagues at the University of Arizona on February 6, 1980. It soon became apparent that 1980S1 was one of the objects that had been seen in 1966. It was seen several more times in France and Arizona and an orbital period of 16.67 hours was determined, matching the orbit of the satellite discovered by

Pioneer (1979S1 = 1979S2). It appeared that the inner satellite was now firmly identified. But life was not to be so simple.

On February 26, 1980, another new satellite, designated 1980S3, was observed by University of Hawaii astronomer Dale Cruikshank at Mauna Kea Observatory; on March 1 it was also picked up by the University of Arizona group, and on

March 15 at Table Mountain Observatory. The orbital period for 1980S3 was virtually identical to that of 1980S1, but the object was different. Here was a unique discovery—two satellites in the same orbit but on approximately opposite sides of the planet! This discovery also introduced a much greater ambiguity into earlier observations, both those in 1966 and those from Pioneer. It was impossible to determine which of the two co-orbital satellites had been seen when. Scientists began to call them S-10 and S-11, but the designation was arbitrary.

On March 1 another new satellite, designated 1980S6, was discovered by P. Laques and J. Lecacheux at the Pic-du-Midi. The same satellite —fainter than magnitude 16, but relatively far from Saturn—was recorded a few hours later by the Arizona astronomers. Subsequent observations and calculations showed that 1980S6 had almost exactly the same period (2.74 days) and was at the same distance from Saturn (6.3 R_S) as the large satellite Dione. The new satellite, called

S-12 or Dione B, was another co-orbital object. Apparently, it was in a stable configuration with Dione, preceding it by about 70 degrees in orbital longitude and occupying one of the permitted Lagrangian points of Dione's orbit. In the space of a few days, two examples of a new phenomenon, co-orbital satellites, had been discovered.

The rings of Saturn were the subject of careful measurements as they appeared edge-on. From their faintness, it was again shown that the rings are extremely thin—almost certainly less than 2 kilometers. A CCD search for the E Ring carried out at Lowell Observatory by William Baum and his colleagues clearly established for the first time the existence of the E Ring and its approximate dimensions. From their measurements, the astronomers at Lowell Observatory found that the E Ring was limited to an area near the orbit of Enceladus. They speculated that Enceladus might be the origin of the E Ring material, although no specific mechanism seemed likely. Was there something special about this satellite?

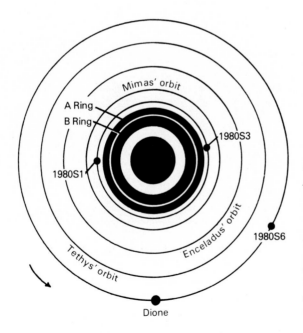

After the 1979 ring plane crossing and before the first Voyager encounter of Saturn, a total of twelve Saturn satellites were known. Two of these, 1980S1 and 1980S3, also called S-10 and S-11, were in essentially the same orbit. One was slowly catching up with the other, apparently headed for a collision in late 1981 or early 1982. Before these two satellites would collide, however, it is expected that they will interact gravitationally, shift orbits, and move slowly apart without damaging each other.

PIONEER JUPITER SCIENCE HIGHLIGHTS

Confirmation that Jupiter emits more heat than it receives from the Sun, and measurement of its internal energy source at 10^{17} watts.

First measurement of the amount of helium in the atmosphere, indicating that the ratio of helium to hydrogen is similar to the value for the Sun.

Location of the minimum temperature in the atmosphere ($-165°$ C) at a pressure of 0.03 bar.

Determination from gravity and temperature measurements that Jupiter is fluid throughout (with the possible exception of a small metallic core), and has no solid surface.

Measurement of the global magnetic field of Jupiter, showing that it is dipolar, with a magnetic axis tilted by 11 degrees and offset 10 000 kilometers from the rotational axis, and a dipolar moment 18 000 times greater than that of Earth.

Improvements in mass determinations for the Galilean satellites, leading to better models for their interior structure.

Discovery from radio occultation data of an ionosphere on Io, with substantial differences between the two locations measured.

Strong ultraviolet emission, possibly due to atomic hydrogen, from a region near the orbit of Io.

Determination that the outer boundary of the Jovian magnetosphere is near 100 R_J in the direction from which the solar wind is flowing, and farther in the downwind direction.

Discovery of a strong current sheet of electrons circling Jupiter in its magnetic equator and extending to about 60 R_J.

Characterization of the strong concentrations of electrons and ions in the inner magnetosphere, trapped in the planet's magnetic field and rotating with it. The peak strength of the radiation belts was located inside the orbit of Io, near 3 R_J.

Measurement of structure in the inner magnetosphere due to particle interactions with the satellites, including the suggestion of an unknown satellite or ring near 1.8 R_J.

PIONEER SATURN SCIENCE HIGHLIGHTS

Discovery of the magnetic field of Saturn, found to be dipolar, with a dipole moment 500 times greater than Earth's, and (surprisingly) to be aligned with the rotational axis of the planet.

Discovery of the magnetosphere of Saturn, extending to about the orbit of Titan in the direction of the solar wind and to greater distances away from the Sun.

Confirmation that energetic charged particles in the magnetosphere are absorbed by Saturn's inner satellites and rings, resulting in radiation intensities hundreds of times weaker than at Jupiter.

Measurements of a magnetic wake produced by the interaction of Titan with the co-rotating Saturn magnetosphere.

Confirmation of an internal heat source on Saturn, with the planet radiating about two and a half times as much energy as it receives from the Sun.

Confirmation of the absence of large spots or other striking cloud features in close-up photographs.

Measurement of ultraviolet glows from Saturn and from a wide region near the orbit of Titan.

Calculation from gravity and temperature measurements that Saturn is composed primarily of liquid metallic hydrogen, with a probable core of heavier material about ten Earth masses in size.

Discovery of a satellite (1979S1 = 1979S2) at 2.53 R_S, about 200 kilometers in diameter, from both imaging and direct measurements of its magnetic wake.

Demonstration from charged particle measurements that there is no satellite in the reported orbit of Janus, but that several other undiscovered inner satellites or rings may be present.

Discovery of the F Ring, much thinner than the other known rings of Saturn, outside the A Ring.

Measurements of the diffuse transmission of light through the rings, including indication of substantial material within the Cassini Division.

Demonstration that a spacecraft can penetrate the E Ring without damage.

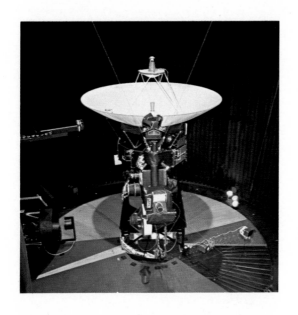

The Voyager Mission

The Voyager mission was conceived in the late 1960s, before the launch of the Pioneer spacecraft or the first manned Apollo landing on the Moon. At that time scientists envisioned a single ambitious program, the Outer Planets Grand Tour, that would send spacecraft to all the planets of the outer solar system. In 1969, the year in which the Pioneer Project received Congressional approval, NASA began serious design work on this mission.

By 1970 NASA had developed plans for four spacecraft launches to the outer planets. The first two spacecraft were targeted to fly by Jupiter, Saturn, and Pluto, with launches in 1976 and 1977. Two years later two more spacecraft were to be sent on a trajectory to Jupiter, Uranus, and Neptune. Several dozen leading space scientists, primarily from universities, were selected in 1971 to carry out the detailed planning of instruments and scientific objectives for the Grand Tour mission, and NASA's plans for fiscal year 1972 called for a Congressional appropriation of $30 million for the Grand Tour.

But this ambitious program was not to be. Planned at a time of rapid growth of U.S. space projects, the Grand Tour was too large and expensive for the reduced NASA expenditures of the post-Apollo years. Almost immediately after the first manned lunar landing, cuts were made in the NASA budget, and one of the items canceled was the Grand Tour. A modest appropriation was made to design a less expensive mission.

The Voyager mission was the product of this redesign. The new mission concept did not include the exploration of Uranus, Neptune, and Pluto. The spacecraft would be smaller than the one designed for the Grand Tour, and less stringent demands would be made for the reliability of its millions of components. Limiting the mission to flybys of Jupiter and Saturn also relieved problems associated with spacecraft power, and with communicating effectively over distances of more than 2 billion kilometers to the outermost planets. The total cost of the new mission was estimated at $250 million, only a third of that planned for the Grand Tour. The mission was initially named Mariner/Jupiter-Saturn; in 1977 the name was changed to Voyager.

The scientific investigators for Voyager were selected in 1972. In response to an Announcement of Flight Opportunity issued by NASA, 77 proposals were received—31 from groups of scientists with designs for instruments, and 46 from individuals desiring to participate in NASA-formed teams. Of these 77 proposals, 24 were from NASA laboratories, 48 were from scientists in various U.S. universities and industry, and 5 were from foreign sources. After extensive review, 28 proposals were accepted—9 for instruments and 19 for individual participation.

The responsibility for carrying out the Voyager mission was assigned by NASA to the Caltech Jet Propulsion Laboratory in Pasadena, California. The Project Manager was Harris (Bud) Schurmeier. Later, Schurmeier was succeeded by John Casani, Robert Parks, Ray Heacock, and Esker Davis. Professor Edward Stone of Caltech, a distinguished expert on magnetospheric and cosmic ray physics, was selected to serve as Project Scientist. The official beginning of the Voyager project was set for July 1, 1972.

The Objectives of Voyager

Voyager is one of the most ambitious planetary space missions ever undertaken. Its objective was the exploration of the two giant planets, Jupiter and Saturn, and their magnetospheres and satellites. Major emphasis was placed on studying the satellites, many of which are planet-sized worlds, in as much detail as possible. The study of Titan, the only satellite in the solar system known to have an extensive atmosphere, was nearly as high a priority as studies of Saturn itself.

The Voyager mission used two identical spacecraft to investigate the Jovian and Saturnian systems. One reason for flying two spacecraft was to provide redundancy. Voyager would penetrate farther and require greater reliability than any previous mission. If one spacecraft failed, the second might be able to continue the mission successfully. Perhaps more important was the complementarity of the trajectories of the two spacecraft. No single flight path could provide close encounters with Jupiter and Saturn and each of their major satellites. For instance, in the Jupiter system a single well-selected path could bring a spacecraft close to three of the large Galilean satellites but not the fourth. In the Saturn system,

Voyager Project Scientist Edward C. Stone.

a trajectory optimized for observations of Titan would not provide the best perspective for viewing the rings. In addition, if the Voyager 2 spacecraft were to continue beyond Saturn to a 1986 encounter with Uranus, it would have to fly on a path that would not bring it close to Titan. Thus the paths of the two spacecraft and the detailed sequence of observations were designed to be complementary. In addition, the second spacecraft could be reprogrammed to take advantage of the discoveries of the first.

Science on Voyager

More than 100 scientists are directly involved in the Voyager scientific investigations. They were selected competitively from universities, NASA laboratories, industry, and abroad. Each team of scientists is associated with a particular instrument, designed specifically for Voyager for the collection of critical data from Jupiter, Saturn, and their systems of rings and satellites. The measurements made by these instruments can be

Ray Heacock, Voyager Project Manager for the Voyager 1 Saturn flyby.

The remote sensing investigations on Voyager are essentially astronomical in nature, measuring the light reflected from or emitted by the planets and their satellites. There are many advantages to making such measurements close to a planet. New perspectives are available, such as views from above and below the rings of Saturn. Operating in space, these instruments can exploit the full spectrum of electromagnetic radiation without concern for the absorption by the terrestrial atmosphere that restricts ground-based astronomers to certain spectral windows. But most important, the remote sensing instruments on Voyager would be a thousand times closer to their targets than any telescopes on Earth's surface or in Earth orbit. Far greater detail could be obtained than what we might hope for from Earth-based observations.

Five of the remote sensing instruments—two TV cameras, the infrared spectrometer, the ultraviolet spectrometer, and the photopolarimeter—are mounted together on a scan platform. This platform can be pointed to any direction in space, allowing exact targeting of the observations. One remote sensing instrument, the planetary radio astronomy receiver, is not on the scan platform. It measures long-wave radio emission without requiring special pointing.

divided into two broad categories, usually called direct or *in situ* measurements and remote sensing measurements. A direct measurement involves the analysis of the immediate environment of the spacecraft; remote measurements are made by analyzing the radiation from distant objects much as astronomers do with telescopes on Earth.

The direct measurement instruments on Voyager measure cosmic ray particles, low energy charged particles, magnetic fields, plasma particles, and plasma waves. Their activity began immediately after launch, monitoring the Earth environment and then interplanetary space. However, their main purpose was the study of the magnetospheres of Jupiter and Saturn, those large volumes of space in which charged particles are trapped by the magnetic fields of the planets. The particles and fields instruments were to continue measuring conditions in interplanetary space as the Voyagers moved beyond their planetary targets. It was hoped that the spacecraft would operate until they reached the heliopause, the boundary between the solar-wind-dominated space within the solar system and true interstellar space beyond.

Esker Davis, Voyager 2 Project Manager.

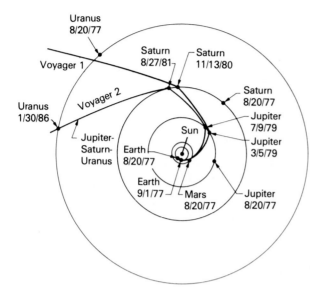

Uranus
8/20/77

Saturn
8/27/81

Saturn
11/13/80

Voyager 1

Voyager 2

Saturn
8/20/77

Uranus
1/30/86

Jupiter-
Saturn-
Uranus

Sun

Jupiter
7/9/79

Jupiter
3/5/79

Earth
8/20/77

Earth
9/1/77

Mars
8/20/77

Jupiter
8/20/77

Each Voyager spacecraft followed a billion-kilometer path to Jupiter, where the gravitational pull of the giant planet was used to redirect the trajectory toward Saturn. Voyager 1 received a larger kick from the gravitational slingshot than Voyager 2, increasing its lead so that it arrived at Saturn in November 1980, about nine months before Voyager 2. Following the Saturn flyby, Voyager 1 continued out of the solar system while Voyager 2 used the Saturn flyby to redirect its path toward a Uranus encounter in 1986.

The Voyager scan platform contains instruments that gather data for Voyager's remote sensing investigations. Five of these instruments—two TV cameras, the infrared spectrometer, the ultraviolet spectrometer and the photopolarimeter—are mounted together on the scan platform, which can be pointed to any direction in space to allow exact targeting of the observations. (373-7146BC)

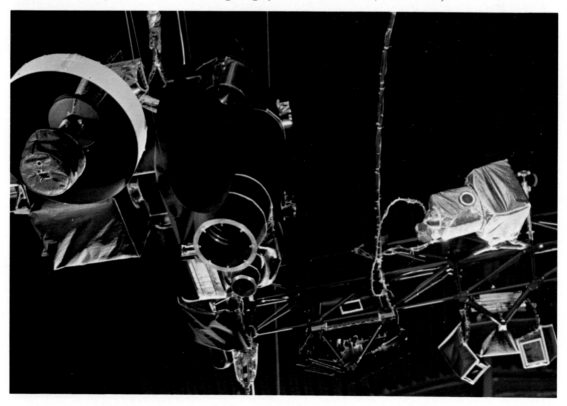

The Voyager Science Team principal investigators and team leaders at JPL for the Jupiter flyby.

A final Voyager investigation did not require a special instrument at all. The radio telemetry link between the spacecraft and controllers on Earth was also used to probe the atmospheres of the planets and satellites, and special tracking of the spacecraft revealed the masses of planets and satellites as the spacecraft passed near them.

Remote Sensing Instruments

The eyes of Voyager are in its imaging system. Two television cameras, each with a set of color filters, look at the planets and their satellites and transmit thousands of detailed pictures to Earth. Unlike other Voyager instruments, the imaging system is not the result of a competition among proposals submitted by groups of scientists. The Voyager cameras were built by the Jet Propulsion Laboratory to be integrated with the design of the Voyager spacecraft and its subsystems. Members of the Imaging Science Team were selected individually on the basis of the scientific studies they proposed to carry out. The Team Leader is Bradford A. Smith, an astronomer from the University of Arizona; the Deputy Team Leader is Laurence A. Soderblom of the U.S. Geological Survey in

Flagstaff, Arizona. Originally there were seven other members of the Imaging Science Team, but by the time of the Saturn encounter, the membership had been expanded to 26 scientists.

Both wide-angle and narrow-angle television cameras are required to obtain the highest possible resolution while retaining the capability to study global-scale features on the giant planets. The wide-angle camera has a focal length of 200 millimeters, providing a field of view of about 3 degrees, similar to that obtained with the 500-millimeter telephoto lens on a 35-millimeter camera. The narrow-angle camera has a focal length of 1500 millimeters and a field of view of 0.4 degrees. The detectors are selenium-sulfur vidicon television tubes, 11 millimeters square, designed for slow-scan readout, requiring 48 seconds to produce each picture. These are black and white television systems, but they can be used to produce color images by combining data from pictures taken successively through different colored filters.

Each image contains a tremendous amount of information, much more than is found in a commercial television picture. In computer termi-

VOYAGER SCIENCE INVESTIGATIONS
Project Scientist: E. C. Stone, Caltech

Investigation	Principal Investigator or Team Leader	Primary Objectives at Saturn
Imaging science	B.A. Smith U. Arizona	Measurement of atmospheric dynamics; determination of geologic structure of satellites; search for new rings and new satellites; determination of structure and properties of the rings.
Infrared radiation (IRIS)	R.A. Hanel NASA Goddard	Determination of atmospheric composition, thermal structure, and dynamics for Saturn and Titan.
Ultraviolet spectroscopy	A.L. Broadfoot U. Southern California	Measurement on Saturn and Titan of upper atmospheric composition and structure, auroral processes, distribution of ions and neutral atoms.
Photopolarimetry	A.L. Lane JPL	Measurement of brightness and polarization of light from Saturn and Titan; occultation measurement of small scale ring structure.
Planetary radio astronomy	J.W. Warwick Radiophysics, Inc.	Determination of polarization and spectra of radio frequency emissions, plasma densities, rotation period of Saturn.
Magnetic fields	N.F. Ness NASA Goddard	Measurement of magnetic fields of Saturn and Titan, magnetospheric structure and interactions with Titan.
Plasma particles	H.S. Bridge MIT	Measurement of magnetospheric ion and electron distribution, solar wind interaction with Saturn, magnetospheric interaction with Titan.
Plasma waves	F.L. Scarf TRW	Measurement of plasma electron densities, wave-particle interactions, low-frequency wave emission.
Low energy charged particles	S.M. Krimigis Johns Hopkins U.	Measurement of the distribution, composition, and flow of energetic ions and electrons; satellite-energetic particle interactions.
Cosmic ray particles	R.E. Vogt Caltech	Measurement of the distribution, composition, and flow of high energy trapped nuclei; energetic electron spectra.
Radio science	G. L. Tyler Stanford U.	Measurement of Saturn's atmospheric and ionospheric structure and composition; determination of surface temperature and pressure on Titan; satellite masses.

nology, there are more than 5 million bits of information in each picture. The primary limitation in the number of pictures that can be taken is the rate of data transmission from the spacecraft to Earth: one picture every 3 minutes from Saturn.

A second scan platform instrument is the infrared interferometer spectrometer (IRIS). The IRIS Team consists of 13 scientists, led by Principal Investigator Rudolph Hanel of the NASA Goddard Space Flight Center, Greenbelt, Maryland. The IRIS measures the spectrum of emitted or reflected infrared light between 4 and 50 micrometers wavelength. Its primary purpose is the measurement of the chemical composition and structure of the atmospheres of Jupiter, Saturn, and Titan.

The third major scan platform instrument is the ultraviolet spectrometer (UVS). The Principal Investigator for the UVS is A. Lyle Broadfoot of the University of Southern California. Associated with Broadfoot are 14 other scientists from the United States, Canada, and France. The spectral range of the UVS is 50 to 170 nanometers, wavelengths at which one sees primarily emission from hot atoms in the atmospheres of the planets or in glowing gas clouds that surround planets and satellites. UVS data can be used to determine the composition of these glowing regions and the temperature and density of matter in them.

The fourth Voyager scan platform instrument is the photopolarimeter, built at the University of Colorado with Principal Investigator Arthur L. Lane of JPL. This instrument did not operate on Voyager 1, but on the second spacecraft it carried out important studies of Saturn's atmosphere, of Titan, and especially of the fine structure in the rings.

The planetary radio astronomy investigation is led by James Warwick of Radiophysics, Inc. in Boulder, Colorado. Together with 30 co-investigators, Warwick used a 200-channel radio receiver and a pair of external antennas to detect radio static from Jupiter and Saturn.

Direct Measurement Instruments

If the remote sensing instruments are the eyes and ears of Voyager, the direct measurement instruments are its organs of taste, smell, and touch.

The primary objectives of these instruments are the measurement and characterization of the magnetic fields and the many kinds of charged particles and plasmas that are trapped within them, both in interplanetary space and in the magnetospheres of Jupiter and Saturn.

The first of the direct sensing instruments is the magnetometer, designed to measure magnetic fields, both those intrinsic to Saturn and its satellites and those associated with the flow of charged particles in the solar wind and the magnetosphere. The Principal Investigator for this instrument is Norman F. Ness of the NASA Goddard Space Flight Center. His co-investigators are four colleagues from Goddard and one from Germany. The magnetometer is mounted on a 13-meter-long boom that was unfurled and extended automatically after launch. It is sensitive enough to measure fields one-millionth as strong as the magnetic field at the surface of the Earth.

A plasma is a dilute gas consisting of charged particles rather than neutral atoms or molecules. These charged particles can be electrons, protons, or any of a wide variety of positive ions. Although there are always equal numbers of positive and negative charges, the fact that the individual particles are not neutral causes them to experience a force when in a magnetic field. The particles in a plasma also undergo physical effects that do not occur in our everyday world, including the generation of plasma waves, which are oscillations in density and electric field that generally cover the audio range of frequencies. The plasma wave investigation on Voyager is directed by physicist Frederick L. Scarf of the TRW Defense and Space Systems Group of Redondo Beach, California. The instrument uses the same pair of antennas to detect plasma waves that are used for the planetary radio astronomy instrument. Direct measurement of the plasma particles is achieved with an instrument built by Principal Investigator Herbert S. Bridge of the Massachusetts Institute of Technology, Cambridge, Massachusetts. This plasma instrument can measure the composition and energy of the electrons and ions as well as the direction of their flow.

The plasma particle detector is sensitive to charged particles with speeds up to about 1 percent of the speed of light, or energies up to a few

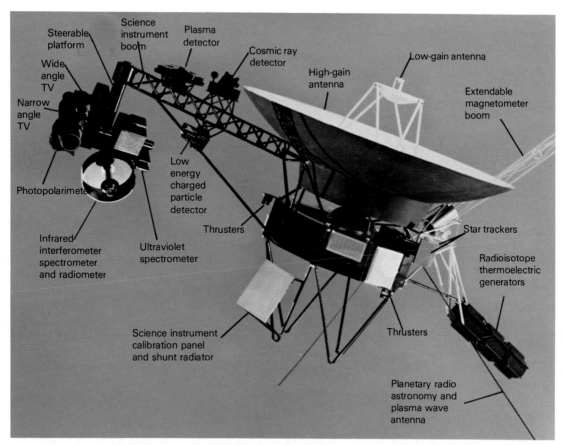

Steerable platform
Science instrument boom
Plasma detector
Cosmic ray detector
Low-gain antenna
High-gain antenna
Extendable magnetometer boom
Wide angle TV
Narrow angle TV
Photopolarimeter
Low energy charged particle detector
Thrusters
Star trackers
Radioisotope thermoelectric generators
Infrared interferometer spectrometer and radiometer
Ultraviolet spectrometer
Science instrument calibration panel and shunt radiator
Thrusters
Planetary radio astronomy and plasma wave antenna

The fully deployed Voyager spacecraft is capable of a wide variety of direct and remote sensing measurements. Because of the exploratory nature of the Voyager mission, every effort was made to fly versatile instruments that could yield valuable results no matter what the nature of the Jovian and Saturnian systems. (P-18811AC)

thousand electron volts. A different instrument is required to measure the smaller numbers of particles that move at higher speeds. The low energy charged particle (LECP) instrument measures energies as high as several million electron volts, corresponding to a few percent of the speed of light. The Principal Investigator for the LECP is Stamatios M. Krimigis, a physicist from Johns Hopkins University, Baltimore, Maryland. The LECP instrument has two parts, designed respectively to measure particles trapped in the magnetosphere of a planet such as Jupiter or Saturn and to measure particles in the lower-density environment of interplanetary space.

A third particle instrument measures very high-energy particles, which are often called cosmic rays.

The Principal Investigator for the cosmic ray instrument is Rochus E. Vogt, a physicist at the California Institute of Technology. Among his six co-investigators is Ed Stone, the Voyager Project Scientist.

The Voyager Spacecraft

The two identical Voyager spacecraft, each with a mass of 815 kilograms, are among the most autonomous, sophisticated robots ever sent to explore other worlds. Each is a self-contained system, carrying its own power, propulsion, communications systems, and science instruments.

Communication between the spacecraft and Earth is carried out via a high-gain radio antenna 3.7 meters in diameter that is always oriented

THE DEEP SPACE NETWORK

A vital component of the Voyager mission is the communications system linking the spacecraft with controllers and scientists on Earth. The ability to communicate with spacecraft over the vast distances to the outer planets, and particularly to return the enormous amounts of data collected by sophisticated cameras and spectrometers, depends in large part on the transmitters and receivers of the Deep Space Network (DSN), operated for NASA by JPL.

The original network of these receiving stations was established in 1958 to provide round-the-world tracking of the first U.S. satellite, Explorer 1. By the late 1970s, the DSN had evolved into a system of large antennas, low-noise receivers, and high-power transmitters at sites strategically located on three continents. From these sites the data are forwarded (often using terrestrial communications satellites) to the mission operations center at JPL.

The three DSN stations are located in the Mohave desert at Goldstone, California; near Madrid, Spain; and near Canberra, Australia. Each location is equipped with two 26-meter steerable antennas and a single giant steerable dish 64 meters in diameter, with approximately the collecting area of a football field. In addition, each is equipped with transmitting, receiving, and data handling equipment. The transmitters in Spain and Australia have 100-kilowatt power, while the 64-meter antenna at Goldstone has a 400-kilowatt transmitter. Most commands to Voyager are sent from Goldstone, but all three stations require the highest quality receivers to permit continuous recording of the data streams pouring in from the spacecraft.

Since the mid-1960s, the DSN's standard frequency has been S-band (2295 megahertz). Voyager introduces a new, higher frequency telemetry link at X-band (8418 megahertz). The X-band signal can carry more information than S-band with similar power transmitters, but it requires more exact antenna performance. In addition, the X-band signal is absorbed by terrestrial clouds and, especially, rain. Fortunately, all three DSN stations are in dry climates, but during encounters the weather forecasts on Earth become items of crucial concern if precious data are not to be lost by storm interference.

As a result of the development of larger antennas and improved electronics, the DSN command capabilities and telemetry data rates have increased dramatically over the years. For example, in 1965 Mariner 4 transmitted from Mars at a rate of only 8⅓ bits of information per second. In 1969, Mariners 6 and 7 transmitted picture data from Mars at 16 200 bits per second. Mariner 10, in 1973, achieved 117 200 bits per second from Mercury. At Jupiter, Voyager operated at a similar rate over a distance six times larger. For the Saturn encounter, however, it was necessary to reduce the rate to 44 800 bits per second to ensure no loss of unique data sent across nearly 1 500 000 kilometers of space.

toward the Earth. The radio transmitters (there are two complete systems to provide backup in case of failure) have only 23 watts of transmitting power, about the power of a refrigerator light bulb. Yet with the aid of the sensitive receivers of the NASA Deep Space Network of tracking stations, this 23-watt radio can transmit data over a distance of 1 billion kilometers at the enormous rate of 115 200 bits per second, almost a hundred times faster than Pioneer. At the greater distance to Saturn, a lower data rate of 44 800 bits per second was adopted. In addition, the Voyager spacecraft carried a digital tape recorder with a storage capacity of about 500 million bits.

The power for each Voyager spacecraft is supplied by three radioisotope thermoelectric generators (RTGs) that produce about 400 watts of electrical power. Each spacecraft is controlled by a set of interconnected electronic brains called the attitude and articulation control subsystem (AACS), the flight data subsystem (FDS), and the computer command subsystem (CCS). Rather than being instructed directly by ground controllers (as were the Pioneers), the Voyager control systems accept precoded sets of several thousand instructions that can provide autonomous operation for days or weeks at a time. These systems also include elaborate error detection and correction routines, so the spacecraft can often locate and correct problems before ground controllers are aware of them. The AACS, FDS, and CCS can be reprogrammed in flight if necessary, allowing great flexibility in responding to changing conditions or science objectives.

Flight to Jupiter

On August 20, 1977, the first of the Voyager spacecraft was launched from Cape Canaveral, Florida, on its long journey to Jupiter and Saturn. Sixteen days later, on September 5, a second Voyager spacecraft followed its predecessor into space. Each was launched by a Titan/Centaur launch vehicle, the largest rocket system in the NASA arsenal since the retirement of the Saturn rockets used for the Apollo Moon flights. The Titan and Centaur rockets were originally developed separately and have been used with other rocket stages for many NASA launches. They were first combined for the two Viking launches to Mars in 1975, and this powerful four-stage launch vehicle was used again for Voyager.

The Titan/Centaur is nearly 50 meters high, and fully fueled it weighs nearly 700 tons. The first stage Titan is powered by both solid and liquid fuel engines. The Centaur stage, 20 meters long and 3 meters in diameter, burns the powerful fuel combination of liquid hydrogen and liquid oxygen. The Titan boosted the Voyager Centaur combination into low Earth orbit, and the Centaur plus a small solid fuel rocket provided the energy for Voyager to escape from Earth orbit and begin the transfer orbit toward Jupiter. Within one hour of launch, each Voyager spacecraft was on its way, moving at a speed of more than 10 kilometers per second.

Both Voyager launches were perfect, but once the vehicles were on their way toward Jupiter, a frustrating series of problems developed with each spacecraft. On Voyager 2, the first problem was an apparent failure of the scan platform boom to lock into place. It was later determined that the error was in the position sensor rather than in the boom itself. A baffling series of difficulties with the onboard computer system arose during the days following launch, and extensive reprogram-

Voyager 1 was launched on September 5, 1977, from Cape Canaveral, Florida, propelled into space on a Titan/Centaur rocket. (P-19480AC)

ming was required to calm down the overreactions that had accidently been built into the system.

Many of the scan platform and control computer problems were avoided on Voyager 1, which was the second of the spacecraft to be launched.

The scan platform did fail two months into flight, but careful adjustments from the ground finally put it back into proper working order.

The most serious problem developed in April 1978. Voyager 2's primary radio receiver failed, and when the spacecraft automatically shifted to its back-up system, it was found that this receiver was also faulty. Because of an electronic failure, Voyager 2 was not able to track precisely the changing frequency of the command signals being sent from Earth. Months of strenuous effort were required to develop techniques to continue communication with the spacecraft in spite of this difficulty. These problems could be solved only because of the great sophistication of the Voyager spacecraft design; with its onboard computers and redundant electronic systems, the spacecraft could work around failures as great as that of the Voyager 2 receiver system. As the engineers and controllers at the Jet Propulsion Laboratory gained experience in dealing with the robot spacecraft, they became adept at providing new instructions and ways of sequencing operations that ultimately made both spacecraft more efficient than had been anticipated before the launch.

Each Voyager flew a long curving trajectory toward Jupiter, and each spent many months in the asteroid belt. But, as demonstrated by Pioneers 10 and 11, there was no significant danger of impact with asteroids or fine debris. Throughout the flight, the direct sensing instruments monitored conditions in the solar wind and the interplanetary medium. By the time the spacecraft were 100 million kilometers from Jupiter some three months before encounter, the quality of the images returned by the television systems exceeded any ever obtained with ground-based telescopes. The three-month period before the encounters constituted Voyager's observatory phase, with primary emphasis on studies of the complicated cloud motions in the atmosphere of Jupiter. The Jupiter observatory phase of Voyager 1 began on January 4, 1979.

In mid-February the observatory phase ended, and the spacecraft began an increasingly complicated series of observations of Jupiter and its satellites using all the remote sensing instruments. More details became apparent every day. On February 28 the spacecraft reached the boundaries of Jupiter's magnetosphere, and the encounter period began. However, rapidly changing pressure from the solar wind caused the highly elastic magnetosphere of Jupiter to swell and contract several times; it was not until March 3, at a distance of only 47 R_J, that Voyager 1 crossed the magnetopause for the last time. On March 3 the spacecraft crossed the orbit of Callisto, the outermost of the four Galilean satellites. For the next three days, a variety of satellite encounters, in addition to views of Jupiter, provided one of the most productive and spectacular periods of exploration in human history.

Jupiter Encounter

The Voyager 1 flyby of Jupiter took place on March 5, 1979, with the spacecraft only 270 000 kilometers from the cloudtops. That morning the spacecraft passed through the flux tube of electric current linking Io magnetically with Jupiter. It also obtained the discovery photograph of the rings of Jupiter. Closest approach to Io took place at a distance of only 22 000 kilometers. That evening, the second close satellite encounter took place, this time with Ganymede at a range of 115 000 kilometers. The encounter with Callisto occurred on the morning of March 6, at a range of 126 000 kilometers. Voyager 1 had only distant views of the fourth Galilean satellite, Europa.

The most spectacular result of the Voyager 1 Jupiter flyby was the discovery of intense volcanic activity on Io, a satellite apparently distorted and heated by the tidal effects of Jupiter. Io was emitting energy at a rate 100 times greater than Earth. The heat produced spectacular volcanoes, sending up fountains of sulfur and sulfur dioxide hundreds of kilometers above the surface. The other Galilean satellites also proved extraordinarily interesting, each a unique world with its own geological history and its own special processes molding its surface.

The two largest satellites of Jupiter, Ganymede and Callisto, were members of a class of objects never before viewed at close range. Each of these satellites has a composition that is about half rocky material, similar to that which makes up

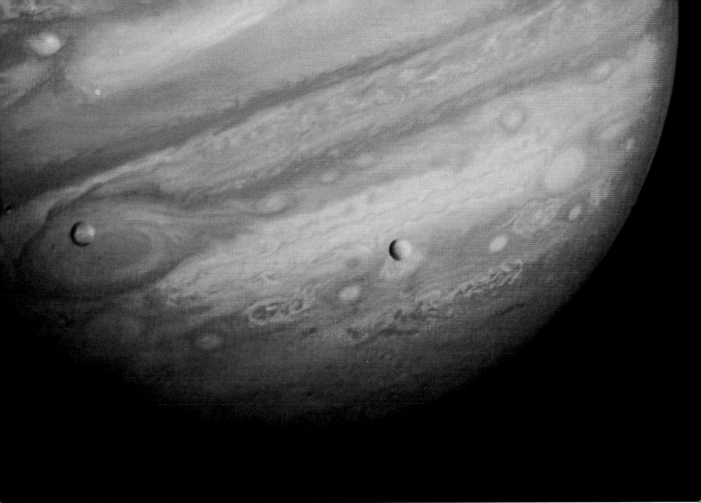

One of the most spectacular Jupiter photographs taken by Voyager 1 was obtained on February 13, 1979, at a distance of twenty million kilometers. Passing in front of the planet are the inner two Galilean satellites. Io (left) already shows brightly colored patterns on its surface, while Europa (right), is a bland, ice-covered world. The scale of these objects is huge by terrestrial standards: Io and Europa are each the size of our Moon, and the Red Spot is nearly twice as large as Earth. (P-21082C)

Earth and the Moon, and about half water, primarily frozen but perhaps including some liquid at great depths. Before Voyager, scientists expected that the geology of such ice-and-rock planets would be different from that of the more familiar rocky worlds, and they were not disappointed. Callisto, although lacking evidence of internal activity, displayed unusual crater forms not seen before in the inner solar system. Ganymede's surface preserved the records of a complex history of melting, mountain building, and slow evolution of the thickness and strength of its crust. In the Saturn system Voyager would find a third giant satellite—Titan—similar in size and composition to Ganymede and Callisto. How would it differ? And why had Titan developed an atmosphere, while Ganymede and Callisto had none?

Jupiter proved a planet of exceptional interest as photographed by Voyager. Its colorful atmosphere was in constant motion, displaying a wide variety of storms, jet streams, and other meteorological phenomena. Some were similar to the circulation of Earth's atmosphere, others unique to this giant gas planet, driven by its internal heat source as well as sunlight. It was already apparent from Earth-based photographs that Saturn lacked highly conspicuous atmospheric features like the Great Red Spot. Why did this difference exist? Would close-up views of Saturn from Voyager prove as exciting to atmospheric scientists as those of Jupiter?

Only four months separated Voyager 2 from Voyager 1, and before the results of the first flyby could be fully processed, the observatory phase for the second spacecraft was under way, extend-

The Great Red Spot of Jupiter is a magnificent sight whether viewed in normal or exaggerated color. These pictures were taken by Voyager 1 at a range of about one million kilometers. On the originals, features as small as 30 kilometers across are visible. South of the Red Spot is one of three white ovals, which are anticyclonic vortices in the atmosphere. The frame at the top is in natural color, while the red and blue have been greatly exaggerated in the lower frame to bring out fine detail in the cloud structure. (P-21430C and P-21431C)

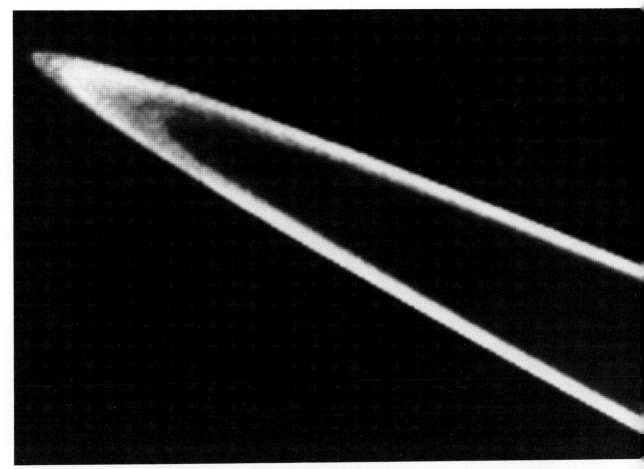

Voyager 1 discovered the rings of Jupiter, and Voyager 2 was targeted to obtain even better ring photographs. Structure can be seen in this Voyager 2 image taken about 27 hours after closest approach to Jupiter. This enlarged portion of a wide-angle picture taken with a clear filter shows a bright core about 800 kilometers across with a dimmer region a few thousand kilometers across on the inside and a narrow dim region on the outside. The Jupiter rings are so tenuous that they would block only a millionth of the light passing through; they are ten thousand times more transparent than the best glass. (260-674)

ing the time base for study of the atmosphere of Jupiter. Although controllers had been concerned over the ailing radio receiver on Voyager 2, their efforts to work around the problem were successful, and the encounter unfolded without any serious communications difficulties.

On July 2, 1979, Voyager 2 crossed the bow shock at 99 R_J and began direct sensing of the Jovian magnetosphere, which had expanded slightly between the two encounters. By July 6 long-range photos of Io confirmed that most of the volcanoes discovered four months earlier by Voyager 1 were still erupting. On July 8 Voyager 2 encountered Callisto at a range of 215 000 kilometers. Early the next day the spacecraft passed just 62 000 kilometers from Ganymede, substantially closer than had its predecessor, followed by

encounter with Europa at 206 000 kilometers. Europa, poorly imaged by Voyager 1, proved as extraordinary as its companions, with a smooth icy surface crossed by hundreds of thin light and dark lines that looked like cracks in sea ice. Here was another satellite with its own special geologic history and an appearance different from any planet or satellite previously investigated.

Although Voyager 2 did not pass closer than a million kilometers from Io, a special observing sequence had been introduced to study the giant volcanic eruptions discovered four months earlier. The Voyager 2 mission was also modified to include photographs of the newly discovered Jovian rings, and the resulting pictures were among the highlights of the July 9 encounter. An added bonus was the discovery of a total of three new

The four Galilean satellites of Jupiter are planet-like worlds revealed by Voyager to be as diverse and fascinating as the terrestrial planets Mercury, Venus, Earth, and Mars. In this composite, all four satellites are shown in their relative sizes as they would appear from a distance of about one million kilometers. Relative color and reflectivity are also approximately preserved. Clockwise from the upper left, the satellites are Io, Europa, Callisto, and Ganymede. (260-499C)

One of Voyager's most spectacular discoveries at Jupiter was the presence of gigantic volcanic eruptions on Io. Especially beautiful views of these eruptions were obtained by Voyager 2 during its ten-hour Io volcano watch on July 9, 1979. On the edge of the crescent image, two volcanoes send up fountains of sulfur and sulfur dioxide about 100 kilometers above the surface. (P-21780)

Jovian satellites from careful study of the thousands of Voyager images of the Jupiter system.

The two Jupiter encounters were celebrated as splendid technological and scientific accomplishments. Thomas A. Mutch, NASA Associate Administrator for Space Science, called Voyager "a truly revolutionary journey of exploration. We're starting a new stage of space exploration, and when history books are written a hundred or two hundred years from now, historians will cite this period of exploration as a turning point in our cultural, our scientific, our intellectual development." But the Voyager mission was less than half over. Ahead remained the formidable challenge of Saturn. Rodney Mills, Voyager Program Manager, noted amid the cheering that "Jupiter has been a nice place to go by, but we wouldn't want to stop there—we're going on to Saturn!"

On To Saturn

Both Voyager spacecraft were aimed to take maximum advantage of the force of Jupiter's gravity to speed them on toward Saturn. Voyager 1 flew closer to Jupiter and received the greater increase in speed. As both craft followed their new trajectories outward across the vast spaces between Jupiter and Saturn, Voyager 1 pulled steadily ahead of its slower-moving sister, increasing the gap from four months at Jupiter to nine months at Saturn.

During the long cruise period, both spacecraft continued to measure the solar wind and the interplanetary medium. By the summer of 1980 Voyager 1 was already close enough to begin test photographs of Saturn. The rings were practically invisible in the earliest pictures, since they were turned nearly edge-on to the Sun. As August and September passed, the resolution approached that of Earth-based pictures, and the A, B, and C Rings could be clearly distinguished.

Even before the observatory phase, important new results had been obtained from Voyager observations of Saturn. Beginning on January 1, 1980, the planetary radio astronomy (PRA) instrument began to detect very long wave radio bursts coming from Saturn. As these observations

VOYAGER JUPITER SCIENCE HIGHLIGHTS

Atmosphere

Atmospheric composition of hydrogen and helium in the ratio 0.11 (± 0.03) helium molecules for every hydrogen molecule.

Anticyclonic motion of the Great Red Spot, the white ovals, and many other major disturbances, indicating that these are high-pressure regions.

Stability of the zonal pattern of east-west winds, indicating that this planet-wide flow is more fundamental than the shifting cloud belts and zones.

Extension of the east-west wind patterns to the polar regions, previously thought to be dominated by convective upwelling and downwelling.

Complex interactions between the Great Red Spot and the zonal flow, including major changes over the four-month interval between encounters.

Cloud-top lightning bolts, similar to terrestrial superbolts, including radio-frequency emission in the form of whistlers.

A temperature inversion in the stratosphere, with the temperature rising from a minimum of about 110 K at a pressure level of 0.1 bar to 160 K at 0.01 bar.

Concentration of ultraviolet absorbing high-altitude haze in the polar regions.

A time-variable ratio of ethane to acetylene in the upper atmosphere that changes by about a factor of 2 with position on the planet.

Polar auroral emission in the visible and ultraviolet, associated with charged particles originating in the Io torus.

Strong ultraviolet emission from the entire disk of the planet, indicating a thermospheric temperature of more than 1000 K.

Satellite and Ring System

A previously unknown ring of material about Jupiter with an outer edge 128 000 kilometers from the center of the planet and an inner edge extending down to the atmosphere.

A typical ring particle size that is extremely small, perhaps a few micrometers, producing strong forward scattering of light.

Indications of extension of the ring material out of the equatorial plane, probably as a result of electromagnetic effects.

Two new satellites (1979J1 and 1979J3) only a few tens of kilometers in diameter orbiting just outside the ring.

First determinations of the size, shape, and reflectivity of Amalthea, showing it to be an irregular, elongated, dark, very red object with a surface probably contaminated by sulfur from Io.

A third satellite (1979J2) about 80 kilometers in diameter orbiting between Amalthea and Io.

Nine immense volcanic eruptions on Io, at least six of which persisted over the four months between encounters. These appear to represent a new kind of volcanism based on sulfur and sulfur dioxide as the driving volatiles.

---

continued over a period of several months, it became apparent that the bursts were not randomly spaced but that they defined a periodic variation, repeating about once every ten hours, close to the known rotation rate of Saturn. A similar periodic variation in radio emission from Jupiter had been used for many years to determine an accurate rotation period for the central core and its associated magnetic field. Apparently, a similar effect was taking place at Saturn.

From an initial survey of 40 days of PRA data, Mike Kaiser of the NASA Goddard Space Flight Center and his colleagues calculated the rotation period of Saturn to be 10 hours, 40 minutes. A later analysis, based on 267 days of observations, refined this value to 10 hours, 39 minutes, 24 ± 7 seconds. Already, months before encounter, Voyager had provided a fundamental new piece of knowledge about Saturn—its period of rotation.

A surface of Io that is uncratered, extremely young, brilliantly colored by sulfur and sulfur compounds, and capable of altering over areas of tens of thousands of square kilometers in a few months.

Hot spots on Io, suggesting (with ground-based observations) a major internal heat source.

A thin and possibly transient atmosphere of sulfur dioxide on Io.

A surface of Europa that is exceedingly smooth with no major topographic features, including a low surface density of impact craters.

An intricate, global-scale network of light and dark lines crisscrossing Europa, suggesting major tectonic stresses at some time in the distant past.

A surface of Ganymede characterized by both heavily cratered and more lightly cratered terrains, with indications of a complex evolution of the bearing strength of the crust.

Extensive linear parallel ridge/valley systems on Ganymede indicative of periods of great internal activity; some suggestion of tectonic motion of crustal plates.

A surface of Callisto characterized by impact cratering, with no indication of significant internal geologic activity.

The first opportunity to study, on Callisto and Ganymede, the effects of impact cratering in a crust dominated by water ice rather than rock; discovery of distinctive crater forms, including the ''bullseye'' basins on Callisto and crater ''palimpsests'' on Ganymede.

Accurate determinations of size and mass for the four Galilean satellites, leading to improved estimates of their bulk compositions.

Magnetosphere

An electric current of more than a million amperes flowing in the magnetic flux tube linking Jupiter and Io.

Ultraviolet emissions from sulfur and oxygen ions in a plasma torus surrounding Jupiter at approximately the orbit of Io, with temperatures in the torus up to $100\,000$ K and electron densities exceeding 1000 per cubic centimeter.

A cold, co-rotating plasma inside 6 R_J with enhanced abundances of sulfur, oxygen, and sulfur dioxide, all probably derived from volcanic eruptions on Io.

A magnetopause in the Sun-facing direction that can vary rapidly in response to changing solar wind pressure from less than 50 R_J to more than 100 R_J.

A region of hot plasma in the outer magnetosphere consisting primarily of hydrogen, oxygen, and sulfur ions.

Low-frequency (kilometric) radio emission from Jupiter with a strong latitude dependence.

A complex magnetospheric interaction with Ganymede extending up to $200\,000$ kilometers from the satellite.

Evidence suggesting a transition from closed magnetic field lines to a Jovian magnetotail at about 25 R_J.

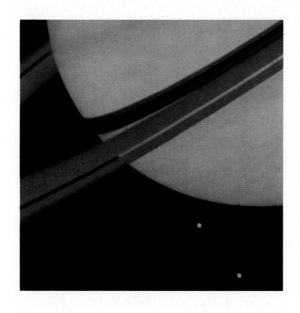

Encounter
With
Saturn

In the autumn of 1980, as the Voyager 1 spacecraft sped toward Saturn, nature provided a remarkable display in the skies of Earth. About every 20 years Jupiter, in its faster circuit of the sky, catches up with and passes Saturn. This is the longest interval between close passages, or conjunctions, involving two of the planets observable with the naked eye, and ancient astrologers called the event the Great Conjunction.

At the beginning of October, just as scientists from around the world were en route to the Jet Propulsion Laboratory (JPL) for the Saturn encounter, Jupiter and Saturn moved together in the morning sky, and for a few days they were joined by the planet Venus. Early risers were treated to a spectacular predawn show. Brilliant Venus, Jupiter, and Saturn and the bright star Regulus were all clustered together; Mars and Mercury were visible not far away. Perhaps this celestial event was a good portent for the events about to unfold.

Voyager had been observing Saturn regularly since midsummer, and a great deal of data had already accumulated at JPL. Day by day, the pace of activity increased, and along with it grew the excitement of the participants. We now follow the events chronologically, describing the drama of planetary exploration as it appeared to the scientists and members of the press who participated.

October 1, 1980 (Range to Saturn, 56 million kilometers)

Six weeks before encounter the cameras on the Voyager 1 spacecraft were able to resolve details of Saturn and its rings as small as 1000 kilometers across, about three times better than had ever been obtained from telescopic observations on Earth. From this distance the rings showed a surprising amount of detail. Instead of smooth sheets of material, banded structures began to show, looking like ripples spreading out from the planet. The prominent Cassini Division between the A and B Rings was clearly not a simple gap; there was at least one faint band of material inside the division. Several new gaps could be seen within the inner C Ring. To the surprise of several scientists on the Imaging Team, the positions of the ring features did not, for the most part,

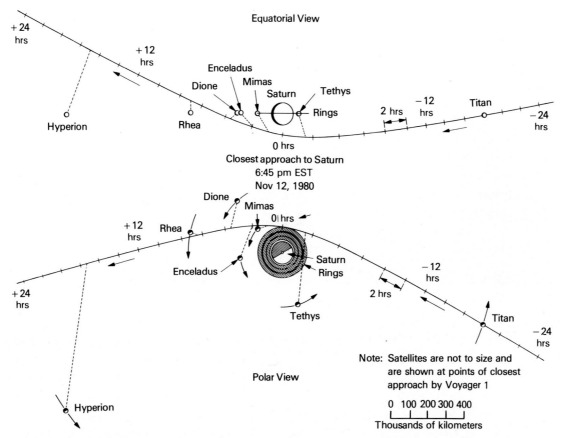

Equatorial View

+ 24 hrs

+ 12 hrs

Enceladus
Dione
Mimas
Saturn
Tethys
Rings

Hyperion

Rhea

2 hrs
− 12 hrs
Titan
− 24 hrs

0 hrs
Closest approach to Saturn
6:45 pm EST
Nov 12, 1980

Dione
Mimas
0 hrs

+ 12 hrs
Rhea

Enceladus

Saturn
Rings

− 12 hrs

+ 24 hrs

2 hrs

Tethys

Titan

− 24 hrs

Note: Satellites are not to size and
are shown at points of closest
approach by Voyager 1

Polar View

0   100 200 300 400
Thousands of kilometers

Hyperion

Voyager 1 studied the large satellite Titan, as well as the planet and its rings. From the time of Titan encounter, about 18 hours before closest approach to Saturn, until 5 hours after closest approach, the spacecraft viewed the dark side of the rings. Voyager 1 provided particularly close views of Mimas, Rhea, and Titan.

coincide with the expected resonances with the inner satellites. Perhaps the gaps were due to other effects, such as the gravitational influence of small satellites orbiting within the rings but invisible to the Voyager cameras.

At a resolution of 1000 kilometers, the cloud structure of Saturn began to appear. Several light and dark spots could be seen, each presumably a large storm system many thousands of kilometers across. None of these was as large as the Great Red Spot or the white ovals that were so prominent on Jupiter, and all were difficult to see because of pervasive haze. Meanwhile, the Voyager spacecraft was rushing toward Saturn at a speed of 1.3 million kilometers per day, and the resolution of the cameras improved steadily.

October 6, 1980 (50 million km)

A dramatic set of photographs of the rings with a resolution of about 900 kilometers had been taken by Voyager over the weekend. As Imaging Scientist Rich Terrile began to scan these pictures, he saw a new kind of structure within the B Ring: dark lanes that extended radially to the planet like the spokes of a wheel. These were the first features ever photographed in the rings that were not symmetric with respect to the planet. Nonaxisymmetric features were unexpected because the differential rotation of the rings should destroy them soon after they form. The dark lanes, which were much more visible on one side of Saturn than on the other, stretched

During the Voyager 1 observatory phase, the spacecraft first photographed the planet and its rings at resolutions greater than could be obtained with Earth-based telescopes. In early September, at a range of about 100 million kilometers, features as small as 2000 kilometers across could be seen. One of these features was the Keeler Gap near the outer edge of the A Ring, which had occasionally been glimpsed by sharp-eyed observers but had never before been photographed. (P-22877)

from about 104 000 to 116 000 kilometers from the center of Saturn. As news of the discovery spread, plans were made for a last-minute modification of the imaging sequence to make a movie of the moving lanes of dark material in the rings.

October 14, 1980 (39 million km)

While the Voyager spacecraft continued its measurements, most of the leading planetary researchers in the United States were in Tucson, Arizona, for the annual meeting of the Division for Planetary Sciences of the American Astronomical Society. Here, for the first time, the new Voyager photographs of the rings were shown to the scientific community.

Another subject of widespread interest was the ground-based and Voyager observations of the two inner satellites of Saturn, now being called S-10 and S-11. First discovered in 1966 and observed again by several astronomers when Earth passed through the plane of Saturn's rings in 1980, these two satellites were now being photographed every day by the Voyager cameras.

Voyager Project Scientist Ed Stone (left) discusses a sequencing problem with his deputy, Ellis D. Miner. (P-23311AC)

They were in almost exactly the same orbit but on nearly opposite sides of the planet. However, the orbital periods differed just enough for the two satellites to approach each other at about 9 meters per second relative speed. Many scientists wondered what would happen in about a year and a half when the two satellites passed very close to each other. Presumably they would interact and shift orbits, but the details were purely speculative.

October 24, 1980 (25 million km)

With imaging resolution better than 500 kilometers and the ring filling the narrow-angle camera field of view, Voyager passed from the observatory phase to the far encounter phase. Scan platform instruments other than the cameras were beginning to observe the Saturn system. The ultraviolet spectrometer (UVS) detected strong emission from hydrogen, not only from the planet but also from a diffuse region extending as far as the orbit of Titan. However, the preliminary observations did not show the doughnut-shaped torus at the orbit of Titan that had been predicted by many investigators.

The infrared spectrometer (IRIS) obtained spectra of Saturn several times each day, from

The scientific data radioed from the Voyager spacecraft were first received at JPL in the science control room. Here scientists could take a quick look at the numbers being produced by their instruments and verify that the spacecraft systems were operating correctly. (P-23162BC)

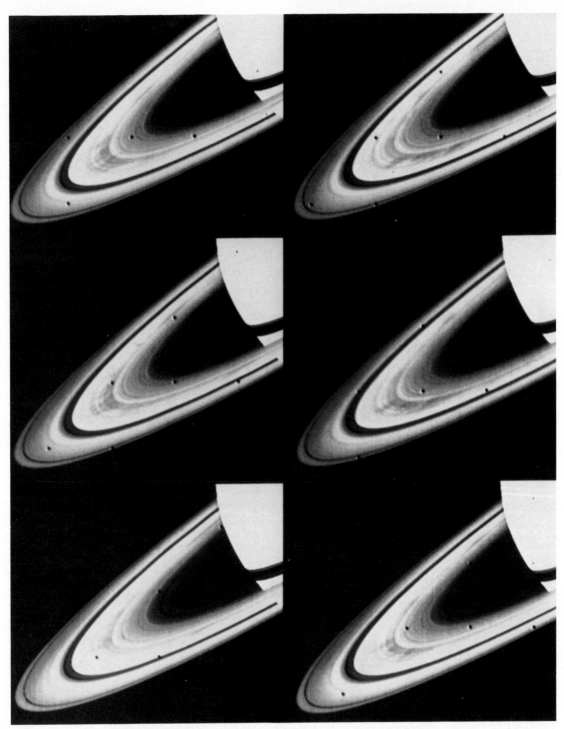

As the Voyager camera resolution improved to about 1000 kilometers, a surprising new kind of structure in the B Ring was photographed for the first time. In these six views, taken on October 25 from a distance of about 24 million kilometers, variable dark streaks (spokes) can clearly be seen. The time sequence, taken from a long series of Voyager photos, shows the dark spokes revolving around the planet. Later in the flyby, when seen from a different geometry, the same dark spokes appeared as bright streaks. (P-23053)

A NOTE ON NOMENCLATURE

Because Saturn is so difficult to study from Earth, the traditional nomenclature of the rings and satellites has not proved adequate to deal with the many Voyager discoveries. Ultimately, new names will be assigned by the International Astronomical Union, but in the meantime some designations will be arbitrary and others ambiguous. In this volume we cope with this confusing situation as well as we can.

The main rings are called the A, B, and C Rings, moving from outside to inside. The gap between the A and B Rings is called the Cassini Division; there is no gap between the B and C Rings. The very faint rings inside the C Ring discovered by Voyager are called the D Ring. For the faint outer rings, we call the thin ring discovered by Pioneer Saturn the F Ring, the diffuse ring beyond it the G Ring, and the still more diffuse ring near the orbit of Enceladus the E Ring. No names are applied to the thousands of individual ''ringlets'' resolved in Voyager images or the tens of thousands detected by the photopolarimeter on Voyager 2.

The main gap between the A and B Rings has always been called the Cassini Division. The next most prominent gap, near the outer edge of the A Ring, is called the Keeler Gap for James E. Keeler of Lick Observatory, who first saw it clearly in 1888; however, it is also frequently called the Encke Gap or Encke Division. No other gaps have been named, although there is interest in assigning the names Huygens, Encke, and Lyot to the most prominent, in addition to Keeler and Cassini.

The first nine satellites have names and numbers, proceeding from the innermost, S-1 Mimas, out to S-9 Phoebe. Those discovered more recently will ultimately be numbered in order of their discovery, but in the meantime the only proper designations are temporary ones that give the order of reporting within a given year, such as 1980S3 for the third satellite of Saturn reported in 1980. Several of these numbers can apply to the same object. Wherever possible, we use informal descriptive names; for instance, the pair 1980S1 and 1980S3 (also called S-10 and S-11) are referred to collectively as the ''co-orbital satellites,'' and 1980S28 is the ''A Ring shepherd.'' The following table may help sort this out.

Official Temporary Designation	Unofficial Number	Informal Name
1980S28	S-15	A Ring Shepherd
1980S27	S-14	Inner F Ring Shepherd
1980S26	S-13	Outer F Ring Shepherd
1980S1	S-10 or S-11	Co-Orbital
1980S3	S-10 or S-11	Co-Orbital
1980S13	S-16	Tethys Lagrangian (leading)
1980S25	S-17	Tethys Lagrangian (trailing)
1980S6	S-12	Dione Lagrangian (or Dione B)

which the composition and the structure of the atmosphere could be determined. The chemicals already detected by IRIS included hydrogen, helium, phosphene, methane, acetylene, and ethane. High in the atmosphere where the pressure was only one-tenth of one percent that of the sea level pressure on Earth, IRIS measured a temperature of − 130° C, somewhat warmer than the value measured at the same altitude by Pioneer. Perhaps the structure in the upper atmosphere varied with time.

October 25, 1980 (24 million km)

In an effort to understand the motions of the dark spokes in the B Ring, controllers repro-

grammed Voyager to devote 10 hours to photographing one of the ends, or ansae, of the rings, producing a "movie" of pictures taken once every five minutes. It was a lazy Saturday afternoon at JPL, but Imaging Science Team member Andy Collins came in to process some of the new pictures as they were received from the spacecraft. In addition to the expected structure in the rings, he spotted a new small satellite orbiting the planet just on the outer edge of the narrow F Ring. As one frame followed another, the small point of light could easily be seen swinging around the planet. The next day, Collins examined the new photos more carefully and found another new satellite, somewhat fainter than the first, orbiting on the inner edge of the F Ring. These were the first new satellites of Saturn to be discovered by Voyager—the thirteenth and fourteenth known satellites of Saturn.

A trained eye is required to make sense from the initial sequences of raw numbers transmitted to JPL. In most cases, days or weeks of additional processing are required to understand the significance of the information received. (P-23312AC, P-23315AC, P-23315BC)

Members of the Imaging Team immediately speculated that the two new satellites on either side of the F Ring might be responsible for the ring's narrow, ribbon-like form. It had been suggested about two years earlier that a similar gravitational focusing effect might produce the narrow rings of Uranus, but in that case the satellites could not be seen and remained hypothetical. Here was a real example that might provide important clues to the nature of both the Saturnian and the Uranian ring systems.

October 31, 1980 (17 million km)

With only two weeks remaining before encounter, increasing detail could be seen in the photographs of the planet and the rings; the

More structure in the rings became apparent as Voyager neared Saturn. On November 6, at a distance of 8 million kilometers, approximately 95 individual concentric features were revealed on specially computer-processed images. In the version shown here, the large-scale brightness differences between the A, B, and C Rings have been suppressed to bring out finer detail, including four rings inside the Cassini Division and a very faint image of the thin F Ring beyond the edge of the A Ring. (P-23068)

satellites, too, began to appear as tiny round worlds rather than mere points of light.

In Saturn's atmosphere the small light and dark spots began to take on a more distinctive character. Along the borders between belts and zones, plumes of material appeared to be rising from below, and many of the clouds took on a characteristic scalloped shape, reminiscent of the high-speed wind areas on Jupiter. Within the rings, every increment in resolution seemed to produce finer detail. For instance, the Cassini Division, already found to contain one interior ring, could now be seen to have five separate interior rings, each just a few hundred kilometers from the one adjacent to it.

Although the images of the satellites of Saturn were still too small to show any surface detail, it was possible to measure them for size. From preliminary examination of the available information, Torrence Johnson of the Imaging Science Team concluded that both Dione and Tethys were slightly larger than had been expected, suggesting that they had a very low density, perhaps as low as 1 gram per cubic centimeter, the density of water. Johnson also noted that in some of the images Enceladus did not look round, a result not confirmed by later observations. As always, scientists push the data as far as possible to try to extract every bit of information from the tiny images. (A common saying in research is "If it were easy, it would have been done already by someone else.") But a fascinating new dimension was added with observations made by Voyager, since each day produced a major improvement in resolution. Results would be superseded, and theories overthrown, from one day to the next—in effect condensing an entire scientific career into a few hectic and exciting weeks.

November 3, 1980 (12 million km)

Saturn's giant satellite Titan, one of the primary objectives of the Voyager 1 mission, began for the first time to assume the character of

Imaging Team Leader Brad Smith and team member Reta Beebe work on the analysis of atmospheric motions on Saturn. On the bulletin board behind them are individual frames from the ring movie that first showed the motion of the dark spokes in the B Ring. (P-23287A)

a planet. Until now the Voyager pictures had shown only a blank face for this cloud-shrouded satellite, but Rich Terrile succeeded in enhancing the contrast in one of the new pictures to show a faint hint of banded structure and perhaps a Y-shaped dark feature in the equatorial part of Titan. The images of this satellite would be watched with increasing interest over the next week as Voyager plunged toward its flyby late on November 11, the day before Saturn encounter.

The photographs of the rings of Saturn, taken as part of the special sequence a week earlier to study the radial dark spokes, had been processed at the JPL Image Processing Laboratory and assembled into a movie sequence. In the afternoon, Project Scientist Ed Stone and several members of the Imaging Science Team had their first opportunity to see this time-lapse movie

Saturn is intrinsically less colorful and exciting than Jupiter. The cloud structure is subdued and nearly invisible in a normally processed photo; only with special techniques of computer enhancement can banded structure and storm systems comparable to those on Jupiter become visible. (P-22993, P-22994)

covering 10 hours of ring rotation. As they watched in fascination, the dark spoke-like features appeared and moved around the ring, changing shape as they went. The more the scientists saw these features, the more baffling they seemed. Torrence Johnson noted that, once again, our expectations had proved wrong. He said, "We never thought we would be able to see the rings spinning like this. When we planned the Saturn movie, we thought we would see the planet turning with the rings as a still life. It now appears to be more nearly the reverse."

With only a little more than a week to go until encounter, the pace at JPL was rapidly accelerating. Most of the participating scientists had arrived and occupied their offices. The press would soon follow. Many people realized that this would be the last opportunity for many years to participate in a major spacecraft encounter with an unknown world. Saturn, with its rings and satellites, lay spread before us. No one knew what discoveries might be made, but everyone was confident that the next 10 days would not be dull.

November 5, 1980 (9 million km)

The first formal science investigators meeting, chaired by Ed Stone, was held at JPL. At these daily meetings, the Principal Investigators for

each instrument would summarize their latest results and exchange ideas and tentative interpretations. Imaging Science Team Leader Brad Smith reported that the narrow F Ring appeared to be slightly eccentric, swinging about 400 kilometers farther from the planet on one side than the other. On the planet a wide variety of atmospheric features were being measured. These included bright halos surrounding dark centers, one long, dark feature similar to the so-called barges at Jupiter, intricately scrolled edges between belts and zones, and one confused spaghetti-like cloud. Perhaps most impressive were the unexpected numbers of belts and zones; in the southern hemisphere of Saturn between the ring and the pole, Smith counted 24.

Lyle Broadfoot reported that the ultraviolet spectrometer was now obtaining spectra of Saturn showing a variety of emission lines, the strongest being Lyman α of hydrogen. In addition, several lines appeared at wavelengths between 80 and 160 nanometers. Although he could not provide individual identifications, Broadfoot noted that these probably represent atomic emission lines due to aurora in the atmosphere of Saturn.

Fred Scarf, reporting results from the planetary radio astronomy and plasma wave instruments, noted that in the past few days a new kind of radio radiation with a frequency of about 10 kilohertz had been observed. He believed that this radiation did not arise at the planet Saturn, but from Saturn's magnetosphere.

November 6, 1980 (8 million km)

Voyager was speeding up as it felt the gravitational tug of Saturn; the approach speed was now 15.4 kilometers per second. The far encounter sequence of observations continued with a major imaging mosaic on the rings once a day and observations of Titan with the full battery of remote sensing instruments once every six hours. Late in the evening searches were carried out for undiscovered satellites, and a long series of observa-

Magnetometer Principal Investigator Norm Ness examines a computer printout for indications that the Voyager spacecraft has reached the magnetosphere of Saturn. (P-23309BC)

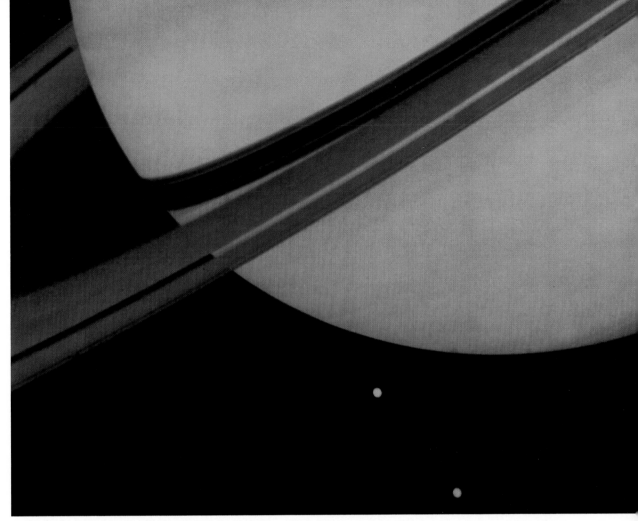

Silhouetted against the face of Saturn, the rings appear partly opaque and partly transparent. In this view, taken November 3 at a distance of 13 million kilometers, the A, B, and C Rings cast clearly separate, individual shadows on the cloud tops of Saturn. Also visible are two of the icy inner satellites, Tethys and Dione, as well as the black shadow of Tethys on the planet. (P-23058)

tions of Saturn were undertaken by the IRIS and the UVS. The resolution of the imaging cameras was now 150 kilometers.

At 10:30 a.m. the first news conference was held in Von Karman Auditorium at JPL. Project Manager Ray Heacock welcomed about 60

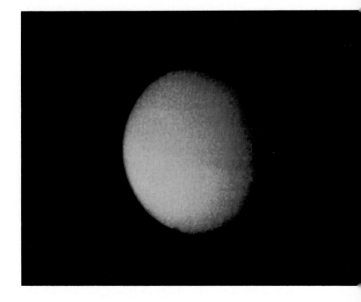

The large satellite Titan was the first main target of the Voyager 1 encounter. In this image, taken on November 9 from a distance of about 5 million kilometers, the cloud-shrouded satellite appears remarkably bland. However, a dark cap can be seen over the north pole, and there is a faint line along the equator separating the slightly darker northern hemisphere from the brighter southern hemisphere. There is no indication of any breaks in the clouds through which the surface might be glimpsed. (P-23076)

61

During the encounter period, daily meetings were held by all the science principal investigators to discuss their discoveries. Here Lyle Broadfoot, the UVS Principal Investigator, describes the bright emission from Titan that first suggested that nitrogen was a major component of the satellite's atmosphere. (P-23316AC)

members of the press and announced that all the engineering subsystems were in excellent condition except the Canopus star tracker. He explained that although the star tracker was not working properly, it was not anticipated that this would cause any difficulty during the encounter. Heacock also announced that the ninth and final trajectory correction maneuver would be carried out that evening to define the aimpoint of Voyager at Saturn. The anticipated change in velocity was only 1.52 meters per second, bringing the spacecraft 650 kilometers closer to Titan and placing it exactly on the desired trajectory through the Saturn system. Finally, Heacock showed the magnificent computer-animated film of the coming Voyager 1 flyby, complete with rotating planet and rings, a complex sequence of spacecraft maneuvers, and a spectacular outbound simulation of the E Ring crossing that drew gasps from the audience. It seemed as if the next week of exploration, condensed into a few moments of film, had been made more real—the long-awaited encounter was actually beginning!

Project Scientist Ed Stone began his presentation by expressing his belief that we were "on the verge of major discoveries." After providing some background discussion of Saturn and its magnetosphere and satellite system, Stone introduced Imaging Science Team Leader Brad Smith. Smith also emphasized the potential for major discoveries by Voyager during the next week and said, "Our long-standing theories, our cherished ideas of the Universe, are likely to become casualties." He showed photographs of the planet Saturn that revealed a variety of features in the atmosphere and a color picture of Titan that showed a ruddy orange color with the first hint of banded structure, as well as a darkening toward the poles.

The highlight of the news conference was the presentation of the ring movie, showing the enigmatic dark spokes swinging around the planet in the middle of the B Ring. Smith emphasized that the Voyager scientists had no explanation for these features, so the press tried out a few ideas of their own.

In response to a question concerning the significance of the Voyager Saturn flyby, both Ed Stone and Brad Smith made interesting comments. Stone said, "It is clear that as we move out through the solar system, we are seeing different examples, presumably related to the fact that the temperatures were different at the time the solar system was formed. This is all a part of trying to understand how planetary systems form. It is clear that the more examples we have to test our theories with, the better idea we're going to have about not only the formation of the Saturn system itself but of the entire solar system."

Smith added, "It is the comparative work that is really important. We can develop theories to explain what we thought we saw on Jupiter, but those theories have to work on Saturn as well. If they don't, we know we're in trouble on Jupiter too."

In the afternoon, a special brainstorming session was held by the Imaging Science Team to see if anyone had a reasonable theory to explain the dark spokes in the B Ring. A variety of possibilities was discussed, ranging from changes in the particles induced by interactions with the magnetosphere to wave-like variations in density

In the last days before the Voyager 1 encounter with Saturn, the planet's atmosphere began to show a greater variety of interesting storm structures. This enhanced color image, obtained on November 5 at a distance of 9 million kilometers, shows convective cloud systems at a resolution of about 200 kilometers. (P-23062)

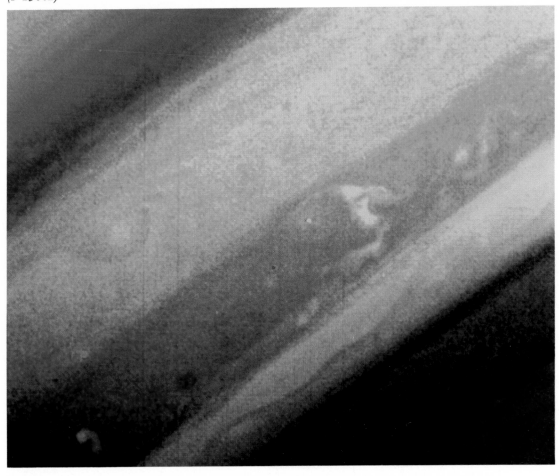

caused by the gravitational perturbations of satellites. None of these ideas seemed very satisfactory.

At the daily science meeting, Rudy Hanel reported that the IRIS might have detected ammonia in the atmosphere of Saturn. Lyle Broadfoot showed additional ultraviolet spectra and explained that he was now fairly certain that the emission from Saturn corresponded to aurora produced by the excitation of neutral atoms caused by the impact of protons and electrons on the atmosphere.

Several fields and particles experimenters discussed the probable time that Voyager would cross the bow shock and magnetopause and enter the magnetosphere of Saturn. It was generally agreed that decreased solar wind pressure would result in a bow shock around 40 R_S from the planet, rather than much closer, as it had been during the time of the Pioneer 11 encounter. Jim Sullivan indicated that measurements of the solar wind as it flowed past the Voyager 2 spacecraft also en route to Saturn should make it possible in the next day or two to predict exactly the solar wind pressure on the magnetosphere and

therefore the size of the magnetosphere. Norm Ness noted that Titan would almost surely be inside the magnetosphere, and therefore it would be possible to obtain a more sensitive search for an intrinsic magnetic field on this large satellite.

November 7, 1980 (7 million km)

The regular science press corps had now all arrived and occupied their desks in the large press room next to Von Karman Auditorium. They were primarily veterans who had worked together covering Voyager Jupiter, Pioneer Saturn, Pioneer Venus, Viking, and other planetary spectaculars of the past decade. Many had been involved in the space program even earlier, in the exciting period of the first manned flights that led up to the Apollo lunar landings. Now they were together again, perhaps for one of the last planetary missions during their careers, unless the trend of declining investment in space exploration were reversed.

At the morning press briefing, Deputy Project Manager Esker Davis announced the successful completion of the last maneuver that would target Voyager exactly for Titan and Saturn. This

The Voyager Imaging Science Team was responsible for interpreting the many hundreds of pictures received each day during the encounter period. Here a meeting of the Imaging Team has been called to discuss possible interpretations for the dark spokes and the very large number of individual rings appearing in the high-resolution images. (P-23318)

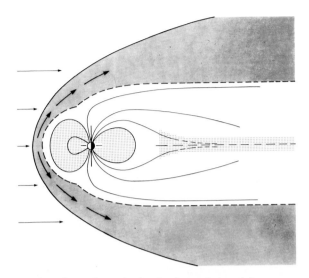

As the solar wind of charged particles nears Saturn, it interacts with the planetary magnetic field to produce a bow shock, shown here as a solid line. The actual limits of the Saturn magnetosphere are marked by the dotted line, which follows the magnetopause. The magnetosphere is compressed toward the Sun and extends out into a long tail away from the Sun. Pioneer Saturn had established the basic outline of the magnetic field and magnetosphere of Saturn, but the Voyager instruments were capable of making more detailed measurements, particularly of the composition of charged particles.

trajectory correction maneuver (TCM) had begun at 8:22 p.m. the previous day, when controllers directed Voyager to turn away from its navigational stars and continue under gyroscopic control instructed by its onboard computers. The spacecraft turned nearly 90 degrees and then fired its rocket motors for 11 3/4 minutes. Two hours passed before the spacecraft began to unwind from this complicated maneuver. By 12:13 a.m. it had returned to celestial lock, and controllers on the ground verified that the proper change in velocity had been achieved. Davis said, "This critical event is now behind us, and we should have smooth sailing from here to Saturn."

The steadily improving resolution of the Voyager photographs provided Brad Smith with new results to show to the press. On Saturn more and more narrow belts and zones were appearing,

primarily in the southern hemisphere. Smith showed pictures of the red spot of Saturn, nothing like Jupiter's Great Red Spot, but still nearly 5000 kilometers long. A ring picture at a resolution of 150 kilometers was shown, and Smith reported that he had counted 95 separate rings.

Strange little Iapetus, the satellite with one dark face and one bright face, had been photographed for the first time the previous day. At this point in the orbit of Iapetus, both hemispheres could be seen and, as had been predicted, the satellite did have a black leading face and a bright, white trailing face, with a sharp boundary between. Pictures with improved resolution would be obtained a day after Saturn encounter, but no very good look at this strange

One of the new Saturn satellites discovered by Voyager orbits just 800 kilometers outside the edge of the A Ring. About 100 kilometers in diameter, this small satellite (1980S28) circles the planet in 14 hours, 20 minutes. Voyager scientists suggested that the gravitational effect of this small satellite, rather than a resonance with the larger, more distant satellites, might be the cause of the sharp outer edge of the A Ring. This overexposed picture, which also shows the F Ring, was taken on November 6 at a distance of 8 million kilometers. (P-23070)

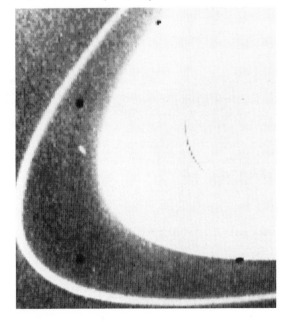

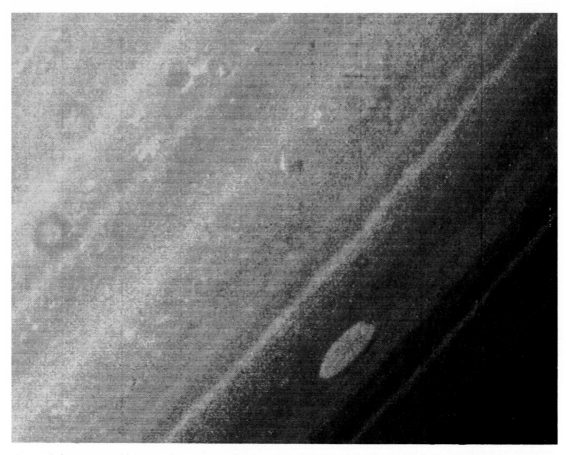

One of the unique features of Jupiter is the Great Red Spot, about twice the size of the Earth. Saturn lacks such gigantic storms, but this false color image, taken on November 6 from a distance of about 8 million kilometers, shows a somewhat similar, although much smaller, red spot on Saturn. False color was used to make the faint spot more visible. (260-1217)

world would be obtained until the closer flyby by Voyager 2 the following August.

During the afternoon, the Voyager spacecraft carried out additional searches for new satellites. Meanwhile, the possible identification of another new satellite near the F Ring had been made from photographs taken the previous day. A major search for ultraviolet emission features from Titan was also carried out.

November 8, 1980 (6 million km)

Bad news opened the daily press briefing. The Voyager data are received on Earth at three NASA Deep Space Network tracking stations located in desert regions of Australia, Spain, and California. These three stations are evenly spaced in longitude around Earth, and there is very little redundancy in their coverage. Thus it is crucial that each station operate if data are not to be lost. The radio signals from the spacecraft can pass through ordinary terrestrial clouds and even light rain, but a heavy rainstorm can wipe out the signal entirely. Ray Heacock opened the morning press briefing by announcing that just such an event had taken place during the early morning hours while the spacecraft was being tracked by the station in Madrid. A series of extremely heavy thunderstorms had caused a loss of about 6 hours of transmission. Not until the spacecraft rose above the horizon could contact be made with the

Goldstone Tracking Station in the Mohave Desert. Another series of storms in the Atlantic Ocean was apparently moving toward Spain. Heacock said, "The rain in Spain has lost all humor for us."

The new satellite—Saturn's innermost—suspected the previous day had been confirmed; it was the third Saturn satellite discovered by Voyager and the fifteenth satellite of Saturn. The new S-15 appeared to be about 100 kilometers across and orbited 800 kilometers outside the edge of the A Ring. Brad Smith suggested that the presence of this satellite may provide the gravitational confinement that defines the outer edge of the ring. This would be an important conclusion, indicating that perhaps much of the structure in the rings was caused by the herding effect of small satellites rather than gravitational resonances with more distant satellites.

At the science meeting, Rich Terrile of the Imaging Science Team showed recently received pictures indicating that the narrow F Ring, no more than 100 kilometers wide, was not uniform in brightness. Two bright condensations or concentrations of matter had been seen and their motion followed for four rotations of the ring. Each condensation was perhaps 1000 kilometers long.

Don Shemansky reported that the UVS was clearly recording emission from a number of lines of neutral atomic nitrogen coming from Titan. This was the first strong evidence of the presence of this gas in the atmosphere of the satellite. It had been suggested that nitrogen was an important component in the models that called for a massive atmosphere on Titan, whereas the cold, small-atmosphere models called for almost pure methane.

Jim Sullivan of the Plasma Team had been using information on the solar wind pressure obtained from the Voyager 2 spacecraft upstream of Saturn to calculate where the border of the magnetosphere of Saturn would be when Voyager 2 arrived. He was ready with his first prediction this afternoon. Voyager 2 had been measuring the solar wind speed at 420 kilometers per second, but Voyager 1, closer to Saturn, was getting a lower value. Now the higher speed streams appeared to be catching up with Voyager 1, which today was reading 400 kilometers per second. This high wind speed was expected to persist for several days. Depending on whether the magnetosphere of Saturn had the compressibility of that of Earth or Jupiter, a bow shock at 30 to 35 R_S was now expected. In any case, Titan should be well inside the magnetosphere, and the spacecraft should encounter the bow shock sometime on Tuesday afternoon, November 11.

November 9, 1980 (5 million km)

Good news today. Although thunderstorm activity had continued in Spain, the heavy rain had held off long enough for the data receipt at Madrid to be completed and transfer to the Goldstone facility accomplished. The weather forecast for Spain suggested improvement, with little likelihood of data loss due to rain on the crucial encounter days.

Titan, which was the first major encounter target of the mission, loomed larger and larger in the Voyager images, but remained disappointingly bland. There was a faint dark band around the equator, and the northern hemisphere appeared distinctly darker than the southern, but there was no indication of holes in the clouds through which the surface might be glimpsed. Brad Smith said, "No fine structure of any kind has been seen on Titan. We'll just have to wait and watch daily to see if anything shows up."

By now the rings of Saturn were too large to fit within the narrow-angle field of view of the Voyager camera. Instead, the cameras were targeted for detailed pictures of individual small areas. Brad Smith showed one of these pictures of the Cassini Division. No longer a simple division, it appeared filled with a variety of light and dark rings. Smith noted that it was difficult to determine the boundaries of the Cassini Division. One of the new rings was exceedingly narrow, rather like the F Ring. Two days later it would be shown to be eccentric as well. In releasing a picture of the clumps found in the F Ring, Smith noted, "We have no explanation of what causes them, what holds them together, or how long they last."

Jim Sullivan had refined his interplanetary weather forecast for the magnetosphere of Saturn and now predicted that the bow shock would be encountered between 22 and 29 R_S on Tuesday, November 11.

Although little had been said recently about the dark spokes in the rings, members of the press persisted in asking the cause of them. Brad Smith, in response to one of these questions, said, "We've known of the finger-like projections for several weeks now, and we really don't have any inkling of an explanation. I don't expect the light to turn on suddenly in the next few hours or days to give us an answer to this perplexing question."

This was the day on which some of the first good pictures of the Saturn satellites were expected, pictures with resolutions substantially better than 100 kilometers. Early photographs of Rhea showed wispy streaks and fuzzy bright spots with filamentary structure on the leading hemisphere. There was as yet no clear evidence of impact craters.

At the science meeting, Lyle Broadfoot had an interpretation for the Lyman α hydrogen emission detected in the ultraviolet from the vicinity of Saturn. It appeared that the source was neither Saturn nor Titan, but a very broad disk-shaped region stretching from about 8 to 25 R_S and perhaps 4 R_S thick. This disk included the orbit of Titan, but it was not clear whether Titan was the source of the glowing hydrogen.

As the spacecraft approached Saturn, there was increasing interest in the possibility of detecting bursts of energetic particles from the planet. Jim Sullivan saw evidence of an upstream burst of electrons in the plasma data, but it could not be confirmed by the other instruments. Tom Krimigis noted that when Voyager was this close to Jupiter, it was possible to detect a great many electrons and heavy ions originating at the planet. Apparently Saturn did not have the same ability to accelerate charged paricles to very high velocities and inject them upstream into the solar wind, or else the Voyager spacecraft was not at the right place to see the bursts.

In the late afternoon many Voyager scientists and engineers, as well as members of the press and dignitaries who had arrived for the encounter, drove to the Caltech campus to hear a distinguished panel (Walter Sullivan, Philip Morrison, Carl Sagan, Ray Bradbury, and Bruce Murray) discuss "Saturn and the Mind of Man." This break from the details of the encounter provided a welcome sense of perspective and brought into clearer focus anticipation for the discoveries of the next few days. This spirit continued later in the evening, when many participated in a fund-raising dinner sponsored by the Planetary Society, an organization newly created by Carl Sagan and Bruce Murray to involve the public in the exploration of the solar system.

November 10, 1980 (3 million km)

This was the day before the anticipated crossing of the magnetospheric bow shock and the first big encounter (with Titan). It was strangely quiet, as though everyone was saving his energy and enthusiasm for the two or three days of frantic activity to come. At the morning press briefing Ray Heacock reported that the spacecraft was healthy and the rain in Spain dispersing. Ed Stone was more

Both the ultraviolet and infrared instruments on Voyager contributed to unraveling the mystery of the composition of Titan's atmosphere. Here, IRIS Principal Investigator Rudy Hanel (right) shows his most recent infrared spectrum to UVS Principal Investigator Lyle Broadfoot. (P-23310AC)

understated than usual in his presentation; and even Brad Smith, usually enthusiastic, seemed exhausted and preoccupied.

The press interest in the Saturn encounter continued to soar. Today, for the first time, every seat in Von Karman Auditorium was taken, and many people stood against the walls. With the national election past, newspapers seemed willing to provide space to report on Voyager. A full-page story with two pictures appeared in the November 10 issue of *Time*; it drew parallels between the ancient Roman festival of the Saturnalia and the gathering of scientists and the press at JPL for the encounter. *Newsweek* quoted Brad Smith: "Every-thing we are seeing on Saturn is brand new." Major stories appeared daily in the *Los Angeles Times*, the *New York Times*, the *Washington Post*, and the *Christian Science Monitor*. George Alexander, writing in the *Los Angeles Times*,

As the Voyager spacecraft sped toward its encounter with Saturn, Jim Sullivan of the Plasma Science Investigation took the lead in predicting when the spacecraft would encounter the magnetosphere of Saturn. Data from both Voyager 1 and Voyager 2 were used to estimate the strength of the solar wind at the time of encounter, and from that the degree of compression to be expected in the magnetosphere. (P-23850)

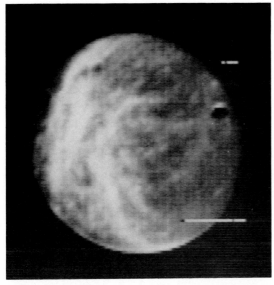

Early pictures of the satellites of Saturn showed primarily light and dark markings on the surfaces, rather than topography. In these images, the resolution on Dione (right) is about 100 kilometers and on Rhea (left) about 30 kilometers. The wispy, bright streaks superimposed on an already light icy surface excited the Voyager scientists because they suggested the possibility of internal geological activity on these two rather small satellites. (P-23085, P-23078)

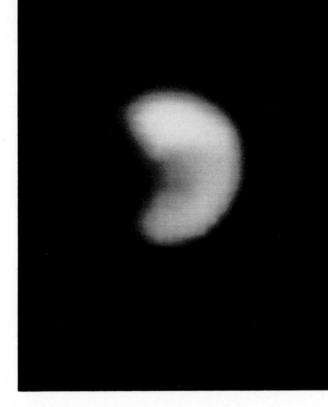

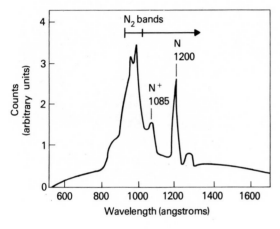

The first indications of the true composition of the atmosphere of Titan were produced by UVS spectra that showed ultraviolet emission from atomic and molecular nitrogen. Subsequent analysis of these data demonstrated that nitrogen was the primary constituent of Titan's atmosphere, whereas the concentration of methane, which had been detected from the Earth, amounted to only about 1 percent.

called the rings "just as breathtaking as people have always imagined them—and twice as baffling."

Meanwhile, the Voyager spacecraft was busy. The first detailed views of the satellites Tethys and Dione were obtained, and a special sequence of "retargetable" images of features in the atmosphere of Saturn began. More and more, the remote sensing instruments were focusing on Titan. By evening, the spacecraft was less than 2 million kilometers from this satellite, and the resolution of the cameras was better than 35 kilometers. If there were holes in the clouds, they should begin to show up soon.

November 11, 1980 (2 million km)

The day began with a full suite of observations alternating among the small satellites of Saturn, the rings, the planet, and Titan. At 10:00 a.m. the spacecraft performed a 384 degree roll turn to a new guide star in order to map out the fields and particles environment. By 11:00 a.m. Titan was too large to fill a single frame of the imaging camera, and 2 × 2 mosaics were made. By the middle of the afternoon, 3 × 3 mosaics were necessary to encompass the satellite.

Voyager scientists eagerly awaited the magnetospheric bow shock crossing, which had been predicted to take place at about 3:00 p.m. The particles and fields experimenters still expected that Titan would be inside the magnetosphere, but not by a very large margin. At about 3:00 p.m. the far encounter phase of observations ended, and near encounter with Saturn and Titan began. The distance to Titan at this time was 493 000 kilometers. There was no sign of the bow shock.

The daily press briefing was moved forward one hour to 9:30 a.m. Esker Davis described the spacecraft maneuver to a new guide star and asserted that the spacecraft was healthy and performing extremely well. Weather forecasts for Spain indicated some chance of rain but little probability of another major data loss. Ed Stone described the

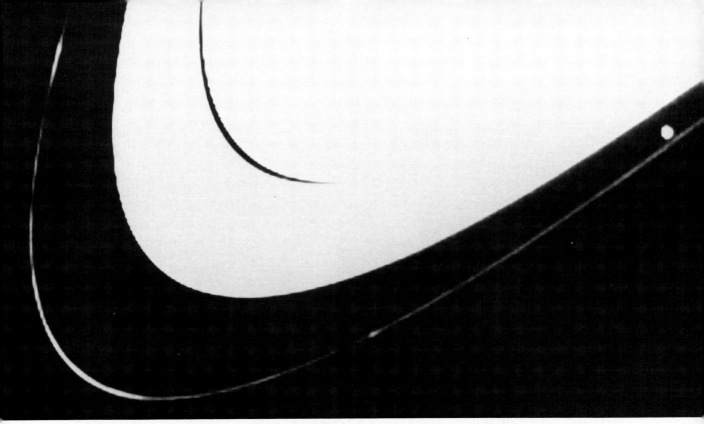

The F Ring of Saturn had been discovered by Pioneer, but not until the Voyager approach was it possible to determine the narrowness of this ring. By November 8, when the spacecraft was still 7 million kilometers from Saturn, it was already clear that the F Ring was no more than 100 kilometers wide. Even more remarkable, the ring was not uniform in brightness, but appeared to show knots or condensations along its circumference. (260-958)

sequence of events that would focus on Titan. From 6:00 to 8:00 p.m. the effort would concentrate on infrared spectra with the IRIS. Then primary observations would be made by the UVS. At 10:25 the scan platform would point to the edge of Titan, and the IRIS would begin a special series of observations to determine trace constituents in the atmosphere above the main cloud deck. Later, the spacecraft would begin to prepare for the radio occultation. Data transmission would be turned off, leaving a pure tone radio signal, providing an increase of thirty times in the signal-to-noise ratio during the occultation period. At about 11:00 p.m., the spacecraft was expected to pass through the magnetic wake of Titan, assuming, of course, that Titan was inside the magnetosphere. It would enter the shadow of Titan at about 11:10 and emerge at about 11:23.

Brad Smith announced a major new discovery in the photographs of Titan. A detached, thin layer of haze, about 100 kilometers above the main cloud deck, could now be seen stretching all the way around the atmosphere. Near the north pole, this detached haze connected with an opaque dark hood of clouds. Strangely, there was no comparable feature near the south pole. Smith then introduced the latest ring pictures saying, "The mystery of the ring structure gets deeper and deeper; it seems like a bottomless pit. We have seen many remarkable things. The thing I perhaps least expected to see was eccentric rings, and now we have not one, but two." He showed photographs of the thin, bright rings, one within one of the C Ring gaps, the other within the Cassini Division, both of which departed noticeably from circularity. He said the phenomenon was most unexpected and there was no explanation; Torrence Johnson later remarked that the rings "are not just eccentric; they are stark raving mad."

Satellite expert Larry Soderblom showed some of the first satellite images to show surface detail. Dione, Rhea, and Tethys all showed distinct, but enigmatic, features. The strangest was a picture of Tethys with a circular feature about 200 kilometers across near the center of the disk. This feature looked very much like a crater ring illumi-

As the first photographs of satellites primarily composed of ice were obtained, Larry Soderblom of the Imaging Team fascinated the press with descriptions and interpretations. Impact cratering had been expected, but the widespread wispy terrain seen on Rhea and Dione represented a new phenomenon in planetary geology.

nated obliquely, with all the bright areas and shadows one would expect. However, the Sun was not coming from the side, but almost directly from behind; the feature was, in a sense, an optical illusion. It probably represented differences of brightness or albedo on the surface and not indications of topography. A similar confusing view of Io had been seen by Voyager 1 when the great circular feature, later identified as evidence of the volcano Pele, also showed up at a great distance as an enigmatic albedo marking on the surface. Unfortunately, the strange feature on Tethys was setting and would not be seen close up during the Voyager 1 flyby.

Some of the scientists were disappointed that the opaque clouds on Titan appeared to be revealing no sign of the surface underneath. Atmos-

pheric scientists might find the structure in the clouds exciting, but there was no hint of information for the geologists. Hal Masursky of the Imaging Science Team remarked, "We cannot see the surface of Titan. If we are going to learn what this extraordinary and fascinating body is like, we will require a Titan orbiting imaging radar such as the VOIR mission being proposed for Venus." Radar could penetrate the clouds and atmosphere and provide a map of the surface, revealing the geologic history of this mysterious world.

During the day, satellite images with increasingly better resolution continued to be received. Measurements of the diameters of the satellites were now accurate to within 20 or 30 kilometers, sufficient to allow reasonable estimates of density. All the densities appeared to be low, in many

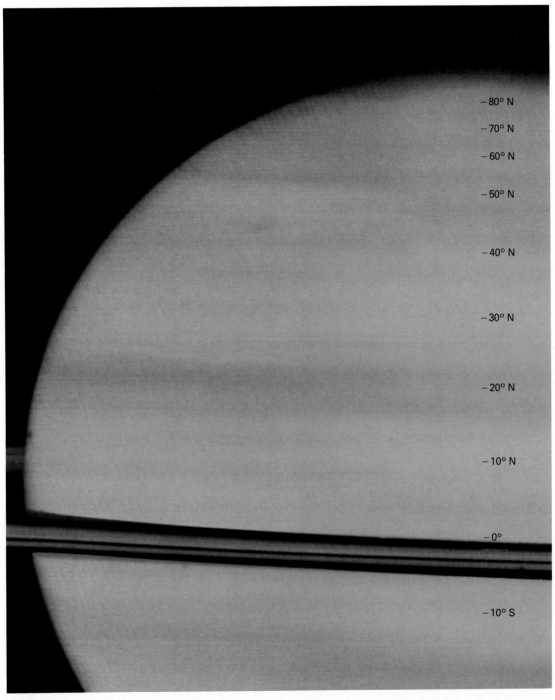

−80° N

−70° N

−60° N

−50° N

−40° N

−30° N

−20° N

−10° N

−0°

−10° S

As Voyager 1 neared the plane of the rings, its perspective on the planet Saturn improved. This picture, taken on November 11 from a distance of about 2 million kilometers, shows features as small as 50 kilometers across. In spite of the low contrast and pervasive haze, a great deal of fine structure is apparent, with many more alternating bands and zones than were visible on Jupiter. (260-1119BC)

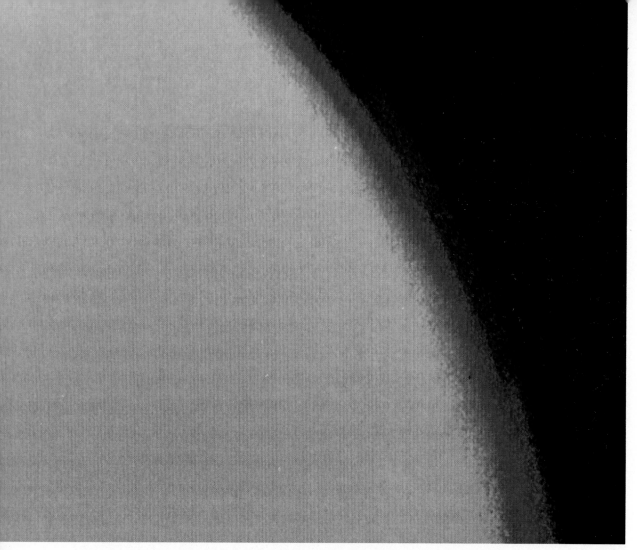

By November 12, Voyager was less than half a million kilometers from Titan, its first major target. Images with a resolution of about 10 kilometers showed an unbroken orange cloud cover, with detached haze layers visible at the edge of the satellite against the blackness of space. By this time, scientists had given up any hope of seeing surface features on Titan and concentrated their attention on the atmosphere. (P-23108C)

cases as small as 1.1 gram per cubic centimeter, strongly suggesting that the satellites of Saturn were basically icy bodies with no more than a small component of silicates, rocks, or metals. More markings on the surfaces showed up, but the spacecraft still had the Sun directly behind it; only a faint hint of topography in the form of craters along one edge of Tethys could really be identified with any certainty.

As the day progressed, activity at JPL became more and more hectic. Dozens of scientific visitors blocked the halls and corridors and stood clustered around television monitors. VIPs from NASA Headquarters and industry congregated in the control building for the spacecraft. In Von Karman

Auditorium the press corps swelled to more than 400 persons, more than had been present for the Voyager Jupiter encounters or the Viking landings on Mars.

At 4:50 p.m., at a distance from Saturn of 26.2 R_S, the Voyager spacecraft encountered the bow shock. As predicted, the magnetosphere of Saturn was larger than it had been at the time of the Pioneer flyby, when the bow shock had first been encountered at a distance of 24.1 R_S. During the evening, as the spacecraft swiftly approached Titan, there were five individual encounters with the magnetopause, the border between the magnetosphere of Saturn and the turbulent area between the bow shock and the magnetosphere. The first magneto-

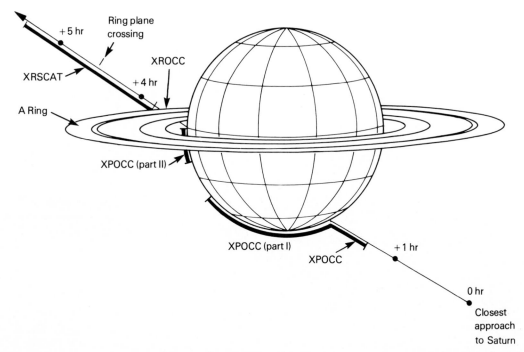

Ring plane
crossing

+5 hr

XROCC

XRSCAT

+4 hr

A Ring

XPOCC (part II)

XPOCC (part I)

XPOCC

+1 hr

0 hr
Closest
approach
to Saturn

At the beginning of the Voyager 1 near encounter period, the spacecraft swooped below the rings, viewing them on their dark side. Then, as seen from Earth, the spacecraft passed behind the planet, reemerged in the small gap between the planet and the C Ring, and crossed successively behind the C, B, and A Rings. Careful analysis of the radio signal as it probed the planet's atmosphere and the rings would provide a particularly powerful tool for studying the Saturn system.

If Titan was located inside the magnetosphere at the time of the Voyager encounter, scientists expected that the atmosphere of this satellite would be a major source of magnetospheric charged particles. The Low Energy Charged Particle (LECP) Investigation provided the main compositional analysis of the magnetosphere. Here LECP Principal Investigator Tom Krimigis describes what he expects to see as Voyager crosses the magnetopause and enters Saturn's magnetosphere. (P-22368BC)

pause crossing took place at 7:19 p.m. at a distance of 23.7 R_S, the final at 8:13 at a distance of 22.9 R_S, when the Voyager 1 spacecraft entered the magnetosphere for the last time. Just three hours remained before Titan encounter.

As Voyager approached Titan, the ultraviolet and infrared instruments held center stage. Spectra of Titan at greater and greater spatial resolution

On November 10, at a distance from Saturn of 3 million kilometers, Voyager 1 had one of its last opportunities to photograph the rings on both sides of the planet. This composite view shows the trailing ansa (top) and the leading ansa (bottom) of the C Ring. Almost all the rings of Saturn are circular, but this technique reveals a single eccentric ring lying within a broad, dark gap. As shown here, the ring varies in width and position between the two photos. (P-23096)

were obtained while imaging continued. At 9:41 Voyager reached its closest approach to Titan, passing just 4000 kilometers above the clouds. High resolution photographs were taken, and the IRIS made a series of spectra of infrared emission from the high upper atmosphere on the edge of the apparent disk of Titan.

At 10:45 the normal telemetry was shut off and the onboard transmitter began sending a pure frequency for the critical occultation experiment, which was about to begin. As Voyager passed behind the atmosphere of Titan, the radio signal was absorbed and changed in phase, providing a sensitive probe of the ionosphere and atmosphere of this satellite. One of the major objectives of Voyager 1 at Saturn was to determine the depth of the atmosphere and the pressure and temperature at the never-seen surface of Titan. At 11:11

the Sun set behind the edge of Titan as seen from the spacecraft. One minute later the Earth set, and communications were lost. After less than 15 minutes, the rapidly moving spacecraft reemerged, repeating the occultation observations on the opposite side of Titan. At almost exactly the same time, 11:22 p.m., Voyager successfully passed through the plane of the rings of Saturn. For the next 24 hours, the spacecraft would be on the opposite side of the rings from the Sun, looking at the darker side, before crossing the ring plane again and leaving the Saturn system.

November 12, 1980 (Encounter Day)

Less than a million kilometers from Saturn, the Voyager spacecraft began its most crucial day of operation. Not only would Voyager pass close to Saturn and provide unique perspectives of the

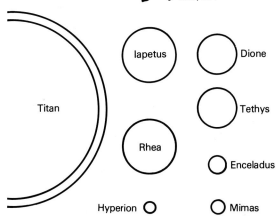

O   ◊ S10, S11

Iapetus   Dione

Titan   Tethys

Rhea   Enceladus

Hyperion ○   ○ Mimas

The satellites of Saturn range in size from Titan, which is nearly as large as the planet Mars, to the tiny dust specks within the rings. Of particular interest to the geologists on the Voyager Imaging Team were the satellites of intermediate size and primarily icy composition—Iapetus, Rhea, Dione, Tethys, Enceladus, and Mimas. This diagram, prepared in the midst of the Voyager 1 encounter, shows the relative sizes of these objects.

The two co-orbital satellites of Saturn first seen in 1966 and accidentally rediscovered by Pioneer (which nearly collided with one of them) are in nearly identical orbits. As these Voyager photos show, both satellites are irregular cratered objects, possibly fragments from a larger parent body broken up in some catastrophic primordial collision. Both satellites are elongated, with their longest dimension directed toward Saturn. The two images on the left are both of satellite 1980S1. In the two photos of 1980S3 on the right, we see the shadow of the F Ring cast on the satellite and moving across it in the few minutes between exposures. (260-1141B, P-23104)

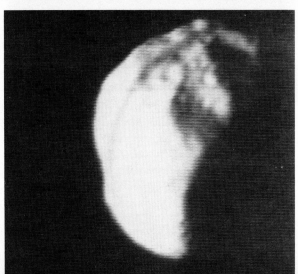

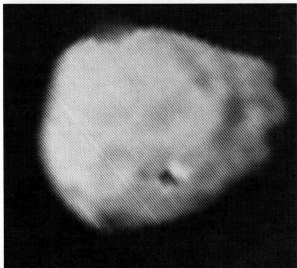
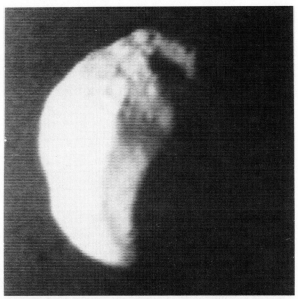

Mimas, the innermost of the moderately large satellites of Saturn, was the first to be viewed up close by Voyager. This photo, taken on November 12, shows features as small as 12 kilometers across. One immense crater, about 130 kilometers in diameter, dominates this face of Mimas. The crater has the raised rim and central peak typical of large impact structures on the terrestrial planets. (P-23098)

rings as seen from below, but close encounters with several of Saturn's satellites would also occur. These included the larger and well-known moons, Mimas, Enceladus, Tethys, Dione, and Rhea, and also the newly discovered inner satellites S-10, S-11, and S-12. Voyager also flew close to S-13, S-14, and S-15, but there had been insufficient time to establish exact orbits for these bodies or to program the cameras to photograph them. The closest approach to Tethys took place at a distance of 400 000 kilometers. Closest approach to Saturn was 124 000 kilometers above the cloud tops. Mimas was seen from 88 000 kilometers. Just 3 1/2 hours after passing Tethys Voyager passed 202 000 kilometers from Enceladus.

At 7:08 p.m. Voyager began its occultation of Saturn. As seen from Earth, the spacecraft disappeared behind the planet, reappeared briefly, and then passed successively behind Rings C, B, and A. During occultation came the closest approach to Dione at a distance of 161 000 kilometers. At 9:00 p.m. Voyager finally emerged from behind the A Ring. Forty-five minutes later the spacecraft crossed the ring plane for the second time, aiming for the Dione clear zone, where it was expected there would be less chance of impact from small particles outside the main rings. The final main event of the day was a very close approach to Rhea; at 10:21 p.m. the spacecraft passed 72 000 kilometers above the surface, the closest encounter with one of the small satellites of Saturn to be obtained by Voyager.

The morning press conference was packed. Every seat was taken 20 minutes early; by the time the briefing began, people were sitting or standing on every bit of available floor space. Ray Heacock happily announced that the spacecraft and all its systems were working perfectly for

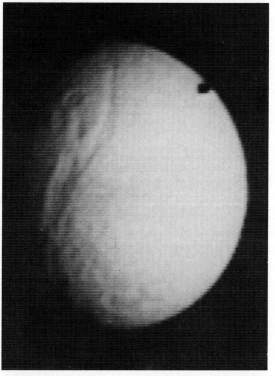

Tethys is an icy satellite just over 1000 kilometers in diameter. On November 12, Voyager took this picture from a distance of 1.2 million kilometers; it shows features as small as about 25 kilometers across. Most of the surface appears heavily cratered, but in addition, there is a large multiple valley structure about 100 kilometers wide and many hundreds of kilometers long, suggestive of major geological activity in the remote past. (P-23095)

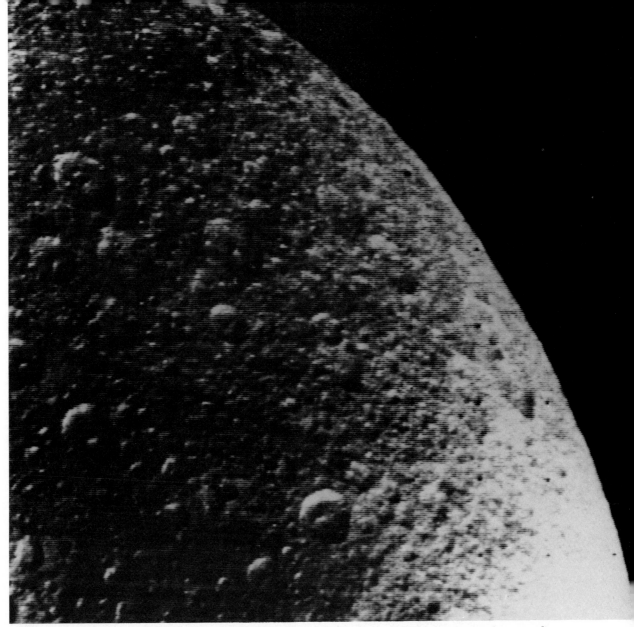

The closest Voyager 1 satellite encounter was with Rhea on November 12; this photo was taken at a distance of 73 000 kilometers and shows features as small as about 1 kilometer across. This view is dominated by impact craters up to 75 kilometers in diameter. Many have sharp rims and appear relatively fresh, while others are very shallow and subdued, indicative of their antiquity. (P-23102)

encounter day. There had been a bad scare the previous day during the Titan occultation when another series of heavy thunderstorms moved over the Madrid tracking station. The rain began just before occultation and persisted for 30 minutes after it; however, it appeared that the occultation signal had been properly received. Heacock also announced that a slight deviation had been found in the spacecraft trajectory, amounting to an exit from Titan occultation 43 seconds early. This time difference meant that the spacecraft was about 200 kilometers off target. Engineers predicted that the ring plane crossing would still take place within the Dione clear zone but about 1500 kilometers from its center.

Norm Ness, the magnetometer Principal Investigator, announced the times that the spacecraft had crossed the bow shock and the magnetopause. Ed Stone had a preliminary result from the Titan occultation indicating that the atmosphere was substantial, almost certainly more than the 20-millibar minimum atmosphere that had been suggested as a possible model for Titan. He also noted that the Titan temperatures obtained by the IRIS appeared to correspond not to the surface but to a cold deck of clouds.

An exhausted-looking Brad Smith reported for the Imaging Science Team. He showed photographs of Titan that clearly indicated a detached high-altitude haze with a polar hood in the north. Smith's manner brightened when he discussed the spectacular pictures of the rings: "In this strange world of Saturn's rings, the bizarre becomes the commonplace and this is what we saw on the F Ring this morning." As the image flashed on the screen, everyone gasped. Instead of a single F Ring, there appeared to be two distinct, separate strands winding around each other. No one offered any explanation for this remarkable picture. In answer to a question, Smith stated that the braiding seen in the new picture of the F Ring defies the usual laws of orbital mechanics. Some other nongravitational forces may be involved. He added, "Obviously, the rings are doing the right thing; it is just that we don't understand the rules." The first pictures of the two co-orbital satellites, S-10 and S-11, were also shown. The larger of the two appeared to be about 150 kilometers across.

Larry Soderblom showed some spectacular bright streaks on the new images of Rhea. From a greater distance, some of these markings had seemed reminiscent of Ganymede, but now they had a character all their own. The bright features looked wispy. Soderblom showed a picture of Dione and said, "We also have wispy terrain on this satellite.

From a range of a quarter of a million kilometers, Dione, which is about the same size as Tethys, shows evidence of a variety of geological structures. Most of the surface is heavily impact cratered, but in addition, bright radiating patterns, presumably surface deposits, extend into view from the trailing hemisphere. Also visible are irregular valleys that suggest old fault troughs degraded by impacts. (P-23101)

I don't believe these can possibly have been produced by impact processes. Their global extent, the connectedness of these features, suggest that they must originate internally.'' The new pictures of Tethys also showed a global-scale feature—in this case, what appeared to be a large valley or trench extending a third of the way around the satellite. Mimas, the innermost of the large satellites, was shown with a gigantic impact crater; again the audience gasped. Soderblom noted that, relative to the size of the body, this may be the largest impact crater we have ever seen.

One of the most exciting photos of the Voyager 1 encounter shows the F Ring from a distance of 750 000 kilometers. At a resolution of about 15 kilometers, this outer ring suddenly revealed a complex braided structure, beyond the wildest imaginings of the Voyager scientists. Two narrow bright rings that appear braided are visible, in addition to a broad diffuse component apparently separated from them by about 100 kilometers. Also visible is a kink, or knot, where the ring seems to depart dramatically from a smooth arc. Finding an explanation for the complexity of the F Ring quickly became one of the prime objectives of theorists studying the orbital motion of ring particles. (P-23099)

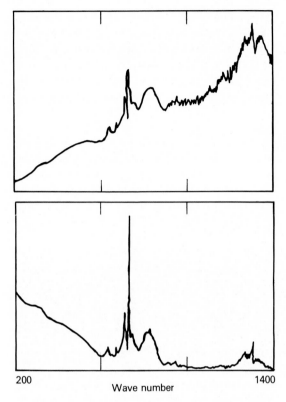

200   Wave number   1400

As the Voyager spacecraft made its extremely close pass by Titan on November 12, the IRIS infrared instrument probed the atmosphere from a variety of angles. Analysis of the infrared spectra, such as that shown in this figure, could yield not only composition but also temperature and pressure analysis of the atmosphere. Particularly sensitive were the scans made at the edge of the atmosphere, which provided a profile of composition at different altitudes. (260-1009BC)

Additional data from the Titan encounter were available at the 1:00 p.m. science meeting. Rudy Hanel showed IRIS spectra that indicated strong emission from methane at an atmospheric temperature of – 100° C. Acetylene, ethane, and hydrogen cyanide were also seen, making "a soup of hydrocarbons." In the IRIS limb scans, the atmosphere was probed at various heights and indeed the spectra showed differences. Hanel called the limb scans "the most spectacular result we had."

Lyle Broadfoot reported that the Titan-Sun occultation experiments had worked extremely well. Additional analysis of Titan's spectra by the UVS Team identified the major emitting gas as neutral nitrogen, N_2. Probably the nitrogen was being excited to glow by the bombardment of energetic electrons.

The first data from the passage of the spacecraft through the magnetosphere near Titan showed a surprisingly large amount of plasma wave turbulence in the wake behind the satellite. Don Gurnett of the Plasma Wave Team reported a remarkable effect in the form of high-frequency radio emissions that were seen only after the spacecraft had passed Titan, as though they were being generated on one hemisphere of the satellite only.

No further information was available from the radio occultation of Titan, but Von Eshleman promised a preliminary result by late afternoon. When the result came in everyone was excited, because Eshleman said that the atmosphere of Titan was definitely dense and deep, that the radio data extended down to a pressure level of 0.5 bar and the surface had not been encountered.

During the afternoon and evening an incredible series of images of the rings of Saturn at resolutions as high as 10 kilometers was received. The closer the spacecraft came, the more rings could be seen. Within the Cassini Division, for instance, it now appeared that there might be as many as 20 or 30 separate rings. The F Ring continued to be a major center of interest. Everyone was mystified by its kinks and braided structure. Looking at the pictures, visiting dynamicist Stan Dermott of Cornell University said, "This is a case where a new discovery is not stimulating, it is just inhibiting."

As the day came to a close, interest focused on the flyby of Rhea. Pictures of a very heavily cratered landscape were flashed back just before midnight, but the highest resolution views were recorded on the Voyager tape recorder for playback the next day. By 1:00 or 2:00 a.m. most of the exhausted scientists and members of the press had finally headed home for a few hours of sleep.

More than 500 reporters had been issued press badges. During the day, live television broadcasts had been sent out to many different countries—Canada, Japan, Finland, and others. Some television coverage had been available to viewers in the United States, but as usual the most extensive reports were sent abroad. No one knew just why the press had chosen to celebrate this encounter so intensely, but the hard-working Voyager staff was delighted to be able to share their results with so much of the public. One especially welcome member of the audience was President Jimmy Carter, who phoned JPL to offer his congratulations and to say that he had watched more than an hour of the television coverage.

November 13, 1980

Voyager had now passed Saturn, safely traversed two ring-plane crossings, and was moving outbound on a trajectory that would take it far beyond the solar system and into interstellar space. Extensive observations continued behind the planet; the rings and the atmosphere were now seen from a new perspective. The official encounter period ended in the middle of the afternoon, and Voyager shifted into its first postencounter phase.

At the morning press briefing, Rudy Hanel reported on the IRIS observations of the atmosphere of Titan. He stated that the main deck of clouds, because of its temperature of about

– 200° C, probably consisted of frozen or liquid nitrogen. Nitrogen was apparently the main constituent of the Titan atmosphere, with the methane that had been known for so many years amounting to no more than 1 percent of the total. Hanel stressed the importance of the detection of hydrogen cyanide (HCN): "This is the first molecule that deviates from the simple hydrocarbon CH band. It has long been considered a building block for more complex organic compounds. Let me hasten to add that at these very cold temperatures of liquid nitrogen, we do not expect any form of life. Nevertheless, we may be dealing with important aspects of organic chemistry. The Titan data are very exciting and much more important than we thought they would be."

Von Eshleman reported on the Titan radio occultation. He stressed the great power of this technique, in which the bending of the radio wave by as little as an inch could be detected over a distance of a billion miles. Because of the tremendous amount of information contained in the occultation, most of the data had been recorded on magnetic tape at the Madrid tracking station and would not be available at JPL for at least 10 days. Thus the current analysis was based on only

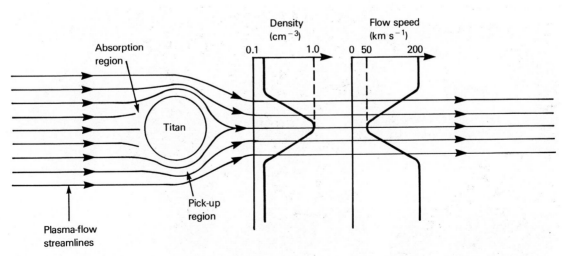

Analysis of the particles and fields data obtained as Voyager swung close to Titan revealed a strong interaction between the satellite and the plasma particles of Saturn's magnetosphere. Immediately behind Titan, the density of particles increased while the flow slowed down. In many ways, the interaction of Titan with the magnetosphere of Saturn was very similar to that of the terrestrial planets interacting with the solar wind. (260-1049AC)

a small part of the total information that would eventually be used to study the atmosphere of Titan. On the basis of this analysis, the surface pressure was probably at least 1 bar. The temperature near the clouds was apparently about $-190°$ C, perhaps cold enough for nitrogen, which was the main constituent of the atmosphere, to condense in the form of liquid nitrogen clouds. Eshelman referred to the idea that the surface of Titan might resemble a murky swamp: "This is a rather bizarre murky swamp. The murk is liquid nitrogen clouds and the swamp is also liquid nitrogen. Titan by size is a terrestrial planet that just happens to be in the outer solar system. We might consider it a terrestrial planet in deep freeze."

Brad Smith began his report for the Imaging Science Team by saying, "I am stunned by the spectacular display of pictures we have seen in the last 24 hours. Perhaps a year from now it will be possible to sort them out, but right now we are simply flooded with new data. I cannot recall ever being in such a state of euphoria at any previous encounter, including the two Voyager Jupiter encounters, as I am this morning." The pictures were indeed remarkable. Imaging of the F Ring showed further views of the interwoven strands, now numbering three, still with no explanation offered. An enormous amount of detail was apparent in the Cassini Division. Smith reported that Rich Terrile had attempted to count the number of rings in the latest images. When he reached 300, he got tired, but he estimated that the number was somewhere between 500 and 1000 individual rings.

Larry Soderblom gave the first geological overview of five new worlds—the inner satellites of Saturn. He began with a tribute to the Voyager Spacecraft Navigation Team, who worked feverishly to revise the spacecraft pointing after the small trajectory error had been found. Without their efforts, we would have missed many of the highest resolution satellite images.

The most important result of the satellite imaging was the demonstration that these objects were different; each had its own characteristics, indicative of a unique geologic history. Only Mimas was "your basic unprocessed ice moon," with no evidence of internal activity. Enceladus, supposedly Mimas' twin, was not imaged up close but clearly lacked the expected large craters. Tethys had a big valley, but other parts were heavily cratered and

This exultant group of Voyager 1 participants returning from the encounter day press conference includes (left to right) Project Manager Ray Heacock, Project Scientist Ed Stone, visiting Parisian scientist André Brahic, and Imaging Team Leader Brad Smith (photo by the author).

Some of the most spectacular views of Saturn were obtained by Voyager cameras just after closest approach as they looked back toward the crescent planet with the rings superimposed in front of it. From this perspective, the rings were open more widely than they had been during approach, and their intricate structure could clearly be seen where they crossed in front of the planet. (P-23110)

therefore geologically inactive. Dione and Rhea showed both smooth and heavily cratered regions; in addition, both had the enigmatic bright wispy terrain. Soderblom emphasized that these are the first members of an entirely new class of worlds never before seen—ice planets, roughly 1000 kilometers across.

As evening arrived, the Voyager team finally began to relax. It had been an intense and hectic encounter, and all had gone extremely well. But now the real work for the scientists would begin, with a vast amount of new data to be analyzed.

November 14, 1980

At the morning press briefing, more discoveries about Titan, the rings, and the satellites were reported. Lyle Broadfoot presented evidence of several discrete cloud layers of unknown composition high in the atmosphere of Titan, above the main cloud deck. Some of these may correspond to the detached haze layers photographed by the imaging system. Further evidence was also presented of the dominance of nitrogen in the atmosphere—Titan is the only body besides Earth that has this gas as its primary atmospheric constituent. Darrell Strobel of the UVS Team explained how sunlight could break up nitrogen and methane molecules in the upper atmosphere of Titan to produce hydrogen cyanide and from that compound build up many complex organic polymers, which probably are responsible for Titan's dark red color.

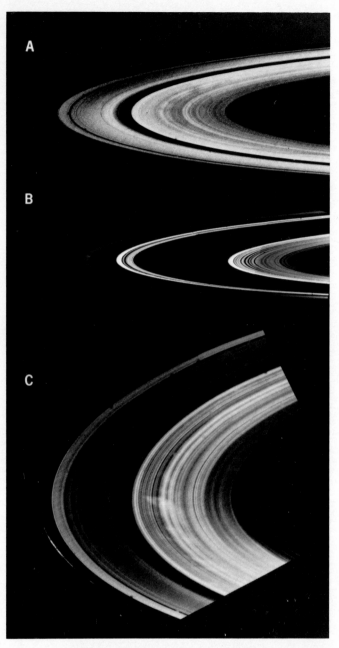

The rings of Saturn change greatly in appearance under different lighting and viewing conditions. The view of the sunlit face, with the Sun behind, is the most familiar (A). From below the rings, Voyager saw the unilluminated face (B), which shines faintly by diffusely transmitted sunlight. A third perspective was obtained after encounter (C), when the sunlit face was seen again, with the spacecraft looking back toward the source of illumination. (260-1204B)

Brad Smith showed spectacular pictures of the rings seen from underneath. Saturn could clearly be seen through many parts of the rings, providing a measure of how closely packed the ring particles are in different regions. Some of the rings, including the narrow F Ring, also appeared brighter when illuminated from behind, which had also been true for the faint ring of Jupiter. This strong forward scattering of sunlight is an indication of small particles; clearly, some parts of the rings contained more small particles than did other areas.

Geologist Gene Shoemaker of the Imaging Science Team attempted to pull all the satellite data into a coherent picture. The satellites are basically icy bodies, although some—most clearly Dione—have a substantial component of rock in their interiors. All have been subject to heavy impact cratering. Shoemaker suggested that impacts were responsible, in one way or another, for most of the features seen. In some cases craters were produced directly, but very large impacts could also melt the ice and fracture the whole body of the satellite to generate the other features seen in the pictures.

For Ed Stone, the highlights of the day's results were in the study of the magnetosphere. He stressed that there was actually more than one magnetosphere: "From the standpoint of magnetospheric physics, we have had not one encounter but two—one with Saturn and one with Titan. Titan is as large as Mercury, and in addition it has an atmosphere. The role of the solar wind is played, for Titan, by the magnetosphere of Saturn. Titan interacts with this co-rotating magnetosphere at a relative velocity about half that of Saturn to the solar wind. An encounter with Titan is thus equivalent to a planetary encounter." Scientists were looking closely at the data from both encounters to provide a better understanding of the general nature of the interaction between a planet and a moving plasma.

The spirits of everyone at JPL were raised by a change in the weather. A brisk desert wind rose and cleared the Los Angeles basin of all traces of smog. Everything looked bright and sharp under

From the new postencounter perspective, the spokes in the B Ring took on an entirely different appearance. Seen with the sunlight coming from nearly behind them, the spokes were transformed from dark streaks to bright streaks, as is apparent in this view taken about one day after closest approach. (P-23109)

a deep blue sky. But residents of the area recognized the danger. This was a Santa Ana wind, and what was a pleasant breeze at JPL could be a 60 mile per hour wind in the desert and the mountain passes. Such a wind could bring danger, both to the tracking station at Goldstone and to the tinder-dry forests surrounding Pasadena.

November 15, 1980

The highest resolution pictures of a satellite surface obtained by Voyager 1 were of Rhea, distinguishing features as small as 2 kilometers across. To realize this resolution it had been necessary to rotate the entire spacecraft during the

One of the last satellites to be photographed by Voyager 1 was mysterious Iapetus. Seen on November 12 from a distance of about 3 million kilometers, some structure is apparent for the first time along the border between the dark leading and light trailing hemispheres. The large circular feature, about 200 kilometers across, might be some kind of impact structure, but the Voyager 1 resolution was not sufficient to provide clear identification of this or any other topographic feature on the satellite. (P-23105)

exposures to compensate for the motion past Rhea, like panning a camera to obtain sharp pictures of a rapidly moving target. During this time, most of the frames were stored on the tape recorder for later playback. These efforts had worked perfectly, and at the morning press conference Brad Smith showed the resulting mosaic of high-resolution views of Rhea. Part of the satellite was very heavily cratered—perhaps the most nearly saturated surface yet seen by Voyager. The crater pattern looked similar to that of Mercury or the Moon. The temperatures of the Saturn satellites render ice nearly as strong as rock, and the icy surface of Rhea seemed indistinguishable from rock except for its brilliant white color.

Norm Ness and Herb Bridge presented new results from the Titan flyby. No shock front formed in front of Titan, but behind it the

plasma was swept in and concentrated. Additional plasma particles escaped from the atmosphere of Titan into the magnetosphere, but the Titan atmosphere was a much weaker source than the volcanoes of Io—about 1 ounce per second, as compared with 1 ton per second from Io. In other respects, too, it was interesting to compare these two satellites, since both generate electrical power as they move through the magnetosphere. Ness reported no evidence of an intrinsic magnetic field for Titan; at most, it could have a field 1/1000 as strong as that of Earth.

The radio astronomy and plasma wave instruments had discovered another new phenomenon on Titan, as reported by Don Gurnett. Apparently, one side of the satellite generated strong radio emissions at frequencies of 30 to 100 kilohertz, but the other side did not. The source appeared to be on the side facing Saturn; its total power was about 20 kilowatts, similar to that of an AM radio station. Gurnett said he did not pretend to understand the details of how this radiation was generated. Subsequent analysis eventually led to the suggestion that Titan was not the actual source.

Pioneer Saturn had made the first study of the magnetosphere of Saturn, but new aspects had been detected by Voyager. Perhaps most important was the depletion of magnetospheric charged particles over one longitude on Saturn. Tom Krimigis suggested that this might be analogous to Earth's South Atlantic Anomaly, in which the magnetic field lines dip low into the atmosphere. This theory might thus provide an explanation for the variation of radio emission as Saturn rotates, although later observations by Voyager 2 would not support this proposal.

Len Tyler had a variety of new results to report from the various radio occultation experiments. First, for Titan, he pushed the atmospheric limits further, announcing that the radio waves had penetrated to a pressure level of at least 1.5 bars. Titan had a larger atmosphere than Earth! The 1.5 bar level was at a temperature of −180° C and a radius of 2560 kilometers from the center of Titan. The true surface might, of course, be substantially lower and warmer.

Tyler also had results from the occultation of the radio signal by the C Ring. The characteristics

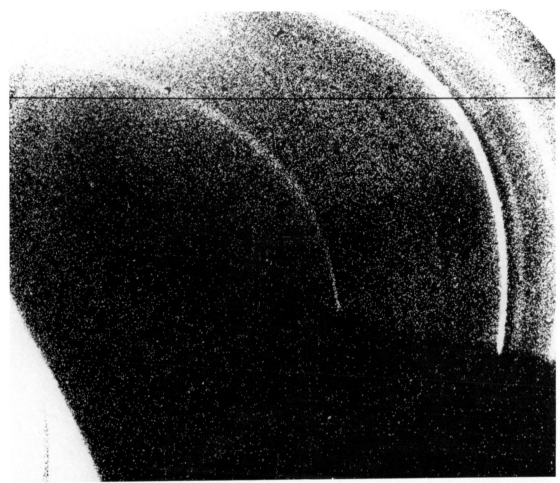

A new ring of Saturn was discovered by Voyager between the inner edge of the C Ring and the top of the planet's atmosphere. Here we see a long-exposure, wide-angle view in which the new ring passes behind the shadow of the planet. Considerable structure is apparent, even in this very tenuous region. This photo encompasses the region identified from ground-based observations with a possible D Ring, but the material shown here is too faint to have been visible before Voyager. (P-23262)

of the absorption of the radio beam showed that the ring particles were relatively large—typically 1 meter in diameter. Tyler described his concept of the C Ring as "boulders flying around Saturn at great velocities in some highly organized manner."

As the day progressed, fires in the mountains turned the clear blue sky over Pasadena dark with smoke. And still-rising winds in the desert endangered the operation of the giant Goldstone antennas. When wind speeds reach 40 miles per hour, the antennas must be stowed and so can no longer track the spacecraft. During the night,

winds gusted above 40 miles per hour but did not quite go beyond the permitted threshold. Meanwhile, as darkness came, the mountains above JPL glowed red from raging fires, while below, inside their windowless buildings, Voyager controllers continued to operate the spacecraft, more than a billion kilometers away and rapidly receding from Saturn.

November 16, 1980

Esker Davis reported that it had been a rough night for the Voyager project. At 1:00 a.m., as

Far beyond the bright rings, near the orbit of Enceladus, Voyager succeeded in photographing the tenuous E Ring. This is near the region in which the Voyager 1 spacecraft crossed through Saturn's ring plane. (260-1175)

the fires in the mountains above Los Angeles worsened, JPL had shifted to standby generators to guard against a power failure. All night the wind had threatened the antenna at Goldstone. By noon, however, the Santa Ana winds had dropped somewhat, and JPL shifted back to commercial power.

The main feature of the press conference, with attendance down to about 30 members of the press, was a detailed tutorial on the rings by Jeff Cuzzi, who had been added to the Imaging Science Team for the Saturn encounter because of his expertise concerning the rings. He noted the great power of the Voyager observations, not just because of higher resolution, but because of the variety of viewing geometries—seeing the rings illuminated from different directions, viewing them from below, photographing the planet through them—all of which provided information on the nature of the particles. Cuzzi said, "We've heard a lot about the things we don't

understand, but I'd like to discuss the things about the rings—admittedly a shorter list—that we do understand." One of these things is the classical resonance theory, which Cuzzi believed explained the Cassini Division but not all other structures. He noted the differences among the rings in the kind of structure seen, particularly the intricate structure in the B Ring, "like grooves on a record," as well as the dark spokes present there. The F Ring and some of the gaps contain small particles, only a few micrometers in size. Other areas, for instance the Cassini Division, do not have many small particles. The dark spokes undergo a remarkable transformation: In forward scattered light, they become bright, as does the F Ring. Thus the spokes too are due to small particles. One important conclusion is the difference in particle size—from meters to micrometers—in different parts of the ring system.

George Gloeckler reported on the identification of specific ions in the Saturn magnetosphere by the Low Energy Charged Particle instrument. The ions, traveling at more than 10 000 kilometers per second, included hydrogen and nitrogen from Titan and hydrogen and hydrocarbon combinations from Saturn. Gloeckler noted the extremely important role of the satellites as sources of magnetospheric particles for both Jupiter and Saturn.

Voyager 1 was now well on its outbound journey from Saturn. It continued to look for new satellites and to carry out further studies of the planet and rings. The JPL television monitors were dominated by a beautiful, ethereal view of the crescent Saturn casting a long black shadow across the wide-open rings—a view of the planet that will be reproduced for decades in books and articles on the solar system.

November 17, 1980

The final press conference of the Voyager 1 encounter drew an audience of about 100 project participants and press for a wrap-up of the mission. The most important new results concerned the increasing interest in electrical and magnetic processes thought to be acting within the Saturn system.

Jim Warwick of the Planetary Radio Astronomy Team reported a new kind of radio burst from Saturn. The bursts had the general character of lightning discharges, but they were of too low frequency to pass through the ionosphere of Saturn, as determined from the radio occultation results. But how could lightning be coming from outside the atmosphere? Warwick suggested the

Not until more than a week after the encounter was it possible to interpret the Titan radio occultation data with sufficient confidence to determine an atmospheric surface pressure and temperature. It was finally revealed that Titan has a surface pressure 1.6 times greater than that of Earth and an atmosphere composed primarily of nitrogen. Several thick absorbing haze layers exist high in the atmosphere, while thick methane clouds are presumably concentrated near the surface. Altogether, the picture that emerged of the atmosphere of Titan was very similar to the models suggested before Voyager by Donald Hunten of the University of Arizona.

Although the clouds of Titan proved to be opaque, it was possible to probe beneath them all the way to the surface of the satellite using the Voyager radio signals. Radio scientist Von Eshelman quickly became the central figure in the determination of the depth of the atmosphere and the surface pressure of Titan. (P-22399BC)

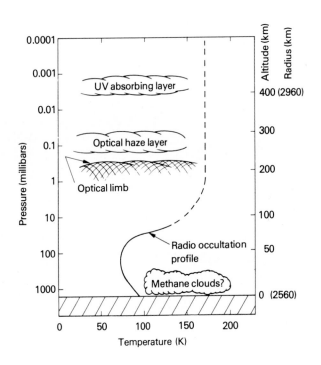

source might be in the rings, where the billions of small particles could become charged by interactions with the magnetosphere. He calculated that lightning-like discharges in the rings could be a million times stronger than those in a planetary atmosphere. Such discharges would not be expected to produce visible flashes of light in the rings, since there was too little gas between the ring particles to generate the high-temperature plasma of a normal lightning bolt.

Larry Soderblom emphasized again the diversity of the satellites of Saturn and showed new pictures that argued for internal geological activity on Tethys, Dione, and Rhea. He then lightheartedly introduced Rich Terrile as a "ringleader" and "spokesman" to provide a final perspective on the spokes in the rings of Saturn.

Terrile reviewed the known facts about the spokes: that they appeared dark in back scattered light and bright in forward scattering; that they were much more evident as they emerged from the shadow of the planet and then faded or broke up as they circled Saturn; and that their velocity was close to that of the co-rotating magnetic field with a period of 10 hours, 40 minutes. The light scattering properties indicated that the particles in the spokes were very small, perhaps suspended like a cloud above the main ring. Electric charging could produce such levitation of particles, and the association with the magnetic rotation period also suggested that electromagnetic forces could be involved. Charging might be more effective in the dark shadow and might then dissipate after the particles returned to sunlight. Finally, Terrile noted that the discharging of such electrified clouds might be the source of the radio bursts reported by Warwick. None of these explanations had been worked out in a quantitative theory, but Terrile believed that electromagnetic effects of this sort might produce the correct framework in which to understand several mysterious properties of the rings, including the braided F Ring as well as the B Ring spokes.

As the press corps departed from Pasadena and the Voyager scientists began to return to their laboratories and universities, the attention of

The press interest in the Voyager 1 Saturn encounter was unprecedented in the space science program. At daily press conferences each new discovery was described and shared with the public almost as quickly as it was made. Here, at the final press conference, Ed Stone makes a point. Seated to his right are Rich Terrile and Larry Soderblom of the Imaging Science Team (photo by the author).

Project officials was turned toward Voyager 2, due to arrive at Saturn in August. The primary changes to be made involved a shift of emphasis from Titan to the rings. Much more time would be spent during the second encounter in imaging the spokes and the F Ring and in targeted observations of the newly discovered small inner satellites. Voyager 2 would be no simple repeat of Voyager 1; rather, it would be programmed to complement and extend the data from the first encounter in every possible way.

During the weeks following encounter, continuing analysis of the Voyager 1 data provided many additional discoveries. The surface pressure of Titan was established at 1.6 bars, but a small revision in the calculated atmospheric temperatures appeared to exclude liquid nitrogen clouds and to indicate that the lowest clouds were composed of methane. On Saturn, a recalibration of IRIS spectra revealed that helium was depleted in the atmosphere, amounting to only half the Jovian abundance; this helium deficiency was seized on by theorists to explain the relatively large internal heat source of the planet. A region of low-energy electrons was discovered trapped in Saturn's magnetotail, and it was confirmed that Titan lacks a measurable magnetic field. Two additional faint rings of Saturn were discovered—the D Ring close to the planet and the G Ring near the region of the co-orbital satellites. Further analysis of the B Ring spokes showed that they revolved about the planet with the period expected for gravitational motion, rather than that expected for charged particles, and dynamists also suggested purely gravitational explanations for the F Ring braids, related to the distributing effects of the two shepherding satellites.

The World Watches

Especially pleasing to those who had worked so hard on Voyager was the wide attention given the encounter by the world's press. The November 24 issues of both *Time* and *Newsweek* featured Voyager Saturn on their covers. *Time* called the encounter a "culmination of Voyager's odyssey, a two-day close encounter of the most extraordinary

kind," and noted that "scientists were staggered by a succession of discoveries." *Time* felt that "space exploration has already paid for itself many times over." *Newsweek* wrote that the pictures from Saturn were "as though Columbus had returned from his first voyage with snapshots of Montezuma's palace and the Grand Canyon," and appreciatively quoted Brad Smith: "I've seen many wondrous things in the last decade, but I can't think of any phenomenon more puzzling than what we've seen this week."

Newspapers, too, continued their special coverage of Voyager. London's *Sunday Telegraph* called the encounter "the most spectacular piece of space exploration since man first stepped on the moon." The *New York Times* described Voyager's astonishing investigation of the rings as being "like a Darwin exploring the Galapagos Islands. Existing theories are tested against the new observations, and when nature turns out to be stranger still, new hypotheses are advanced and debated." The *Wall Street Journal* editorialized that "Not since Neil Armstrong alighted on the surface of the moon have television audiences world-wide marvelled at such remarkable images as those sent back from Saturn by the Voyager spacecraft. It is the linkage of the bits and pieces of past scientific discoveries which now affords us the benefits of our modern, technological world. As Voyager probes the outer reaches of our solar system, man expands the boundaries of knowledge. For that future generations will be forever indebted to us."

Columnist George Will found the Voyager photos inspiring: "The day God created Saturn, He must have been feeling on top of the world, so to speak. The dazzlingly precise flight of Voyager 1 is a smashingly successful government program. Voyager 1 has increased immeasurably—literally immeasurably—knowledge about our relatively close neighbor, Saturn. Extraordinarily useful discoveries have flowed from the fanciful, playful, serendipitous elements of scientific research, from the pure pleasure of discovery pursued without a thought to practicality. It is the height—or depth—of hubris to imagine that we know what it is that we need to know, or to imagine that we imagine all that we are capable of imagining."

SATURN AND THE MIND OF MAN

On November 9, as the Voyager spacecraft was preparing for its historic encounter with Saturn, a special public program, dedicated to a discussion of the place of Saturn and of the Voyager exploration in a cultural and historical sense, was being held at the California Institute of Technology. Similar programs had been held at the time of the Mariner 9 orbit of Mars, again just before the first Viking landing on Mars, and in 1979 as Voyager 1 approached Jupiter. The panel discussions attracted a wide audience and were filmed for later television broadcast. Although aimed at the general public, the discussions were also fascinating for the Voyager scientists who were happy to spend a few hours away from the intense concentration on the minutia of the encounter to reflect on the broader historical importance of the exploration in which they were participating.

Five distinguished scientists and humanists were on the panel to discuss Saturn and the mind of man. The Chairman was Walter Sullivan of the *New York Times*, considered the dean of science writers in the United States. On the panel were Philip Morrison of the Massachusetts Institute of Technology, who was making his first appearance on one of these panels; Carl Sagan of Cornell University; novelist and poet Ray Bradbury; and Bruce Murray, Director of the Jet Propulsion Laboratory.

The panel was introduced by Marvin Goldberger, the President of Caltech, and concluding comments were made by the Governor of California, Jerry Brown, and his science advisor and former astronaut Rusty Schweigert.

Walter Sullivan began the discussion by reviewing the mythology associated with Saturn and its satellites. Philip Morrison continued with the thought that Saturn, in a sense, gave the world time, since its period of revolution around the Sun provided the longest natural time period to ancient peoples, a period not much less than a typical human lifetime. He also emphasized the extraordinary hold that this planet has on our imaginations because of the beauty of its rings. Morrison said, "Of everything revealed by the telescope, the most meaningful to most people is the rings of Saturn." These beautiful features are very real and well known to us, yet invisible without the telescope. They are vast, but nearly transparent, "all surface and no volume, all show and no substance."

Carl Sagan also mentioned the significance of Saturn for ancient peoples. He noted that "the following of the motions of the planets, an attempt to understand them, led to modern science and modern civilization." But to our ancestors, "the planets were not places, not something to be visited." That is a new concept for humanity and it is, after all, only in the last two decades that we have had the capability to visit other worlds and to make them seem real to us. In many ways the Voyager flyby of Saturn was the culmination of this period of exploration. Sagan said, "We are at the end of the first extraordinary stage of planetary exploration where all the wandering lights known to ancients are about to be visited and scrutinized by these wonderful, sophisticated robots we send out to explore the solar system. I believe we are at a moment that will be remembered for tens, hundreds, perhaps even thousands of years. It is with no small rapture that we now, today, view the system of Saturn's rings and fifteen moons. The Voyager results so far are truly stunning. We now see more than 100 separate rings. We see markings on tiny disks, little worlds that have never individually been the subject of a single scientific paper. We are at a moment of extraordinary discovery. There are six or eight new worlds up there that we are about to see for the first time." How much does this exploration cost? Sagan estimated that Voyager was costing about 1 cent per world explored per person on Earth. "The exploration of the solar system is an extremely strong affirmation of being alive, of being curious about our place in space."

Ray Bradbury emphasized the importance of exploring the solar system for our sense of humanity, especially in a period in which we have so much uncertainty about so many other things in our lives. He said, "We have been living in an affluent period of despair." But we are exploring our solar system and we are learning a great deal. "The day mystery dies is the last true day on Earth."

Bruce Murray examined the achievement of the Voyager program. "Voyager is the climax of a glorious decade of exploration. This has been an American cultural, as well as technical, triumph. We have come an enormous distance in space and in time and in intellectual development." Voyager is an extraordinary achievement. Murray emphasized that for the first time in history, a major exploration had to be done truly remotely. The spacecraft had to travel for years through space unattended, and during an encounter at the distance of Saturn the light travel time is so great that controllers could not even operate it by telemetry. We had to build an independent robot craft. "If we try to do things that are nearly impossible, we will develop muscles, and those muscles are important."

Carl Sagan articulated the thoughts of many when he said in a concluding statement that there is an unsaturated zest for scientific exploration that we all share. Mankind has always been characterized by this desire for knowledge. "The exploratory instinct which has taken us to the vicinity of Saturn is part of the reason for our success as a species."

Discussing the implications of Saturn and the Mind of Man are (left to right) Philip Morrison of MIT, Carl Sagan of Cornell, Walter Sullivan of the New York Times, Bruce Murray of JPL, and author and poet Ray Bradbury. (P-23340AC)

In the weeks after the encounter, as the Voyager 1 spacecraft sped outward beyond Saturn, it transmitted this spectacular view of the ringed planet from a perspective never before witnessed by humanity. (P-23254)

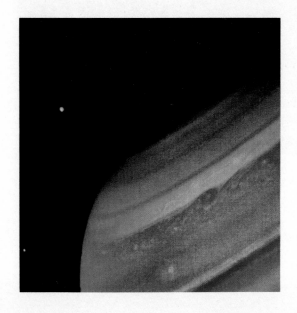

The Last Picture Show

On June 5, 1981, the Voyager 2 spacecraft began its encounter with Saturn. Like its twin, Voyager 2 was to carry out a ten-week observatory-phase study of the planet before the intense near-encounter activity began. During this time, observations would be made to trace out the time history of atmospheric motions and the enigmatic dark spokes in the B Ring. Then, between the first satellite encounter (with Iapetus on August 22) and the last (with Phoebe on September 4), Voyager 2 would undertake an even more detailed look at the Saturn system than had its predecessor. A total of more than 18 500 photos were to be taken, in addition to the flood of data from the ten other investigations on the spacecraft. The Saturn encounter would officially end on September 28, with Voyager safely on its way to a rendezvous with distant Uranus in 1986.

The health of the Voyager 2 spacecraft was a matter of constant concern to project officials at JPL. The main radio receiver had failed in the first year of flight, and the back-up system had proven faulty. Apparently, the shorting of a critical capacitor disabled the part of the circuit that locked the receiver into the frequency of the signal transmitted from Earth. Without this automatic lock, commands sent to the spacecraft were likely to miss their target. It required great ingenuity to develop ways to keep the transmitted signals right on the mark so that the spacecraft could receive them properly. But all had gone very well with the Jupiter encounter, and Voyager engineers were confident that they could carry out a full mission at Saturn in spite of the receiver problems.

All through the summer, as Voyager raced toward Saturn at nearly a million kilometers per day, the planet and its rings loomed larger and larger in the images transmitted to JPL. By August 1, the range was down to 25 million kilometers. But for most of the scientists the real action would not start until the near-encounter sequences began. Not until the middle of the month, during the hottest summer season in the history of Los Angeles, did the adventure of the encounter begin in earnest—an encounter that would mark the end of the formal objectives of the Voyager project, as well as defining a high-water mark in the twenty-year history of planetary exploration.

The rings of Saturn appeared much brighter to Voyager 2 than to Voyager 1 because of increasing solar illumination during the nine-month interval between encounters. On July 21, from a distance of 34 million kilometers, several prominent cloud features were already visible—evidence of increased activity in the atmosphere of Saturn, as well as of a more sensitive camera on the Voyager 2 spacecraft. (P-23883)

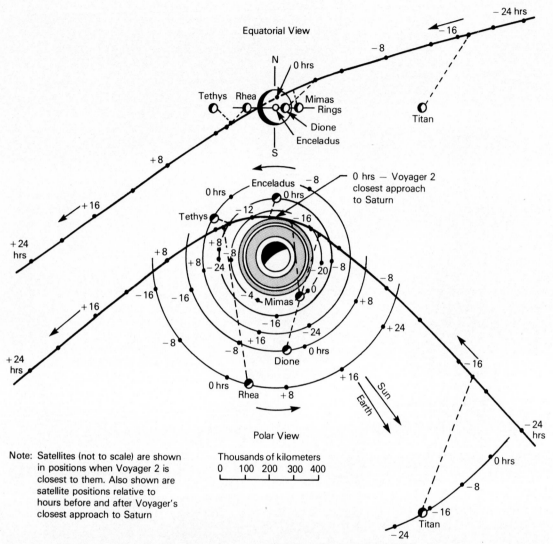

Equatorial View

N — 0 hrs

Tethys   Rhea   Mimas
                     — Rings
              Dione
          Enceladus

S

−24 hrs
−16
−8

Titan

+8
+16
+24 hrs

Polar View

Enceladus   −8
0 hrs   0 hrs
0 hrs — Voyager 2
closest approach
to Saturn

Tethys   −12
−16

+8
+8   −24
−8
−20   −8
−4   Mimas
−16   −8
+8

−16   −16
−16
−8   +16   0 hrs
Dione
+24

0 hrs   +16
Rhea   +8

+16

Sun
Earth

−16

+24 hrs
+16
+24 hrs

−24 hrs
0 hrs
−8

−16
Titan
−24

Note: Satellites (not to scale) are shown
in positions when Voyager 2 is
closest to them. Also shown are
satellite positions relative to
hours before and after Voyager's
closest approach to Saturn

Thousands of kilometers
0   100 200 300 400

*The Voyager 2 Saturn encounter differed in many ways from that of Voyager 1, in part because of the
requirement that Voyager 2 continue on to Uranus and Neptune. In addition, efforts were directed
toward making the second encounter as complementary as possible to the first. Voyager 2 approached
Saturn looking down on the northern lighted side of the rings and crossed the ring plane only once, very
close to the time of its closest passage by Saturn. The spacecraft exited from the Saturn system looking
back at the south or dark side of the rings. This trajectory provided for close flybys of the satellites
Iapetus, Hyperion, Enceladus, and Tethys.*

August 20, 1981 (Range to Saturn, 8 million
kilometers)

On the fourth anniversary of its launch from
Cape Canaveral, Florida, the Voyager 2 spacecraft
was rushing toward Saturn at a speed of 11 kilometers per second. Already, features as small as

150 kilometers across could be seen with the imaging cameras, and the ultraviolet and infrared
instruments were making extensive observations
of the cloud tops and upper atmosphere. One day
earlier, the spacecraft's rocket engine had been
fired briefly to make a final adjustment in the trajectory, moving the targeted point 900 kilometers

nearer Saturn. The final trajectory would take Voyager to within 101 000 kilometers of the cloud tops of Saturn, and 54 minutes later the spacecraft would cross the plane of the rings 112 000 kilometers from Saturn, 32 000 kilometers beyond the F Ring. The path was chosen to produce just the right amount of gravitational acceleration to speed Voyager toward its 1986 rendezvous with Uranus, as well as ensure an optimum Saturn encounter.

It was already apparent that the Voyager 2 imaging system was going to reveal a great deal more about Saturn and its rings than had been seen by Voyager 1. Project officials had become convinced that the television camera had about 50 percent additional sensitivity, resulting in pictures that would be sharper and "snappier." In addition, Saturn was being more cooperative. Greater atmospheric activity was providing a variety of spots, waves, and storm systems; even at this distance, details of developing weather patterns could be followed that had only been seen by Voyager 1 within a day or two of closest approach. Finally, the rings were brighter. Between the two

encounters, the Sun had risen on the rings from an elevation of 4 degrees up to 8 degrees. For several weeks the dark spokes in the B Ring had been clearly evident, and a number of ring movies were made to follow their formation, movement, and eventual break-up as they circled Saturn.

For this final Saturn encounter, scientists and members of the press arrived at JPL in record numbers. Nearly 50 percent more requests for press accreditation had been received than for the Voyager 1 encounter. The intense interest generated by the spectacular results of the previous encounter had not abated, and, in addition, everyone realized that this would be the last planetary encounter for many years. Thus it was with a sense of sadness, as well as enthusiasm, that the participants at JPL greeted old friends and acquaintances and turned their attention a billion kilometers away, to the spacecraft rushing toward its rendezvous with Saturn.

August 21, 1981 (6 million km)

Esker K. (Ek) Davis, who had succeeded Ray Heacock as Voyager's Project Manager, greeted

With the Voyager 2 observatory phase drawing to a close, Science Investigation Support Team Leader Charles Stembridge discusses the encounter phase sequences with Project Manager Esker Davis and his deputy Richard Laeser. (P-24026BC)

Data on the health of the spacecraft and its scientific instruments are continually transmitted to Earth and received at JPL. Here Project Scientist Ed Stone and his deputy Ellis Miner confirm the correct operation of one of the science instruments. (P-24116BC)

One new aspect of the Voyager 2 spacecraft was the presence of the photopolarimeter, a scan platform instrument that unfortunately had failed on Voyager 1. In addition to making many measurements of the brightness, color, and polarization of light reflected from Saturn and its rings and satellites, the photopolarimeter would make the critical measurements on August 25 of starlight transmitted through the rings, thus tracing out a very-high-resolution profile of the ring structure. Here Lonne Lane of JPL, Photopolarimeter Principal Investigator, discusses this experiment with his colleague Larry Esposito of the University of Colorado. (P-23309AC)

the first press conference with word that "everything on the project is going very well!" He explained that, although there had been a failure some weeks earlier of one of the memory chips in the flight data system computer, a new and even better encounter sequence had been worked out. As he explained, "We found better ways to do the sequencing, so we end up with more capabilities than were present in the original sequences."

Project Scientist Ed Stone walked in front of the press with his usual springy step to assert that he believed Voyager 2 would provide an even better look at Saturn than had Voyager 1. The spacecraft would come much closer to the planet, as well as to the lighted side of the rings. In addition, a new instrument was available—the photopolarimeter—which had failed to function on the Voyager 1 spacecraft. One of the most exciting experiments planned for Voyager 2 was the observation of the occultation of a bright star by the rings. By carefully measuring the variations in the starlight transmitted through the rings, the photopolarimeter would be able to map out (in one dimension) the distribution of particles with a resolution ten or twenty times greater than could be achieved in the best images.

A new computer animation film showing the Voyager 2 encounter turned out to be even more spectacular than the three similar films that had preceded it. Data from Voyager 1 had been entered into the computer and were now played back to show an accurate rendition of the planet and its rings and satellites in all their awesome splendor. But perfection has its price, and the forthcoming close encounter with Enceladus was omitted. Voyager 1 images had revealed no detailed structure on this satellite, and the film makers were unwilling to guess what the spacecraft might see.

A real movie of Saturn taken by Voyager 2 during its approach was shown by Imaging Team Leader Brad Smith. Most of Smith's presentation focused on the dynamics of the atmosphere of Saturn, where many unusual cloud structures

With two weeks to go before encounter, the Voyager cameras were concentrating on the dynamics of the atmosphere of Saturn. This view, obtained on August 11 at a distance of 14 million kilometers, shows storm clouds and small-scale spots in midnorthern latitudes. The thin ribbon-like feature in the white cloud band marks a high-speed jet at about 47 degrees north. The fact that banded cloud structures retain their visibility almost to the edge of the disk demonstrates that the low contrast of the Saturn clouds is intrinsic and not the result of an overlying haze. (P-23907)

Modifications in the Voyager 2 imaging sequence following the discovery of the dark ring spokes by Voyager 1 permitted the second spacecraft to obtain improved resolution and to track the evolution of these enigmatic features. This high-resolution picture was obtained on August 22 at a range of 4 million kilometers. Some of the dark spokes appear to be sharp down to this resolution limit of about 100 kilometers. (P-23925)

The particles in Saturn's rings are composed primarily of water ice, but differences in color across the rings can be used to determine the presence of possible trace constituents of other materials. These color differences are too subtle to show up in ordinary light, but can be brought out by special processing. This image, obtained on August 23 from a range of 3 million kilometers, shows an enhanced color image of the inner rings made from three pictures taken through separate filters—ultraviolet, blue, and green. Particularly impressive is the color difference between the C Ring, which occupies most of this picture, and the yellow-appearing B Ring in the upper part. This image also reveals three ringlets within the blue C Ring that have the same pale yellow color as the B Ring. Such apparent compositional differences within the C Ring were unexpected and suggested that ring particles remained confined to individual ringlets. (P-23927)

were being photographed. He also emphasized the importance of the search that would be made for small satellites embedded within some of the prominent gaps in the Cassini Division. Theoretical work done since the first flyby had indicated that these gaps were likely to be produced by the gravitational sweeping out of small particles by satellites large enough to be clearly visible in the Voyager images, and high priority was being placed on this search. Smith asserted that at that time the embedded satellite theory was the only one that seemed to explain the empty gaps; the theory was memorably summarized by Jonathan Eberhard of *Science News* as "moonlets between ringlets cause gaplets."

In answer to questions from the press, Ed Stone asserted that everyone on the Science Team felt "a great deal of anticipation. We expect a lot of surprises. We have done a great deal of preparation and our hopes are high." Asked about the possible danger to the spacecraft from its passage through the ring plane so close to the G Ring, Stone said, "I think we're all confident, but on the other hand, we'll all be much happier to hear the transmission when the spacecraft comes out on the other side." At least he said *when*, not *if*!

During the afternoon, Jim Sullivan and his colleagues on the Plasma Science Team prepared their first estimate of the location of the bow shock and magnetopause for this encounter. For Voyager 1, they had had data on the pressure of

the solar wind from the Voyager 2 spacecraft about 300 000 kilometers closer to the Sun. Now there was no upstream "weather station," but Voyager 2 showed a very high level of solar wind activity with considerable gustiness. They predicted that the magnetopause might be compressed as far as 18 R_S, or inside the orbit of Titan. Sullivan admitted ruefully that "the rings, at least, are still likely to be inside the magnetosphere."

August 22, 1981 (4 million km)

The first satellite Voyager 2 encountered was Iapetus, the outermost of the large icy satellites and one of the most bizarre objects in the Saturn system. Iapetus is the moon with a black leading face. Voyager 1 had only a distant view of Iapetus, but Voyager 2 would come close enough to resolve details less than 20 kilometers across. The examination of Iapetus late in the day would also inaugurate the first near-encounter sequence for Voyager 2.

All the seats in Von Karman Auditorium were occupied at the morning press briefing. Fred Scarf of the Plasma Wave Investigation described the observations that had been made by Voyager during the previous months, as it played tag with the long magnetospheric tail of Jupiter that extends beyond the orbit of Saturn. As a result of the same close alignment of Jupiter and Saturn that made the Voyager Grand Tour possible, Saturn had apparently moved repeatedly in and out of the magnetospheric tail of Jupiter, with possible important effects on its own magnetosphere. To the disappointment of some, however, Scarf predicted that the Jovian magnetotail would miss Saturn during the Voyager 2 encounter.

Brad Smith showed some beautiful exaggerated and false-color pictures to illustrate the cloud motions in the atmosphere of Saturn. He also explained that analysis of both Voyager 1 and

Within the Imaging Science Team, primary responsibility for analysis of the ring pictures was assumed by Jeff Cuzzi of NASA-Ames, Ed Danielson of Caltech, and Rich Terrile of JPL. This group was sometimes known as the Imaging Team ringleaders. (P-24126AC)

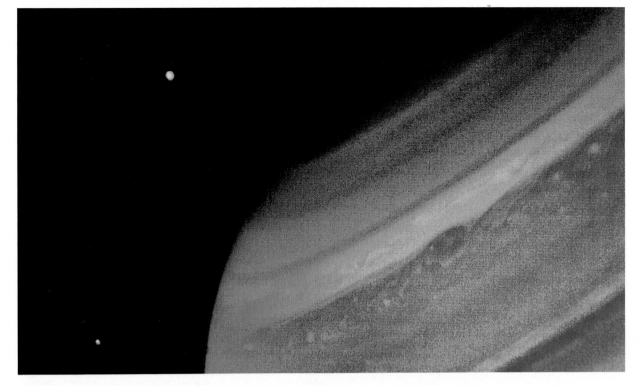

Enhanced color was used to bring out details in the atmospheric structure of Saturn. These images of the northern hemisphere of the planet were assembled from ultraviolet, violet, and green images; they approximate the appearance the planet would have if our eyes were sensitive to shorter wavelengths. The top picture, taken on August 11 from a distance of 15 million kilometers, shows features as small as about 300 kilometers across. The more detailed view, obtained on August 19 from a distance of 7 million kilometers, shows features as small as about 125 kilometers. The weather patterns include three greenish spots flowing westward at a speed of about 15 meters per second. The largest spot, which has a diameter of about 3000 kilometers, is rotating in an anticyclonic direction, indicating a high-pressure region. The ribbon-like feature to the north bordered by the bright yellow below it marks a high-speed jet with wind speeds that approach 150 meters per second. (P-23914 and P-23922)

Voyager 2 pictures showed that the primary reason Saturn presented such a bland face compared to that of Jupiter was not the presence of a pervasive atmospheric haze—rather, the clouds of Saturn were intrinsically less colorful and had less contrast than those of Jupiter. Apparently, there was something in the atmosphere of Jupiter to keep the different colored clouds separate, whereas on Saturn either less intense colors were generated in the first place or the circulation of the atmosphere tended to mix different clouds, producing an almost uniform butterscotch color.

Pictures of Iapetus taken a day earlier at a resolution of about 40 kilometers showed the striking contrast between the icy surface and the dark leading hemisphere. Imaging Scientist David Morrison noted that the contrast between the light and dark material was equivalent to that between snow and asphalt.

The flyby of Iapetus took place between about 4 p.m. and midnight, with several sets of pictures

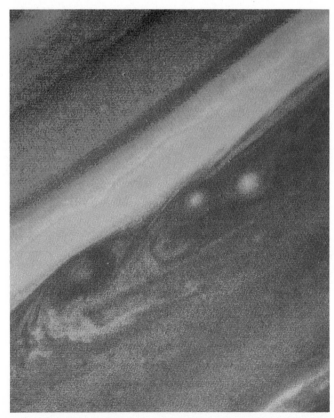

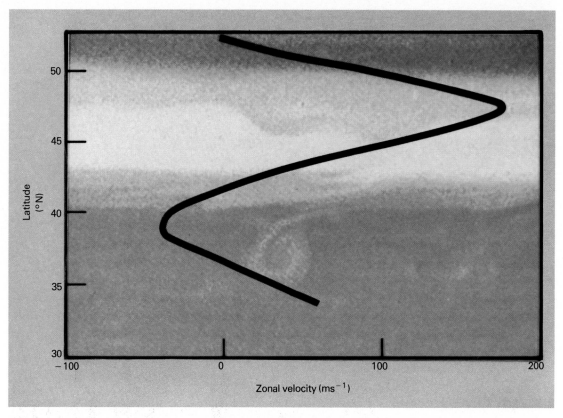

When images of Saturn taken many hours apart are compared, it is possible to trace out from cloud motions the speeds of winds high in the atmosphere of the planet. Here, the plot of wind speeds in the northern hemisphere is superimposed on a picture of the cloud structure. The ribbon at 47 degrees north corresponds to a local maximum in Saturn wind speed. (260-1302)

taken as the spacecraft crossed the north pole at a distance of about 1 million kilometers. The icy part of Iapetus was revealed to be heavily scarred by impact craters. Seen from the bright side, Iapetus looked a lot like its twin in size, Rhea. Considerable structure could be seen along the now-ragged border between the light and dark hemispheres, but no obvious clues were apparent to indicate the source of the dark material. As David Morrison lamented, it was probable that these were the best pictures of Iapetus we would ever see; if they did not resolve the nature of the dark deposit, we might never succeed in doing so.

August 23, 1981 (3 million km)

As Voyager 2 moved into its period of greatest activity, mission controllers prepared to make a final adjustment in the pointing of the scan platform for the high-resolution satellite images. The most recent navigation information was fed into the JPL computers to generate one more input to the preprogrammed pointing sequence. This correction would be sent to the spacecraft early the next day.

At the morning press briefing, Ek Davis reported on the good health of the spacecraft and explained that the day's program called for an intricate set of roll maneuvers to map out the particles and fields environment in the outer magnetosphere of Saturn. It was hoped that Voyager would be inside the magnetosphere by afternoon, although Jim Sullivan's predictions suggested that the spacecraft might still be in the solar wind at that time.

Both Ed Stone and Brad Smith discussed the search for satellites embedded in the ring gaps.

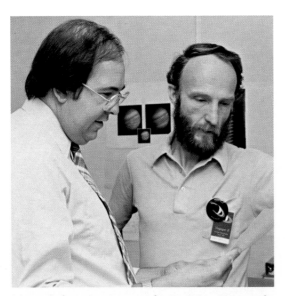

Two of the scientists on the Imaging Team who played leading roles in the interpretation of photographs of the planet are British meteorologist Gary Hunt and Caltech physicist Andy Ingersoll. (P-24126BC)

The most promising target was the gap about 500 kilometers across at the inner edge of the Cassini Division, where calculations by Imaging Team member Jeff Cuzzi and his colleagues predicted a 20- to 30-kilometer-diameter satellite. Images had been taken of this region for one complete ring rotation. If the satellite were present, it would pass through the camera's field of view at least once in this interval. At the time of the press conference, Cuzzi had made a preliminary search of one-third of the frames without finding an embedded satellite. Brad Smith also showed a ring spoke movie in which a single group of spokes was followed around the ring, from its emergence from behind Saturn to its disappearance into the shadow nearly one rotation later. In following these spoke features, the camera seemed to pan around the rings, causing this film to be dubbed the "Saturn 500."

During the afternoon, Voyager obtained the first good photographs of Hyperion, the satellite between Titan and Iapetus. It was immediately evident that Hyperion was a very strange looking object, surprisingly irregular for its size, more than 300 kilometers in diameter. The first pictures showed an almost square profile in which the satellite looked something like a dented can or chipped brick. An analysis presented at the daily afternoon science meeting suggested that the long axis did not point toward Saturn as, according to all gravitational theories, it should. In disbelief, Ed Stone asked, "Are you sure you know where Saturn is?" Imaging Team members assured him that they did know where Saturn was, but that further pictures of Hyperion would be required to determine for sure the orientation of its longest axis.

Press interest in this Voyager 2 encounter was extraordinarily high. Yet there was a big difference from the same stage in Voyager 1, in that relatively few startling new discoveries had been generated. Freelance writer Jim Loudon commented that little hard news should be expected at this stage, since Voyager 2, as a follow-up mission, was seeking to get detailed observations of

The ultraviolet spectrometer was the Voyager instrument most sensitive to the composition of the upper atmospheres of Saturn and Titan and of the extended gas torus arising from the atmosphere of Titan. Here Darrell Strobel and Jack McConnel of the UVS team examine spectra of auroral emission from the polar regions of Saturn. (P-24023BC)

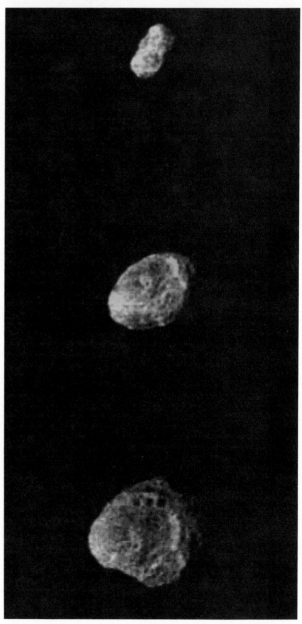

Hyperion is a small satellite between the orbits of Iapetus and giant Titan. These three views of Hyperion were obtained as Voyager flew past this satellite looking at it from different directions. They were taken on August 23 and 24 from distances of 1.2 million kilometers, 700 000 kilometers, and 500 000 kilometers, respectively. Hyperion is an icy object, roughly 400 by 250 by 200 kilometers in size, with a surface pockmarked by meteorite impact craters. (P-23932)

The first satellite encountered by Voyager 2 was Iapetus, the outermost of Saturn's large icy satellites. Iapetus is remarkable for having a leading hemisphere less than one-tenth as bright as the icy trailing hemisphere. This picture was taken on August 22 from a distance of 1.1 million kilometers; it shows features as small as 20 kilometers across. The northern trailing hemisphere is in view, including the north polar region on the right and a band of dark terrain near the equator that extends around from the dark leading hemisphere. Unfortunately, even at this resolution the origin of the dark material that covers a third of this satellite could not be readily determined. (P-23961)

unexpected phenomena that had been discovered by Voyager 1. He said, "When it's all over and the histories are written, the pictures selected to illustrate those phenomena will no doubt be mostly from Voyager 2, not Voyager 1. The Voyager 2 pictures will be better because we now know what to take pictures of. With the first encounter, things that had happened by this stage were easy to make into news stories. You described the discoveries, and that was enough to fill your column or newscast item. Now it's a different situation. For instance, although the ring pictures are even better than those from Voyager 1, we already know the startling fact that there are

At the time of the Voyager 2 encounter, the magnetosphere of Saturn was even more compressed by high-speed streams of solar wind particles than it had been at the time of Voyager 1. Here, plasma physicists Jim Sullivan and Herb Bridge monitor the rapidly varying solar wind pressure in order to predict the time the Voyager spacecraft would enter the magnetosphere of Saturn. (P-24023CC)

a thousand rings. You can't write a story about that now. This time the pictures are being taken to find out *why* there are a thousand rings, and we can't answer that instantly. It will take analysis. Maybe the analysis will be quick enough to give answers in a few days while the press room is still open, but maybe not.''

During the afternoon, two items dominated the attention of the more than one hundred Voyager scientists now gathered at JPL. For the Imaging Team, the dominant concern was the failure to find the embedded satellites. By evening, two-thirds of the images had been searched, and no satellites had been discovered. Jeff Cuzzi and Rich Terrile worked late into the night, but when they had finished looking carefully at every one of the targeted images, they sadly concluded that there were no satellites down to a diameter as small as 10 kilometers within the gaps in the Cassini Division. Meanwhile, the Particles and Fields

scientists were searching for the first evidence of the bow shock as Voyager neared the magnetosphere of Saturn. Earlier predictions had indicated the shock might be reached very soon. However, the increasing levels of solar wind pressure made it more probable that Voyager 2 would not cross the bow shock until midmorning of the next day.

August 24, 1981 (2 million km)

At 8:05 a.m. the telemetry signals received at JPL finally indicated that the spacecraft had crossed the bow shock and had begun its encounter with the magnetosphere of Saturn. The initial shock was seen at 31.7 R_S, but the shock wave was highly unstable and, as it oscillated back and forth, the spacecraft recrossed at 11:35 a.m. at 29.1 R_S and at 12:56 p.m. at 28.1 R_S. It was expected that Voyager would reach the magnetopause a few hours later.

At the morning press briefing, Brad Smith had to admit that the search for embedded satellites in the rings had been a failure. There were definitely no satellites as large as 10 kilometers in diameter within any of the four major Cassini gaps, and it looked increasingly as though efforts to press the limits of detection as low as 5 kilometers would be equally unsuccessful. Rather ruefully, he admitted that, ''We now find ourselves at the point where we hoped not to be. We are desperately looking for an alternative hypothesis to explain the gaps.''

On the brighter side, Smith pointed out that so far Voyager 2 had had incredible success in targeting images of specific storms in the atmosphere of Saturn. Following the Voyager 1 encounter, Andy Ingersoll, atmospheric dynamicist on the Imaging Team, had predicted from the weather patterns on Saturn where each of these long-lived storms would be nine months later when the Voyager 2 craft arrived. Almost all the images targeted on the basis of these predictions were coming out right. Terrestrial weather forecasters might well envy Ingersoll's success in projecting so accurately the turbulent weather on Saturn.

At the afternoon science meeting, a good deal of attention was directed to questions of ring dynamics, particularly to a search for alternative

As encounter approached, Voyager returned ever more spectacular views of the rings. This picture, taken on August 23 from a range of 3 million kilometers, shows the edge of the planet seen through the C Ring and the inner part of the B Ring. Part of Saturn is shadowed by the rings. Clearly visible is a bright band corresponding to sunlight transmitted through the nearly empty Cassini Division. The Cassini Division itself is the darker gap that extends from the lower center of this picture to the upper left. Outside this division is the A Ring, which contains the narrow Keeler Gap. (P-23931)

hypotheses to explain the major gaps. Some concern was also expressed over the failure, so far, for Voyager 2 images to show twists or braids in the F Ring. Since Voyager 1, there had been a good deal of speculation about unusual gravitational,

or even electromagnetic, mechanisms that might produce such bizarre structure, but Voyager 2 had found no further examples of such features.

As the Voyager spacecraft had swung past little Iapetus two days earlier, the gravitational pull of

Voyager 2 revealed that Saturn's large satellite Tethys, more than 1000 kilometers in diameter, was scarred by an ancient impact crater larger than any other discovered in the Saturn system. This circular feature, about 400 kilometers in diameter and large enough to hold the satellite Mimas, is visible in these three views as it rotates from the center of Tethys to the edge. The pictures were taken at four-hour intervals on August 24 and 25. The large crater has a raised floor, clearly visible on the closest image. Also seen on the final image is another enigmatic ring marked on the surface by different contrast material rather than by topography. Note that this albedo ring lies at the border of a darker part of Tethys' surface. (P-23941)

the satellite had bent the orbit of the spacecraft slightly. A detailed analysis of the spacecraft's trajectory could therefore yield a value for the mass of Iapetus. Previously, the best mass estimate had been derived from Pioneer 11, but the uncertainty was so large that no meaningful estimate could be made of the density. In the afternoon John Anderson of the Radio Science Team reported a new value for the mass with an uncertainty of less than 10 percent. Having heard through the grapevine that the Iapetus mass would be presented at the science meeting, David Morrison had quickly measured the size of the new Iapetus images to derive an improved radius for the satellite of 740 kilometers, about 20 kilometers larger than the Voyager 1 estimate. A quick calculation, combining the new value for mass and radius, yielded a density of 1.1 grams per cubic centimeter, a clear indication that Iapetus is nearly pure ice. Therefore, almost surely the bright trailing face of the satellite is representative of the bulk composition, and the black material on the leading face represents a superficial coating on a basically icy object, or, as one member of the press put it the next day, the zebra was revealed as a white animal with black stripes, not the other way around.

At about 5 p.m., the rapidly shrinking bow shock once again caught up with the spacecraft; not until 6:52 p.m., at a distance of about 22 R_S, did Voyager cross the bow shock for the last time.

The high-resolution satellite images were received at JPL and computer enhanced using interactive terminals available to the Imaging Team scientists. (Left) JPL's Torrence Johnson examines one of the first high-resolution views of Enceladus. Later, the pictures are mounted on cardboard sheets for comparison and analysis. (Right) Joe Boyce of NASA and Gene Shoemaker of the U.S. Geological Survey discuss the interpretation of pictures of Iapetus. (P-24124BC and P-24015AC)

Just past midnight, at 18.6 R_S, Voyager reached the magnetopause, which was so highly compressed by solar wind pressure that it lay inside the orbit of Titan. Meanwhile, the scan platform instruments were concentrating alternately on the planet, its rings, and several of the inner satellites. At about 7 p.m., the highest-resolution pictures of Hyperion were received from a range of about 500 000 kilometers. At midnight, Voyager was just over 1 million kilometers from Saturn.

August 25, 1981 (Encounter Day)

All morning, the scan platform on the Voyager spacecraft kept up its rapid pace of observations, with an ever-increasing emphasis on the satellites. The Voyager scientists were particularly anxious for the images of Enceladus, the satellite that had appeared so bright and lacking in large craters as seen from Voyager 1. At 4 a.m. six pictures were obtained at a range of 1.2 million kilometers; a little after 6 a.m. two more pictures were obtained from 790 000 kilometers, and just before 9 a.m. five more at a range of only 660 000 kilometers. Between 8 and 9 a.m., a series of high-resolution

views of the F Ring was expected to reveal whether the gravitational tug of the shepherding satellites might indeed produce the sort of kinks and braiding seen by Voyager 1. Other pictures were targeted for the small, newly discovered satellites that shared orbits with Tethys and Dione. By noon the spacecraft was only about half a million kilometers from both Enceladus and Tethys, the two major satellite targets for the Voyager 2 trajectory.

At the morning press briefing, Ek Davis reported that a final navigational analysis had shown that Voyager 2 was within 50 kilometers of the aim point and would arrive approximately three seconds ahead of schedule. Ed Stone described this as ''the day of challenge. Everything we see today will be new.'' He was particularly excited about the opportunity Voyager 2 would present to view the rings at close range on their illuminated side. ''The images of the rings we receive today will be of much higher resolution than anything we have ever seen before.''

Brad Smith showed enhanced color pictures of the rings that drew gasps from the press. Von Karman Auditorium was overflowing by this time; to make room for the reporters, everyone else, even

The best color view of Tethys was obtained by Voyager 2 on August 25 from a distance of 600 000 kilometers. It shows features as small as 10 kilometers across. Tethys has two distinct types of terrain — bright, densely cratered regions and relatively dark, more lightly cratered plains that extend in a broad belt across the satellite. The densely cratered terrain is believed to be part of the ancient crust of the satellite. The lightly cratered plains are thought to have been formed later by internal processes. A large valley system, Ithaca Chasma, was discovered by Voyager 1 and is seen in this Voyager 2 image to stretch into the other hemisphere of the satellite, wrapping about 270 degrees around Tethys. (P-23948)

leading NASA officials from Washington, was relegated to standing room around the edges of the auditorium. Smith noted that during the Voyager 1 encounter, the estimate of the number of rings had gone from tens to hundreds to a thousand. He said that it was clear that the number should be several thousands.

The first high-resolution views of Tethys were exciting. Smith showed one picture of an immense crater, about 400 kilometers across, which appeared to be even larger in comparison to the size of Tethys than the big crater on Mimas was— relative to Mimas' diameter. In fact, all of Mimas could fit inside the newly discovered crater on Tethys.

Fred Scarf provided an entertaining, as well as informative, version of the sounds of Saturn. Plasma waves are basically electrical waves in the audio range of frequencies, that is, the frequencies that we could hear if the waves were sound instead of electromagnetic. To make this point, Scarf played back his plasma wave observations through a music synthesizer, providing an eerie sort of music that some compared to a cross between early Stockhausen electronic music and today's Steve Reich or Philip Glass. The assembled members of the press applauded the tape, one of the few times that applause was afforded to nonimaging data.

In response to a question, Voyager Mission Design Manager Charlie Kolhase estimated about a 65 percent probability of a successful Uranus encounter, based on what was known of the current performance and estimated reliability of the Voyager spacecraft. Brad Smith added, "It's best to apply these arguments tomorrow after we've gotten through the ring plane." The audience laughed; after all, no one was really very worried about this ring plane crossing, since it was so close to the place successfully penetrated by the Pioneer 11 spacecraft in 1979.

At 3 p.m. a special press conference was held to celebrate (perhaps a few hours prematurely) the successful Voyager 2 encounter with Saturn. Present were James Beggs, the new NASA Administrator, Andrew Stofan, the head of the NASA Office of Space Science, and Bruce Murray, Director of the Jet Propulsion Lab. All three had high praise for Voyager and the Voyager team, but they also referred to the five-year hiatus to be expected in planetary encounters, with nothing new to come before the Voyager 2 Uranus encounter in 1986. In answer to many questions from the press, Beggs affirmed his personal support for a strong program of planetary exploration in the late 1980s, but he gave no specifics on how the program might be revitalized in the near future.

As encounter time approached, hundreds of VIPs arrived at JPL to share this moment of exploration—industrialists, educators, scientists, movie stars. Presidential Special Counselor Edwin Meese arrived by helicopter from the summer

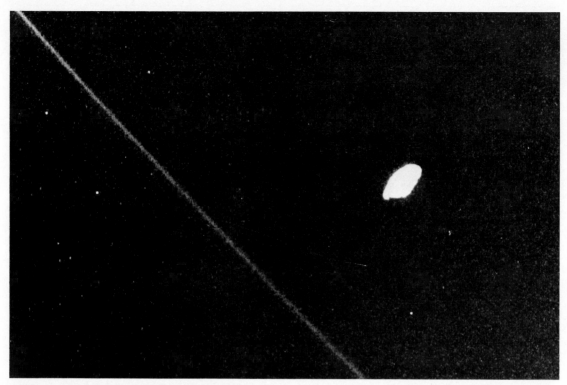

Saturn's narrow F Ring is gravitationally confined between two shepherding satellites. This close-up view obtained on August 25 from a range of 365 000 kilometers shows the ring and its inner shepherding satellite. The satellite is elongated and irregular, with its longest axis pointing toward the center of Saturn. As seen here, the F Ring is thin and does not show the multiple braided structure Voyager 1 photographed, nor is there any indication of a bend or kink in the ring at its closest point to the shepherd satellite, as had been predicted by some theories. (P-23951)

White House for a quick tour. The main events of the evening would be the photopolarimeter trace of a high-resolution profile of the rings, the radio occultation probe of the atmosphere of Saturn, and the drama of ring plane crossing, to be followed in the early hours of the next morning by the closest approaches to Tethys and Enceladus.

This was to be the big moment for the photopolarimeter. This instrument had had problems on both spacecraft during the Jupiter encounters and had not operated at all when Voyager 1 passed Saturn the previous November. But now, measuring the light from the star δ Scorpii as it twinkled on and off behind the individual ringlets, the photopolarimeter could be expected to resolve ring structure as small as about 100 meters across. Two and a half hours of the most valuable time during the encounter—time when the spacecraft was extremely close to Saturn and its rings—had been allocated to the exclusive use of the photopolarimeter to carry out this experiment. More than a hundred people crowded into

James F. Blinn and Charles E. Kohlhase in the JPL Computer Graphics Laboratory.

THE MAGIC OF COMPUTER GRAPHICS

Any true space fan has often dreamed of beholding the spectacular views possible from different vantage points within the Saturn system. Imagine what it would be like to fly along with Voyager 2 as it swings around Saturn and crosses the ring plane just beyond the whirling sea of ice particles and bergs. From a visual standpoint, this wish has been fulfilled by the amazing computer programs of James F. Blinn of JPL.

Computer programs can be written to display rapidly hundreds of dots and lines using a high-speed vector graphics display system. This allows a user to interact with the computer in fractions of a second. However, if more realistic shaded color scenes are desired, it is necessary to compute and store several hundred thousand numbers in a large buffer memory that can control the brightness levels of the red, green, and blue colors at each of the roughly 500 × 500 dot locations comprising the screen of a typical raster-graphics display device.

It is first necessary to construct a mathematical model of "Voyager's world" in the computer data base. This involves such details as the size and appearance of Saturn and its rings, the orbital elements of Voyager's flightpath and the seventeen known moons of Saturn, the appearance of the spacecraft, the locations of Sun and Earth, and the locations of some 6000 of the brightest stars. Since the data base is extensive and complete in a three-dimensional sense, perspective views projected on a two-dimensional screen are of far greater accuracy than would be possible from an artist's conception or conventional animation. Computation times, however, can be as long as a few minutes for each full picture.

Charles E. Kohlhase, Voyager Mission Design Manager, has made frequent use of Blinn's software for mission and science design purposes, as well as for Voyager flyby computer movie simulations, which have been shown around the world. Much of their popularity stems from the realistic visual effects achieved by Blinn and the mission fidelity ensured by Kohlhase.

Three computer graphic views shown here indicate locations of Voyager 2 during its Saturn flyby on August 25, 1981. A large field of view of 75 degrees was used in the first scene to capture the moment of closest approach. This simulation guided space artist Don Davis, whose painting appeared on several magazine covers. The other two computer graphic views have fields of view of 45 degrees and were extracted from the Voyager 2 Saturn flyby movie. They reveal the changing appearance of Saturn's rings a few minutes before and after ring plane crossing.

the room where the electronic signals from the spacecraft would be received. At 6:18 p.m, exactly on schedule, the signals from δ Scorpii were received at JPL, and twenty-two minutes later the star began to dim as it partially disappeared behind the C Ring. As soon as it was clear that the experiment was working, a pandemonium of cheers and congratulations filled the crowded room. During the next two hours, more and more people stopped by to see how the experiment was going and to offer their best wishes to Lonne Lane

and his team. At one point Brad Smith stuck his head in and managed to admit, "It was worth it after all to give up all those images for this occultation." By 8:40 p.m. a profile of 82 000 kilometers of the rings had been obtained that would require half a mile of chart paper to record, at ten points per centimeter.

Soon the Voyager 2 cameras were active again, concentrating now on a last look at Enceladus before ring plane crossing. To everyone's delight, the images showed great detail and a variety of

A tremendous amount of detailed structure in Saturn's B Ring is revealed in this 6000-kilometer-wide photograph taken on August 25 from a distance of 743 000 kilometers. The narrowest features seen here are about 10 kilometers across. At this resolution, about ten times more ringlets are shown than had been suspected from Voyager 1 pictures. (P-23946)

features. Some parts of the icy surface appeared to have been wiped clean by recent geological activity. A few ridge systems appeared that were reminiscent of the mountain-and-valley terrain of Ganymede. In the Imaging Science area, about twenty people clustered around geologist Gene Shoemaker, who excitedly poured out idea after idea as each new image appeared.

Shortly after 10 p.m. the imaging sequence ended and the spacecraft prepared itself to disappear behind the disk of Saturn. From 10:26 p.m. until one minute after midnight, Voyager would

be out of touch with its controllers on Earth. During that period, the radio signal would make critical probes of the atmosphere. Images, including those of the ring plane crossing, would be recorded onboard, and at 10:44 p.m. the spacecraft would pass through the rings at 2.86 R_S, about 3000 kilometers outside the G Ring. Of course, no one at JPL would know whether the passage had been accomplished safely until the radio signal was reacquired at about midnight. Many of the scientists and most of the VIPs went home, while those who remained watched anxi-

Voyager 2 not only discovered many more ringlets than had been visible to Voyager 1, it also demon-strated that the fine structure in the rings is not static. This spectacular composite image shows two views of the outer edge of the B Ring and the inner part of the Cassini Division taken on opposite sides of the planet on August 25 from a range of 610 000 kilometers. Although the major features line up in the two images, there are many differences in the location of the fine structure. In addition, the edge of the B Ring differs by about 50 kilometers between the two images. Scientists believe the distorted shape of the B Ring is due to the gravitational influence of Mimas. Apparently, the rings are in a highly dynamic state with constant variation of fine-scale structure. (P-24064)

ously for the first signal to be received. At about two minutes before midnight, a faint whisper of a radio signal, bent through Saturn's atmosphere, was picked up. Once again, champagne corks popped at numerous locations around JPL. Voyager had made it through and was on the way to Uranus!

August 26, 1981

As the Voyager spacecraft reemerged from be-hind Saturn, its radio signals were received at the Deep Space Network Station in Australia and transmitted directly to JPL. In the windowless control room, mission managers and engineers watched the signal carefully to make sure that all

was well before they headed home for the night. Their initial delight at the reacquisition of the signal quickly turned to worry and despair. The telemetry signals were not normal, with several instruments showing unexplained and peculiar transmissions. Engineering data indicated that near ring plane crossing the small control thrusters on the spacecraft had made several unprogrammed and unexpected firings. Worst of all, the scan platform, with its cameras and spectrometers, was not pointed where it was supposed to be. Within minutes the members of the press remaining in Von Karman Auditorium also recognized the problem, as the expected high-resolution pictures failed to appear on the television monitors.

This was no time for panic, and panic wouldn't do any good anyway. The events being seen at JPL had actually transpired more than an hour and a half before, and it would take another hour and a half for a radio signal traveling at the speed of light to reach the spacecraft with new commands. Nothing precipitous must be done that could endanger the spacecraft, especially with the important Uranus encounter still five years in the future.

As more engineering data from Voyager accumulated, it became evident that the scan platform was frozen in its back-and-forth, or azimuth, motion, although it appeared to have continued moving properly in elevation (up and down) until the onboard computers, sensing a problem, had commanded it to stop. Unfortunately, it had stopped in a place where the sensitive instruments could be damaged by sunlight; thus the first step taken, at about 2 a.m., was to transmit instruc-

tions to move the scan platform to a safe position. Other commands turned off the preprogrammed sequencing and put the instruments into a standby mode. By 6 a.m. it was apparent that the spacecraft had responded to these commands and that the initial problems with other systems had apparently repaired themselves, leaving only the scan platform to be dealt with. Little more could be done until the data on Voyager's tape recorder could be played back; only then would it be possible to tell exactly when the problem had occurred and to identify its cause.

At 8:15 a.m. Mission Director Dick Laeser convened a special press conference to describe the scan platform problem and the actions that had been taken during the night. At the same time, he sent most of the exhausted engineers and programmers home to catch a few hours sleep so that they would be fresh to interpret the information from the tape recorder playback. Meanwhile, the

 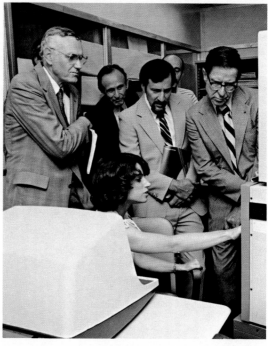

On Encounter Day, NASA Administrator James Beggs and other administration officials arrived at JPL to participate in the historic event. (Left) JPL Director Bruce Murray discusses the forthcoming encounter activities with Associate Lab Director Robert Parks and Andy Stofan, head of NASA's Office of Space Science. (Right) Beggs and his party see a demonstration by Linda Morabito of Voyager's optical navigation facility. (P-23994AC and P-24000AC)

closest encounters with Enceladus and Tethys had come and gone, with the blind spacecraft unable to take advantage of them. Also lost were stereo views of the F Ring, close-up views of the ring from the dark side, and another photopolarimeter ring occultation that would have yielded even higher resolution of the A and F Rings.

Most of the Voyager scientists had by now heard the bad news. Brad Smith had been awakened after only an hour and a half of sleep. His first reaction was, "Thank God it happened when it did and not a few hours earlier."

At 9 a.m. the critical playback from the onboard tape recorder began. A sense of gloom per-

vaded the Imaging Science area. Everyone realized that these would be the last close-up views of Saturn or its satellites they would ever receive—what Rich Terrile called "our last best data." It was like watching each labored breath, waiting for the sick scan platform to expire. Some of the first pictures were of the F Ring, beautiful high-resolution views, closer than any obtained by Voyager 1. Multiple strands were clearly visible, but still no sign of bending or twisting. At 9:56 a.m. a lovely crescent image of one of the F Ring shepherd satellites was received. At 10:10 a.m. the highest-resolution views of Enceladus were due, but instead of satellite images, only a blank

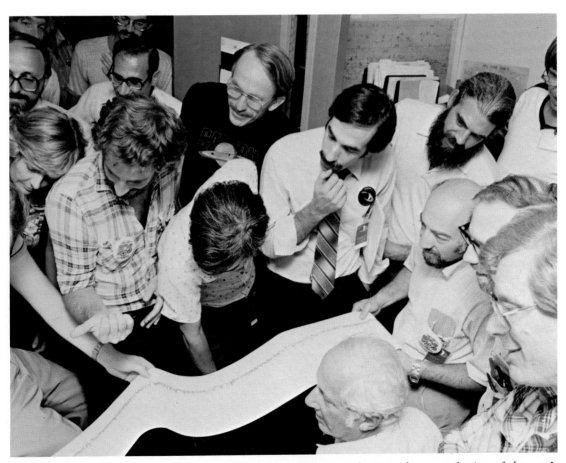

One of the most exciting events of the Voyager 2 encounter was the 2 1/2 hour occultation of the star δ Scorpii by the rings of Saturn. During this period, the photopolarimeter monitored the rapid changes in brightness of the star as it twinkled through gaps in the rings. Here Lonne Lane, Photopolarimeter Principal Investigator, stretches out one of the first printouts of data from the occultation experiment, while members of other science teams and the press look on. (P-24022BC)

screen appeared, prompting someone to refer to "the final images of the planetary program."

But these were not quite the last pictures. As the spacecraft approached ring plane crossing, the wide-angle views still appeared to be approximately on target, and a series of beautiful pictures of the rings nearly edge-on was received. When the time came for the highest-resolution narrow-angle mosaic of Tethys, however, every picture was a blank except for one where, down in the corner, a small edge of the satellite had been photographed. After this, only the wide-angle views of the rings appeared to be anywhere close to target. At fifty-five minutes after ring plane

Enigmatic Enceladus was a major target for Voyager 2. This small satellite is the brightest and smoothest of the icy moons of Saturn. As shown in the color image obtained on August 25 from a distance of 120 000 kilometers, the surface of this satellite proved to be remarkable in many ways. Part is crater free, indicating a recent upwelling of liquid water from the interior. Even the cratered parts of Enceladus show modifications indicative of a thin plastic crust over a liquid interior. In many ways the surface of this satellite resembles that of Jupiter's largest satellite, Ganymede. Enceladus, however, is only one-tenth Ganymede's size, and it must long since have dissipated any primordial heat that could maintain a liquid interior. Yet detailed views such as the one shown at right evidence repeated episodes of surface flooding over a time span that must range to billions of years. Voyager scientists concluded from these images that some unknown source of energy has continued to heat the interior of Enceladus, even up to the present time. (P-23955 and 260-1341)

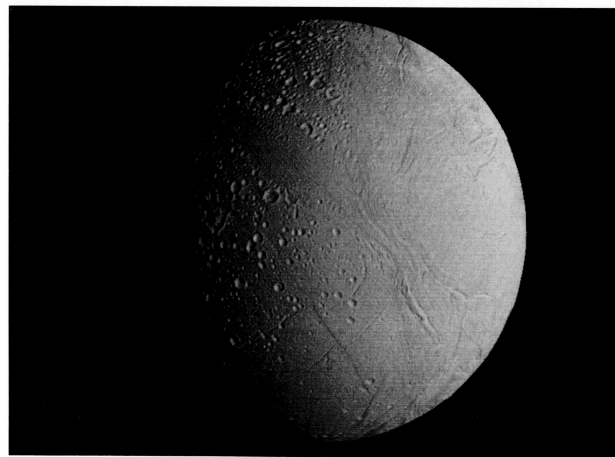

crossing, the azimuth froze up completely, although the spacecraft continued to move in elevation for two more pictures. One of these misdirected views provided a serendipitous discovery—an unprogrammed picture of the Keeler Gap that showed an inner ring at one edge instead of running down the center where it had been expected.

A gloomy mood pervaded the 10:30 a.m. press conference, far different from the elation of the previous day. Dick Laeser—clearly very tired—again explained what actions had been taken to protect the spacecraft. Even after the tape recordings had been received, it was still not evident how the failure had occurred. It did not seem to be a discrete event associated with the ring plane, but rather a progressive degradation of the capability of the scan platform to move as directed. One could not even be sure that the problem really was with hardware, as opposed to the software that provided the commands to the scan platform. The difficulties of dealing with the situation were made even worse by the faulty receiver on the Voyager 2 spacecraft. Ever since the main receiver had failed on April 5, 1978,

special procedures had been required on the ground to keep the transmitted frequency tuned with the ailing receiver. Now, following the Saturn occultation, several repetitions of each command load were required before the transmission and receiver could lock up and the instruction could be acted on. Apparently the difficulty was caused by a small change in the temperature of the spacecraft receiver while it was in the shadow of Saturn. Laeser expressed particular thanks to the engineers who had anticipated this temperature problem and had been prepared to deal with it; without their efforts, it would not have been possible to send the critical signals to protect the scan platform instruments from further damage.

The mood of the press brightened as the conference moved from data lost to data gained. Brad Smith had a series of spectacular pictures received the previous day, including a view of the rings in enhanced color and a close-up of the Keeler Gap that showed a narrow kinky ring running right down the center; these were the first kinks seen since the Voyager 1 photos of the F Ring. Larry Soderblom presented some of the first high-resolution satellite pictures, saying that, "In terms of data quality, without question, we have had a total success. We have completed our first reconnaissance of Iapetus and Hyperion, and had a new much closer look at Enceladus and Tethys." On Tethys, the gigantic valley, Ithaca Chasma, seen by Voyager 1, could now be traced 270 degrees around the satellite—a distance of more than 3000 kilometers. Enceladus showed "a surface that is truly different from that of Mimas, its twin in size," with at least four separate geological terrains. Most remarkable were the flat areas that appeared to have been flooded by fresh water from the interior, probably within the last hundred million years—just yesterday in geological terms. Soderblom noted that there was no reason to expect that such activity had ceased and, indeed, that we might expect further volcanic-type eruptions to take place on Enceladus. He even managed to draw a laugh out of the audience when he described the ridges on Enceladus as being "like something we saw many moons ago" on Ganymede.

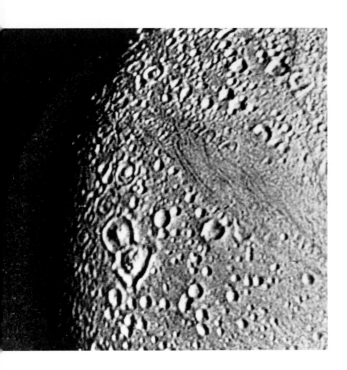

On the evening of August 26, while out of sight of Earth in the shadow of Saturn, the Voyager 2 spacecraft plunged through the ring plane at 2.86 R_S, not far from the tenuous G Ring of Saturn. Photographs taken at that time were stored on the onboard tape recorder and played back for receipt at JPL the next day. (Top) A high-resolution view of the F Ring obtained shortly before ring plane crossing. At least four distinct components are visible at this resolution, which is about 10 kilometers. (Bottom) This wide-angle view was the last picture taken before the satellite crossed the ring plane. It shows the entire ring system highly foreshortened, from the prominent F Ring in the foreground to the loops in the center distance caused by structure within the B Ring. Bright streaks visible within the B Ring are the famous spokes appearing prominently in forward scattered light. (P-23962 and P-23964)

During the occultation of the spacecraft by Saturn, the atmosphere of the planet was probed deeply by the dual-frequency radio signal from Voyager. The Radio Science Team Leader was Len Tyler of Stanford University.

At 1 p.m. the Imaging Team meeting began with a painful debate over just how much data had been lost. It seemed unbelievable that there really were no more pictures coming in. It was with some effort that the scientists turned their minds from this unhappy state to a consideration of the new satellite data.

Gene Shoemaker kicked off the science discussion with a description of the new pictures: "Enceladus unfolded before our eyes last night, far beyond my wildest expectations. We had hoped to see some surface features in order to study topographic relaxation, the degradation of craters due to slow flow in a viscous crust. As it turned out, we have the full range of topographic relaxation, from which we can derive the thermal structure and history of the crust." Shoemaker's student, Quinn Passey, had already computed the way craters might be deformed on an icy surface in anticipation of just such pictures. On the basis of these calculations, Shoemaker expected to be able to calculate the thickness of the solid crust and to differentiate between the histories of different parts of the surface of Enceladus within the next twenty-four hours.

At the 2 p.m. science meeting, the most spectacular results were presented by Fred Scarf. Very close to the time of ring plane crossing, the plasma wave instrument had recorded activity a million times the normal energy level. The high frequency of the signal proved that it could not be ordinary plasma waves, but more likely an electrical phenomenon taking place at the spacecraft. Scarf suggested that such an effect could be caused by the bursts of plasma generated by impact at 10 kilometers per second with very small dust grains, only a micrometer or two in diameter. The quantity of such impacts was truly staggering—thousands upon thousands, not just at the moment of ring plane crossing, but extending for several minutes on either side. The roaring sound of these impacts on the tape that he played, sounding almost like a hailstorm striking a tin roof, sent chills down the spines of the seventy-five scientists attending the meeting. But did this unexpected plasma activity really have anything to do with the scan platform failure? No one could tell.

Late in the afternoon a new series of spacecraft commands was prepared. Even though the exact cause of the platform failure had not been identified, controllers felt it was important to begin trying to determine the extent of the problem, so they prepared commands calling for a slow 10-degree motion in azimuth. Meanwhile, the spacecraft continued pathetically to transmit blank frames. Each empty frame was displayed on the monitors at JPL, complete with the commanded exposure time, filter, and so forth. They kept on coming, one after another, all day. On the positive side, of course, only the scan platform instruments were disabled. All the particles and fields data continued to be returned in a normal mode.

One concern felt by everyone was, "Will Voyager be able to carry out the reconnaissance of Uranus in 1986?" As long as the scan platform continued to move in elevation, it would be possible to point in azimuth by rotating the entire spacecraft. Rotation of the spacecraft used control fuel, but Charlie Kohlhase calculated that there should be enough fuel left at Uranus for about 150 rolls, enough to carry out a very respectable mission even if the scan platform could not be repaired. Indeed, some people within the project advocated making no effort now to resurrect the scan platform in time to continue Saturn observations. Their thought was to declare the Saturn encounter a success and button up the spacecraft

a

b

c

d

Press coverage of the Voyager 2 Saturn encounter exceeded that afforded any previous unmanned space mission. During the days around encounter, Von Karman Auditorium at JPL was packed with hundreds of members of the press, as well as Voyager scientists and engineers. (a) Behind the assembled press is a full-scale mock-up of the Voyager spacecraft. (b) Project Manager Ek Davis, Project Scientist Ed Stone, and Imaging Team Leader Brad Smith in a familiar pose answering questions from the rostrum. (c) A view of the busy press room. (d) JPL's Al Hibbs prepares to interview Gary Hunt for the daily television coverage that was beamed nationwide by the Public Broadcasting System. (P-24128DC, P-24051BC, P-24127AC, and P-24127BC)

to save it for Uranus. Many scientists, on the other hand, asked why some effort could not be made to move the scan platform to point at Saturn. Even if the usual intricate maneuvers were given up, just photographing Saturn and its rings instead of blank space seemed the logical thing to do. Project managers set a middle course, not trying at once to turn the platform back toward Saturn, but beginning to exercise it a step at a

time to see if they felt confident enough to return to the planet.

August 27, 1981

At the regular morning press briefing, Ek Davis reported some progress in bringing the scan platform back to operational status. During the night the spacecraft had successfully responded to the

command to move the scan platform by 10 degrees in azimuth. A second similar command had been sent, and again the platform moved, but this time jerkily rather than smoothly. He commented that the playback of tape recorded information had really not helped solve the problem. "We are not yet at the point of fixing the problem. We are still trying to define the problem, to gain understanding of what is happening." In response to increasing behind-the-scenes pressure to get the platform pointed once again toward Saturn, both Davis and Stone reiterated that "our principal objective is to recover the scan platform capability for Uranus. We will do nothing to increase risk by premature activity now."

The previous day, one of the first reactions to news of the scan platform failure had been to ask what percentage of Voyager 2 science was being lost because of this failure. The problem with such a question is that it is impossible to quantify what you don't have. No one could ever know what discoveries might have been made if the system had continued to operate as planned. However, Ed Stone said that he had thought about the question for the last twenty-four hours, and he did have an answer to the percentage of success for Voyager 2: 200 percent. As he further explained, the spacecraft had so far exceeded the scientific objectives set at the beginning of the project that even the loss of the scan platform at this time left us with twice as much as we had hoped for at the beginning.

Fred Scarf presented his "sounds of the ring plane crossing," commenting that, although "these sounds may be unpleasant to you, they are the things we plasma investigators love." Referring to the mysterious million-fold increase in energy in the minutes around ring plane crossing, Scarf described the cacophony as "impulsive sound—it sounds very much like material impacting the spacecraft. I think the most likely explanation must be impacts of small dust grains."

Brad Smith showed some of the best pictures from near the time of ring plane crossing, culminating in an image of the outer part of the B Ring at a resolution of about 10 kilometers, better than anything that had been obtained by Voyager 1 in its more distant flyby of the rings. Smith explained that, "This is about as far as imaging can take us" in ring resolution. If the intricate structure visible in these highest-resolution pictures were typical of the rings as a whole, there were many thousands of individual features—far more than had been seen by Voyager 1.

For greater resolution, it was necessary to turn to the photopolarimeter occultation results that were now beginning to be analyzed. Lonne Lane proudly walked to the front of Von Karman Auditorium stating that, "It has taken us three years to traverse the 75 feet from the back of this room to the front. We have a superb collection of ring data. There is no question about that." This was the first time in the four Voyager encounters that the photopolarimeter had been featured at a press conference.

Just to display the occultation data would require a piece of chart paper about half a mile long. Lane showed just one stretch of the rings, 340 kilometers wide, showing the profile of the Keeler Gap with many fine features that had not been seen in imaging. He also had a first estimate for the thickness of the A Ring derived from the apparent sharpness of the edge as it blanked out the light from the occultation star. His estimate was less than 300 meters; the best previous estimate from ground-based observations was that the rings were less than about 2 kilometers in thickness.

With no new images being received, attention at the afternoon science conference turned more toward results from the other investigations, primarily the infrared spectrometer, radio science, and the photopolarimeter. Measurements of Titan showed a surprisingly high degree of polarization of the reflected sunlight. Since the Voyager 1 photopolarimeter had failed, this was the first opportunity to obtain data of this type, which were diagnostic of the size of the particles in the upper haze layers. The ultraviolet spectrometer

Voyager 2 discovered two kinky ringlets inside the Keeler Gap in Saturn's A Ring. These pictures show the kinky ring at two different positions as photographed on August 25 from a distance of about 700 000 kilometers with a resolution of about 15 kilometers. The kinks, clearly visible on the right, appear to be more closely spaced than those seen in Saturn's F Ring. Voyager found no shepherding moons associated with this peculiar ring structure. (P-23952)

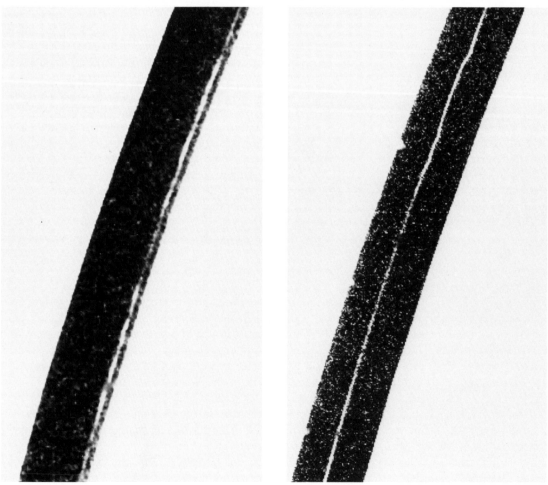

was also concentrating on Titan, but not on the satellite itself. Rather, observations from different angles were being used to map out the toroidal cloud of glowing hydrogen gas that surrounds Saturn near the orbit of Titan.

Tom Krimigis reviewed the picture that was developing of the magnetosphere, which he characterized as "a bag that encloses plasma and energetic particles." The densest concentration of energetic ions was well inside the orbit of Titan,

The photopolarimeter occultation observations probed the rings at high resolution, tracing out a profile of their opacity. In thin regions the star shows through, while dense regions could not transmit the starlight. These two profiles of parts of the B Ring were among the first occultation data to be presented to the press during the Voyager 2 encounter. (Top) A region near the inner edge of the B Ring. Note the plateau on the right that is striking for its unique lack of structure. (Bottom) A region farther out, characterized by a regular pattern of ringlets presumably representing a wave pattern in the ring material. (260-1366 and 260-1368)

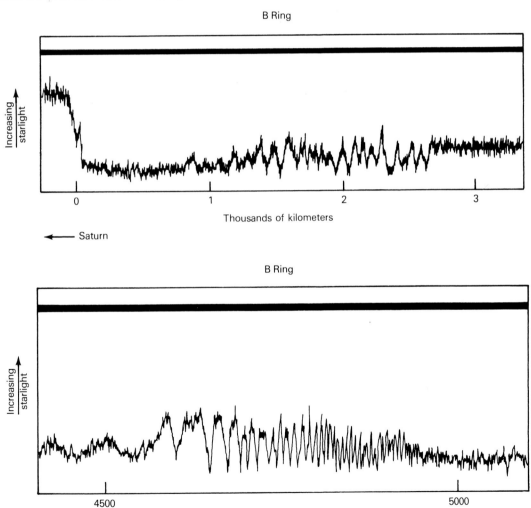

The highest-resolution image of the F Ring was obtained on August 26 from a distance of 51 000 kilometers. To achieve this resolution of a few kilometers, it was necessary to roll the spacecraft slowly during the exposure to compensate for smear due to spacecraft motion. This image shows that the ring is made up of at least four distinct components. However, no kinks or braiding, such as that photographed by Voyager 1, are evident. The small bright dash in the middle right is the trailed image of a star. (P-23966)

but bounded on the inside by the rings. A great deal of structure was imposed on the ion population by the orbits of the inner icy satellites. Herb Bridge had extensive plasma data on the Titan hydrogen torus, which extended inward as far as the orbit of Rhea. Don Gurnett described how the passages of the inner satellites—especially Tethys and Dione—created discontinuities in the plasma, which in turn generated radio noise detectable with the radio astronomy and plasma wave instruments. The E Ring also had an absorb-

ing effect on magnetosphere particles and possibly contributed to these strange radio emissions.

August 28, 1981

Dick Laeser began the press briefing by saying, "If I have a smile on my face this morning, it's because there's a good chance that Saturn will be on our TV screens again by the end of today." As the result of three diagnostic tests, it appeared that "our tentative conclusion is that the plat-

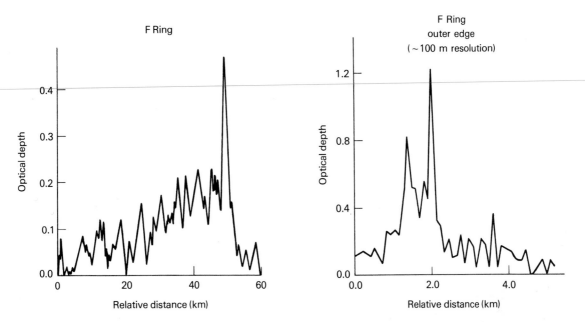

The occultation of a star by the rings provided a profile of ring structure with much higher resolution than could be obtained by imagery. Here we see two preliminary photopolarimeter plots of data from the occultation by the F Ring. The low-resolution view on the left shows a variety of faint ringlets in addition to the primary ring. On the right, a more detailed presentation of the data shows that the central part of the F Ring is broken up into finer structure. (260-1352 and 260-1382)

form improves with use.'' He explained that they had decided in their next test to move from the present position at azimuth 270 degrees to 209 degrees. Then, with just a small change in elevation, Saturn could be brought into the field of view of the scan platform instruments. If all went well, the first image could be received as early as 5:38 that afternoon.

Ed Stone noted that the Voyager spacecraft was still inside the magnetosphere of Saturn, but should be expected to exit sometime that day. He then introduced Lonne Lane, commenting that, ''We will now hear the results on about 400 city blocks out of the 400 000 that they have yet to do.''

This time, Lane concentrated on the occultation results for the F Ring, presenting not only a trace across the ring, but a pseudo-image of the bright central feature of the F Ring at an effective resolution of about 1 kilometer. The central F Ring broke up into about ten smaller features,

right down to the resolution limit of the occultation technique. Lane emphasized that at this level of detail there was no reason to expect that the structure was static. ''The F Ring is a dynamic phenomenon. All we have is one snapshot of one place at one instant in time.'' Of course, a second effort to get an occultation profile of the rings had been lost as a result of the failure of the scan platform.

More of the highest-resolution images of both rings and satellites had now been processed and were presented by Brad Smith and Larry Soderblom. A new B Ring movie showed spokes forming and being torn apart by the differential rotation of the rings. Soderblom emphasized the wide range of geological styles and ages apparent in the surface of Enceladus. ''The oldest terrains on Enceladus are similar in crater density to the least cratered plains of Dione, which were previously the youngest regions seen in the Saturn satellites.'' The smooth regions of Enceladus are

The photopolarimeter occultation trace across the Keeler Gap near the outer part of the A Ring showed considerably more structure than could be seen in television images. Here we see a picture, generated in a computer, of the appearance of the Keeler Gap at a resolution of about 1 kilometer, produced on the assumption that all the structure seen in the occultation trace corresponds to rings rather than individual moonlets. Approximately in the center of the gap is a substantial ringlet, presumably the same as the kinky ringlet photographed by the imaging system. A number of much fainter ringlets also appear, as well as prominent wave patterns in the A Ring near the border of the Keeler Gap. (P-23960C)

probably at least ten times younger, meaning that "parts of Enceladus that we see are younger than the age of the dinosaurs on Earth."

The remarkable aspect of Enceladus is that a satellite of such small size should have retained enough heat to keep the interior fluid and allow these repeated outbursts onto the surface. Indeed, it seemed impossible that primordial heat could still be having such an effect. Rather, Enceladus must contain a sort of "heat engine" that continues to generate energy in a way that does not take place on any of the other satellites of Saturn. Presumably this heat engine has something to do with tides, such as those that heat Io and Europa in the Jovian system, but the details of a tidal heating mechanism for Enceladus were not well

The photopolarimeter observations of the occultation of the star δ Scorpii by the rings generated a profile of ring opacity. But these data can also be used to produce a picture of the appearance the rings would have, on the assumption that the trace along a single line was representative of the opacity at other positions in azimuth—in other words, that the structure seen represented rings, not moonlets. Here is such a picture of the bright central position of the F Ring as it might appear at an effective resolution of 1 kilometer. The detailed structure in this image is below the resolution limit of the Voyager television cameras. (P-24069C)

understood. Nevertheless, Soderblom emphasized that the observations told us that some such heating must be taking place, whether or not the theoreticians had identified the details of the mechanism.

During the afternoon, the critical commands were sent to move the scan platform back toward the planet. It was planned to send a series of commands, in case the platform did not respond properly or failed to turn at the correct speed. If it responded properly, the first picture would be received at 5:38 p.m.; if not, it might be several more hours before the planet was again in view.

All over JPL, people gathered around the television monitors as 5:30 approached. The three-minute delay between pictures always seemed

One of the remarkable events associated with Voyager's plunge through the Saturn ring plane was the million-fold increase in energy measured by the plasma wave instrument and perhaps associated with impacts with fine ring material. Here Plasma Wave Principal Investigator Fred Scarf discusses these results with Bill Kurth and visiting UCLA physicist Chris Russell. (P-24010AC)

long, but in these final moments time seemed almost to stand still. Then, at last, the critical picture began to be displayed, line by line, on the screens. And there it was! The frame was not properly centered, but clearly visible to one side was a bit of the planet with the rings, now seen for the first time on their dark side, arching up across the field of view. A sharp black shadow was cast across the rings by the planet. A vast collective sigh of relief was expressed all around the lab. People went home that night with a lighter step than had been seen since the failure, nearly three days before.

August 30, 1981

The final press briefing of the encounter took place on a sunny Sunday morning. About fifty

members of the press were still in Pasadena, but the auditorium was filled with Voyager people— not just the scientists, but managers, engineers, programmers, and technicians. Ek Davis assured the audience that all was well; the scan platform continued to respond (although somewhat fitfully), and prospects for a successful Uranus encounter were improving. Meanwhile, a new sequence was being prepared for the final event of this encounter on September 4, when Voyager would fly past Saturn's outermost satellite, Phoebe, on its way out of the Saturn system.

New science results continued to pour in as the data from the preceding week were becoming available to the investigative teams. Norm Ness described how the magnetic field of Saturn was aligned almost exactly with the rotational pole, being tilted by only 0.7 degree from the axis of the planet's rotation. The field was also highly symmetric, and Ness discounted the possibility that a distortion in the field over one longitude was the cause of the pulsed kilometric radio emission from Saturn. The origin of this radiation remained a mystery.

Len Tyler, Radio Science Team Leader, discussed the radio probes of the atmospheres of Saturn and (from Voyager 1) of Titan. One big surprise was the absence of an ionosphere on Titan—making its interaction with the magnetosphere different from the planetary cases studied before. Joe Romig of the Planetary Radio Astronomy Team described calculations of how high-speed impacts with tiny dust particles might have produced the effects detected by Fred Scarf at ring plane crossing. If enough impacts occurred, a plasma cloud could have enveloped the spacecraft. Romig also played recordings of the giant electric discharges believed to be associated with the rings. These had been detected by Voyager 2 as well as Voyager 1, but at a lower rate (thousands of sparks, rather than tens of thousands), even though Voyager 2 had come closer to the rings. Perhaps it required a special geometry for the emissions from these discharges to reach the spacecraft, or perhaps conditions on Saturn had changed between the two encounters.

Brad Smith, Andy Ingersoll, and Larry Soderblom discussed the Imaging Science results as the final Voyager press release pictures were distributed. As one speaker followed another, the briefing grew to an excessive length, but no one left. Finally, Ed Stone rose and apologized for the lateness, but added that "this is the last chance we will have to do this." It was a poignant moment. When the conference was finally over, freelance writer Mark Washburn rose on behalf of the press corps and thanked Ed Stone, Ek Davis, and the whole Voyager team for a wonderful job of doing the mission and getting the results out quickly and accurately to the press. The whole press group rose for an extended standing ovation.

The question and answer session, coming as it did at the end of four incredibly successful Voyager encounters, turned to the future. Ed Stone emphasized that there would now be a long dry spell and that the problem was not limited to planetary exploration. "In all of space science, we are launching only one-fourth as many missions as we were a decade ago. Nowadays, you have to be an optimist to work in this field." Ingersoll commented sadly that "the world will be a very dull place if we stop posing important and difficult questions—or finding questions we don't even know how to pose." Smith spoke for the whole science community when he said, "We have hopes for the future, but they are only hopes. With no new planetary missions launched during the past few years, and none to be launched before 1985, we face a data gap of many years. It will be hard to keep the science and engineering teams together. It will be difficult to get new students to enter the field. This could indeed be the last picture show."

At 1:30 p.m. JPL Director Bruce Murray hosted a farewell champagne party for the press and scientists. The party, intended to last only an hour or so, continued as time passed. Nobody wanted to go home, because they all knew this really was the last event to mark the end of an era. Eventually the press became the hosts, and the party migrated back to Von Karman Auditorium, where

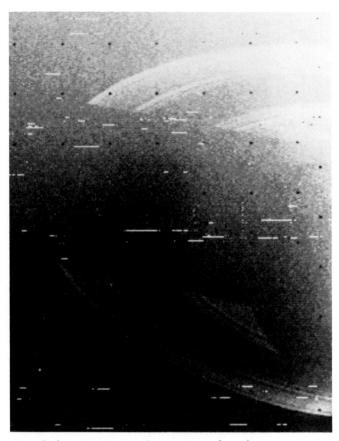

Just before 6 p.m. on August 28, after almost three days without images, the scan platform responded to commands and swung the cameras back toward Saturn. This underexposed, noisy, but extremely welcome image was received at JPL at 5:40 p.m. It shows the dark side of the rings with the shadow cast by the planet falling across them. The noise is the result of temporary ground communications problems between the Australian Deep Space Network Tracking Station and Voyager mission control in Pasadena. The picture was received in Australia in perfect condition, and the noise removed later by subsequent processing. (P-23969)

the television monitors continued to show the beautiful image of the crescent planet and its amazing rings. Dinner time came and went, but the party continued. Finally, at 9 p.m. people wandered away, many to pack their bags and

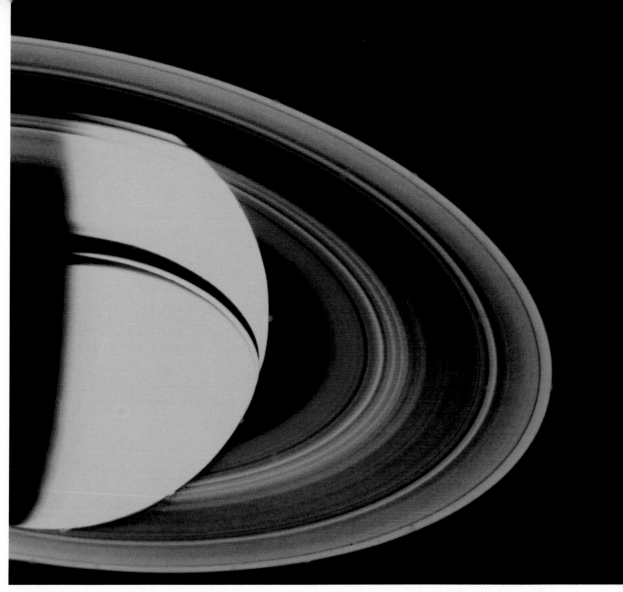

Saturn's appearance from the receding Voyager 2 was quite different from that seen by Voyager 1. This time the spacecraft was looking back at the dark southern side of the rings, whereas its twin had a departing view of the northern illuminated face. This picture was taken on August 29 from a distance of 3.4 million kilometers. It clearly shows the bright disk of the planet seen through the tenuous C Ring and the prominent ring shadow cast on the equator of Saturn. Also faintly visible is the F Ring, which is so tenuous that it is nearly as bright seen from underneath as from the sunlit side. (P-24062)

return to a more mundane existence. No one knew when they would see each other again or when this experience would be duplicated. Jurrie van der Woude of the JPL Public Information Office summed it up: "I love these guys. We've been together to explore Mars, and Jupiter, and Saturn. We've been to a dozen new worlds. It's like breaking up with your shipmates at the end of Columbus' first voyage to America."

The Voyager spacecraft was now 1.5 billion kilometers from Earth and more than 2 million kilometers beyond Saturn. The next destination: Uranus, five years and more than a billion kilometers to go.

The final major event of the Voyager 2 encounter took place on September 4, when the spacecraft passed within 2.2 million kilometers of Saturn's outermost known satellite, Phoebe. Little Phoebe was shown to be a very dark, approximately spherical object about 200 kilometers in diameter. Its appearance and apparent composition are very similar to that of the common dark reddish asteroids that are thought to represent chemically primitive condensates from the original solar nebula. Phoebe is in a retrograde orbit, circling Saturn in the opposite direction from the other satellites, and it is probably a captured asteroid. (P-24137)

The elusive braids in Saturn's F Ring, which had been photographed by Voyager 1 but not seen in the second encounter, were finally confirmed several weeks later by Voyager 2 scientists. A single image overlooked during the encounter period showed two narrow strands that swung apart and then merged again as illustrated in the two-frame mosaic released in early December 1981. (P-24379)

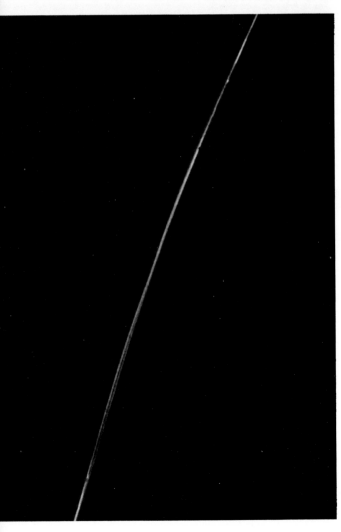

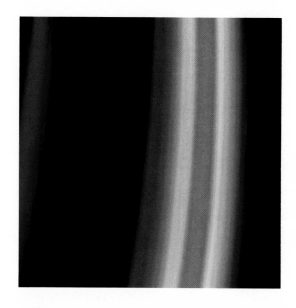

The New Saturn System

Saturn is more than a planet—it is a system. With its multiplicity of rings and satellites, Saturn may be the closest thing we have to a solar system in miniature, a system that reproduces some of the fundamental physical processes that relate to the formation and early evolution of our planetary system. When these considerations are coupled to the sheer magnificence of Saturn and the bewildering variety and complexity revealed by Voyager, it is easy to argue that the exploration of the Saturn system has been one of the highlights of the space program—indeed, one of the highlights of human history in the second half of the twentieth century.

The Pioneer and Voyager encounters have yielded an increment in our knowledge of the Saturn system greater than has been achieved for any other planet in so short a time. Before spacecraft visited Saturn, its distance prevented us from perceiving or understanding it with any great clarity. In many cases scientists simply did not know which were the important questions to ask. A few years ago it was guessed, for instance, that Iapetus was a remarkable object, but who could have predicted the extraordinary nature of

Enceladus, with its mysterious water volcanism apparently persisting to the present day? And what scientist or poet or artist had ever imagined the awesome complexity of the tens of thousands of rings that we now recognize circling Saturn? It can truly be said that the spacecraft encounters, brief though they have been, revealed a new world in Saturn and its system. It is that new, post-Voyager perspective that is briefly described in this chapter.

The Planet Saturn

Saturn is a giant planet, second in size to Jupiter, and sharing with it the basic properties of a solar-type composition, rapid rotation, a substantial magnetic field, and an intrinsic internal heat source. Its diameter is 120 660 kilometers at the equator, but 10 percent less at the poles, a consequence of its rapid rotation. The length of its day, determined from periodic variations in radio emission, is 10 hours, 39 minutes, 25 seconds. The mass of Saturn is 5.69×10^{29} grams, about 95 times the mass of Earth; its density of 0.70 gram per cubic centimeter is the lowest of

Saturn is unique among the planets in having a bright spectacular ring system. It also has 17 known satellites, more than any other planet. This Voyager 2 mosaic shows three of the inner icy satellites (and the shadow of one) in addition to the planet and its bright A and B Rings. Although the atmosphere of Saturn shows considerable banded structure, the color is almost uniform butterscotch, lacking the psychedelic appearance of the complex cloud structure of Jupiter. (P-23887)

any planet, indicating that much of Saturn is in a gaseous state.

As far as we know, Saturn is composed of "star stuff," the same mixture of elements that formed the Sun and the initial solar nebula out of which the planetary system formed some 4.6 billion years ago. Of course, we have not actually measured the composition of Saturn's interior, but calculations suggest that a solar-type composition is consistent with the low density and high degree of polar flattening observed on Saturn. In addition, there is no particular reason to expect so large a planet to have selectively lost any of the gases that were originally available to form it. The most abundant element is the simplest—hydro-gen, believed to constitute nearly 80 percent of Saturn by mass. We believe that the great majority of the remainder, nearly 20 percent, is made of the second most common element, helium. All the other elements together constitute only a little more than 2 percent; the most abundant presumably are oxygen (1.0 percent), carbon (0.4 percent), iron (0.2 percent), neon (0.2 percent), nitrogen (0.1 percent), and silicon (0.1 percent). In the atmosphere, some of these elements should combine to form simple compounds: oxygen and hydrogen to form water (H_2O), carbon and hydrogen to form methane (CH_4), and nitrogen and hydrogen to form ammonia (NH_3).

Jupiter and Saturn are the two largest planets in the solar system. Both are fluid bodies composed primarily of hydrogen and helium. In these Voyager images, we see them to scale with about 1000 kilometers resolution. The lack of bright colors and complex structure on Saturn is evidence that its upper atmosphere is fundamentally different from that of Jupiter. (260-1159AC)

The Interior

Theoretical models of the deep interior of Saturn predict that most of the silicon, iron, and other heavy elements should be concentrated in a core, together with much of the water, methane, and ammonia. These materials exist at extremely high temperatures and pressures, and are probably in the form of a dense liquid. Outside the core and extending as much as halfway to the surface is a region of liquid, metallic hydrogen, capped by a deep hydrogen atmosphere, gaseous in the upper layers and grading into a liquid at great depths. The planet's magnetic field (discussed later) presumably originates in the metallic hydrogen region.

One of the most interesting properties of the interior of Saturn that is accessible to observation is the heat that is being released there and leaking up to the surface. Pioneer and Voyager infrared measurements confirmed that Saturn was significantly warmer than would be expected from solar heating alone. The value for the internal heat source is 10^{17} watts. At first it was assumed that all of this radiated energy was primordial in origin, as it is for Jupiter. But the Saturn heat source is greater than that of Jupiter, in spite of the smaller size of the planet, and theorists calculated that some other process must still be providing excess heat today. The most attractive theory postulated a separation of helium from hydrogen in the interior. If part of the helium could form drops and rain down to deeper levels, it would release enough heat by its fall to provide the observed excess radiation.

Voyager provided dramatic support for this theory when the IRIS infrared instrument not only confirmed the large energy source but also measured a depletion of helium in the observable part of the atmosphere. IRIS measured the fraction of helium as 11 percent by mass, as compared with the anticipated value of approximately 20 percent. Although the arguments are circumstantial, most scientists believe that the missing atmospheric helium is deeper inside Saturn, and that the separation process is responsible for much of the observed thermal excess of the planet.

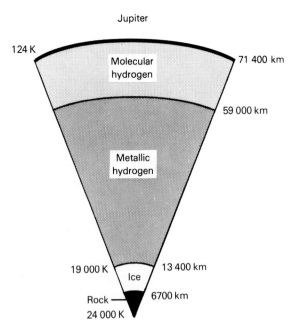

Jupiter

124 K

71 400 km

Molecular hydrogen

59 000 km

Metallic hydrogen

19 000 K

13 400 km

Ice

Rock — 6700 km

24 000 K

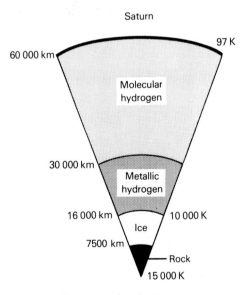

Saturn

97 K

60 000 km

Molecular hydrogen

30 000 km

Metallic hydrogen

16 000 km — 10 000 K

Ice

7500 km

Rock

15 000 K

The internal structures of the giant planets Jupiter and Saturn are probably quite similar, as shown in this cutaway diagram. Temperatures are given in degrees Kelvin (0 K corresponds to − 273 °C). The cores labeled ice and rock in these diagrams exist at such high temperatures that they are probably in a liquid state.

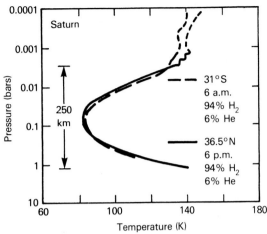

Saturn

31°S
6 a.m.
94% H_2
6% He

36.5°N
6 p.m.
94% H_2
6% He

250 km

Pressure (bars)

Temperature (K)

Direct measurements of the variation of temperature and pressure with altitude in the atmosphere of Saturn were made by tracking the radio signal as the Voyager spacecraft disappeared behind the planet. Here we see the derived structure for the radio occultation entrance and exit of Voyager 2. Except for possible small variations at high altitudes, the atmosphere at these two positions on the planet appears to be nearly identical in structure.

The Atmosphere

The composition of the deep interior of Saturn may not be accessible to observation, but the Voyager IRIS provided direct measurements of the molecules in the visible part of the atmosphere. In addition to hydrogen and helium, it detected ammonia (NH_3) and methane (CH_4) and trace quantities of phosphene (PH_3), ethane (C_2H_6), acetylene (C_2H_2), methylacetylene (C_3H_4), and propane (C_3H_8). At higher elevations, auroral emissions from hydrogen and helium were also observed by the ultraviolet spectrometer. Particularly prominent is a narrow auroral arc between 78 and 82 degrees latitude caused by magnetospheric electrons striking the upper atmosphere.

Both the IRIS and the radio occultation experiments provided probes of atmospheric structure at a variety of latitudes. In the high stratosphere, where the pressure is only 0.1 percent of that at the surface of Earth, the absorption of sunlight

During the nine months between the two Voyager encounters, the weather patterns in the atmosphere of Saturn changed significantly. Here we see two views, each at about 1000 kilometers resolution, in which false-color techniques have been used to enhance the visibility of atmospheric features. The photo taken by Voyager 1 is on the bottom, and the Voyager 2 photo is on the top. In addition, the brightness of the rings increased between the two encounters. (P-23876)

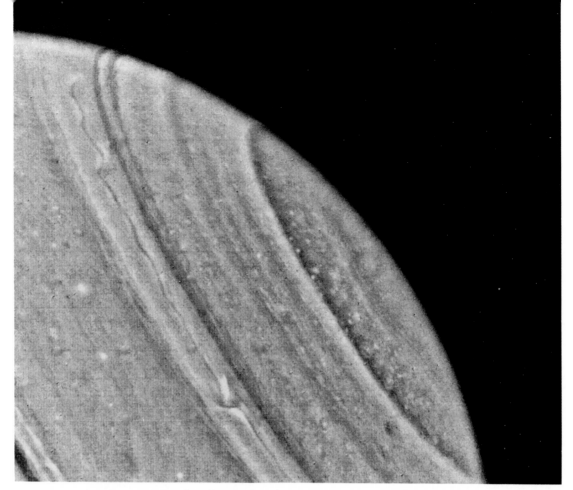

As seen by Voyager 2, the northern hemisphere of Saturn showed considerable small-scale cloud structure and banding extending toward the polar region. This picture has a resolution of about 200 kilometers. The wavy, ribbon-like structure at 47°N latitude marks a high-speed westerly jet. (P-23910)

results in a relatively high temperature (– 130 °C). The temperature then drops with increasing depth, reaching a minimum (– 180 °C) at a pressure level of 0.07 bar. Below the minimum, which corresponds approximately to the top of the convective troposphere, the temperature rises steadily, reaching – 140 °C at a pressure level of 1 bar. The uppermost clouds, which are composed of frozen ammonia crystals, extend over a height range of about 100 kilometers, from below the 1-bar level up to the top of the troposphere. Other cloud layers presumably exist at greater depths, but they are not observable. There are occasional holes in the upper clouds of Jupiter that allow radiation to escape from deeper layers, but apparently these cloud breaks are rare or absent altogether on Saturn.

Although we cannot see below the ammonia clouds, we can make some reasonable guesses about conditions in the middle and lower atmos-phere. The energy escaping from the interior forces the gas to circulate, with bubbles of warm hydrogen rising and colder gas sinking. This con-vection in turn imposes a nearly constant increase of temperature with depth, at a rate of 0.85 °C per kilometer. There is, of course, no solid sur-face—just gas of ever greater density and higher temperature, down to the level at which hydrogen changes from gas to liquid.

None of the expected major clouds on Saturn, even at considerable depth, are colored. The colors we see must represent the effects of trace chemical constituents of unknown composition.

Weather on Saturn

The Voyager images have provided a unique insight into the circulation of the Saturnian atmosphere. Earth-based telescopes show almost no identifiable features on Saturn, but the space-craft cameras revealed a wealth of cloud structure.

By following the motions of these features from day to day, Voyager scientists have mapped out the major wind systems that dominate the giant planet.

The most prominent visible features seen on both Jupiter and Saturn are the narrow contrasting bands that gird the planets parallel to their equators. The primary dynamic features are counterflowing easterly and westerly winds, also confined to narrow latitude strips. The wind speeds in these bands are measured relative to the underlying core of the planet, which has a rotation rate the same as that of the magnetic field. On Saturn, most winds flow eastward (what meteorologists call "westerlies"), with speeds up to 500 meters per second (almost 1500 kilometers per hour) near the equator.

On Jupiter, the easterly and westerly winds alternate with latitude and follow fairly closely the prominent belts and zones. Before Voyager arrived at Saturn, atmospheric scientists expected similar circulation patterns there. But surprisingly, the measured winds turned out to be quite different. Much of the atmosphere—that between latitudes of ± 35 degrees—is involved in a single equatorial jet stream moving at nearly supersonic velocity, about four times faster than the fastest wind speeds on Jupiter. At higher latitudes the winds alternate between east- and west-flowing jets in a remarkably regular way, with almost no measurable difference between the northern and southern hemispheres. If there are seasonal effects in the atmosphere of Saturn, they do not show up in the circulation patterns measured by Voyager.

At latitudes where the wind speeds are low, the rising warm air from the interior can break into sight in the form of large, circulating storm systems. The smaller of these eddies may last only a few days, but the larger features have lifetimes of a year or more. A number of these storm systems, seen by Voyager 1, were successfully reacquired nine months later by Voyager 2.

The largest storms on Saturn are oval spots rather like the great white ovals of Jupiter but substantially smaller. They are anticyclonic in rotation, indicative of high pressure, unlike the

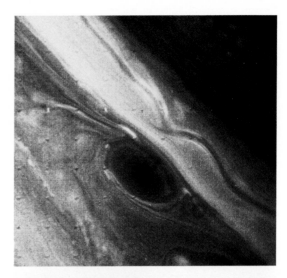

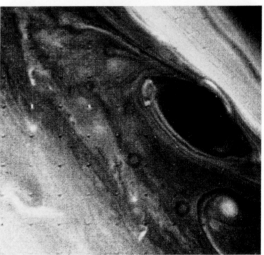

Circulation around a large brown spot in Saturn's atmosphere can be seen in this pair of Voyager 2 images taken about 10 hours apart. These views demonstrate that the large spots move in an anticyclonic direction (counterclockwise in the northern hemisphere), indicative of high-pressure regions. The resolution in these green filter images is about 50 kilometers. (P-23938)

low-pressure cyclones that dominate the temperate-zone weather on Earth. Other features visible on Saturn include a curving, ribbon-like streamer at about 47°N latitude that is thought to represent a wave pattern in a particularly unstable jet stream.

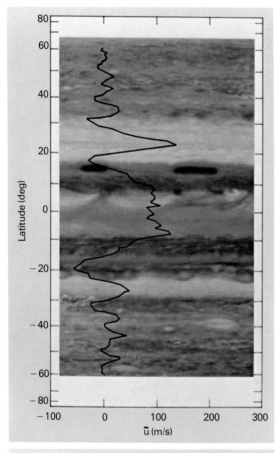

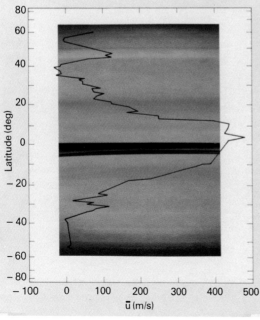

By measuring the relative displacement of clouds on Voyager images taken one or two rotation periods apart, atmospheric scientists are able to map the wind speeds on Jupiter and Saturn. In these two figures wind velocities are expressed relative to the underlying rotation period of the planet. On Jupiter, the velocity profile shows many ups and downs, generally following the horizontal banded structure of the planet. On Saturn, the wind speeds have a different character with a very rapid equatorial jetstream of about 50 meters per second. Only at latitudes above ± 40 degrees do the winds on Saturn begin to mimic those on Jupiter. (260-1126AC and 260-1126BC)

One of the interesting results of the Voyager Jupiter encounters was the discovery that eddies power the horizontal jet streams, rather than the other way around. Thus thermal energy from the interior is transformed into atmospheric energy to maintain the rapidly moving winds. Perhaps the same thing is true for Saturn, which has still faster winds and a proportionally larger internal heat source. Detailed study of the Voyager images will be necessary to prove or disprove this hypothesis.

Since the axis of rotation of Saturn is tilted by 27 degrees, the planet should experience seasons rather like those of Earth but lasting 30 times longer. An additional effect on the atmosphere is provided by the rings, which block out a substantial fraction of the sunlight and induce additional seasonal variations near the equator as their shadows shift in width and position. The IRIS instrument detected some differences in atmospheric temperature between the two hemispheres, but, in general, seasonal effects are small. Calculations suggest that the atmosphere is so large that it cannot respond rapidly to seasonally varying illumination, so perhaps there really are few differences between winter and summer on the planet.

Titan: The Earth-Like Satellite

Saturn has one truly outstanding satellite: Titan. This object, intermediate in size between

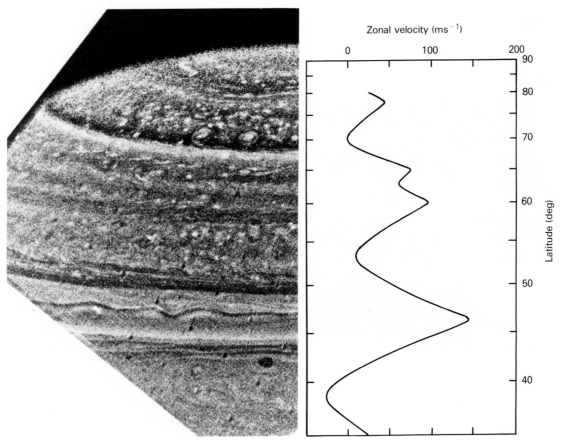

Voyager 2 was able to observe closely the northern hemisphere of Saturn and to map wind speeds nearly up to the pole. Here we see the profile of wind velocities compared with a photograph of the cloud structure at high latitudes on Saturn. (260-1457)

Mercury and Mars, is the only satellite with a substantial atmosphere. The presence of methane gas was discovered in 1944 and further indication of dense clouds was obtained in the early 1970s, but not until Voyager 1 arrived in 1980 did we learn that Titan's atmosphere actually exceeds the Earth's in mass and surface pressure. For Voyager, Titan was a target of investigation only less important than Saturn itself, and for the distant future it seems likely to inspire missions to probe its atmosphere and explore its surface.

When we look at Titan with our eyes (or the Voyager cameras), we see a bland orange sphere with only the faintest markings. The atmosphere of the satellite is opaque, with multiple layers of aerosols, ranging from tenuous smog-like hazes to deep clouds of frozen (or perhaps liquid) methane. Of all the Voyager instruments, only

the dual-frequency radio signals from the spacecraft telemetry system could penetrate through the atmospheric gas and clouds to detect the solid surface, at a radius of 2575 kilometers from the center. The IRIS also was able to probe deeply into the atmosphere at a wavelength near 20 micrometers, where the atmosphere is relatively transparent, to measure a surface temperature of − 180 °C. Everything else that we can conclude about the surface and interior must be determined indirectly from measurements of the atmosphere and inferences drawn from comparisons with other objects.

Bulk Properties

In many respects, Titan is a near twin of the largest Jovian satellites, Ganymede and Callisto.

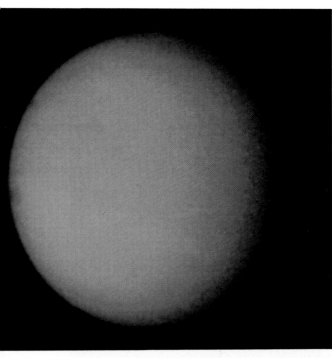

Titan, shrouded in a deep atmosphere and opaque clouds, appears dark red and almost without structure. The only significant feature is the slightly darker color of the northern hemisphere. This Voyager 2 view has a resolution of about 10 kilometers. (P-23929)

Their sizes agree to within 5 percent, and, even more important, their densities are all between 1.8 and 1.9 grams per cubic centimeter. Similar bulk density usually implies similar bulk composition: in this case, 45 percent ice (H_2O) and 55 percent rocky and metallic materials. If, as seems very likely, the interior ice were once liquid, then the heavier materials should have sunk to form a core, resulting in a layered structure. Such a "differentiated" interior would have a core that extended about two-thirds of the way from center to surface, followed by layers of various high-pressure forms of ice, topped by a crust of ordinary ice about 100 kilometers thick. This same basic structure should apply equally to Ganymede, Callisto, and Titan.

Yet something has happened to make Titan very different from its Jovian siblings. Ganymede and Callisto have no atmospheres, while Titan is shrouded in a thick envelope rich in nitrogen and methane. Why this striking difference? Probably the main reason is that Titan, in the colder part of the solar nebula where it was born, managed to incorporate ices of methane and ammonia, as well as water ice, into its inventory of materials. As Titan's interior heated, these gases escaped to form an initial atmosphere. The action of sunlight on ammonia (NH_3) resulted in a conversion to nitrogen with associated loss of most of the hydrogen, whereas much of the more stable methane survives to the present. The methane and nitrogen in turn react to create more complex organic compounds in the atmosphere and on the surface. In this way, the addition of a mere fraction of a percent of methane and ammonia may have been enough to cause Titan's evolution to diverge dramatically from that of Ganymede or Callisto.

When illuminated from behind, the tips of the crescent Titan extend to form a bright ring produced by sunlight scattering through the high atmosphere of the satellite. Most of this scattering is caused by very fine aerosols several hundred kilometers above the main clouds. The resolution in this Voyager 2 picture is about 2 kilometers. (P-23949)

This spectacular view of the edge of Titan was obtained by Voyager 1 from a distance of only 22 000 kilometers. Several tenuous high-altitude haze layers, which appear blue, are visible above the opaque red clouds. The highest of these haze layers is about 500 kilometers above the main cloud deck and 700 kilometers above the surface of Titan. (P-23107)

The Atmosphere

We can only speculate about the past history of Titan, but its atmosphere was subject to direct observation by Voyager. The ultraviolet spectrometer first detected a strong emission from nitrogen in the upper atmosphere, suggesting that this was the dominant gas and that its glow was excited primarily by the impact of electrons from the magnetosphere of Saturn. This emission extended to a height of about 1000 kilometers above the surface and was strongest on the side facing into the rapidly moving magnetospheric plasma. The power associated with this excitation is about a billion watts. Also visible at high alti-

tudes is the ultraviolet glow of atomic hydrogen, which is a trace constituent of the upper atmosphere, having been produced by the action of sunlight on methane (CH_4). This hydrogen escapes from Titan at a rate of about 10^{27} atoms per second, spreading out around the orbit of the satellite to produce a huge torus of dilute hydrogen gas.

Our primary knowledge of atmospheric composition comes from the IRIS infrared spectra. The IRIS could not measure nitrogen, but it did detect methane (CH_4) and the more complex hydrocarbons ethane (C_2H_6), acetylene (C_2H_2), ethylene (C_2H_4), methylacetylene (C_3H_4), propane (C_3H_8), and diacetylene (C_4H_2). All of these

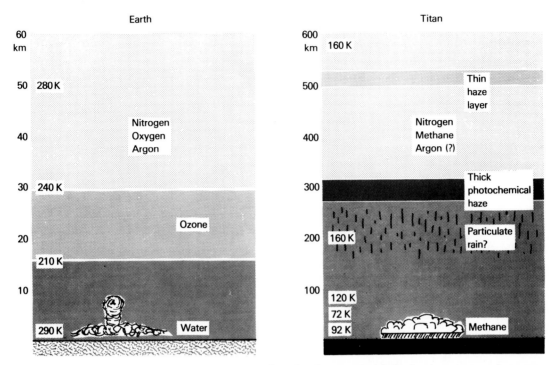

Earth

60 km	
50	280 K
40	Nitrogen Oxygen Argon
30	240 K
20	Ozone
	210 K
10	
	290 K · Water

Titan

600 km	160 K
500	Thin haze layer
400	Nitrogen Methane Argon (?)
300	Thick photochemical haze
200	160 K · Particulate rain?
100	120 K
	72 K
	92 K · Methane

The atmospheres of Earth and Titan are compared in this diagram. Both bodies have atmospheres composed primarily of nitrogen, and the surface pressures are somewhat similar: 1 bar on Earth and 1.6 bars on Titan. The atmosphere of Titan is much more extended, however, because of the low gravity of this satellite. As shown on the right, there are several thin, high haze layers, a main thick smog layer between 200 and 300 kilometers, and a troposphere, probably containing methane ice clouds, below about 40 kilometers altitude.

more complex molecules can be produced from the action of sunlight on methane. Even more exciting was the detection of carbon-nitrogen compounds: hydrogen cyanide (HCN), cyano-acetylene (HC_3N), and cyanogen (C_2N_2). Hydrogen cyanide is a key component of living matter, and it plays a critical role in the chemical synthesis of amino acids and the bases present in nucleic acids. The existence of carbon-nitrogen compounds is possible on Titan because of the high abundance of both nitrogen and hydrocarbons. Titan is unique in providing in abundance all of these building blocks of complex organic compounds; on the giant planets the nitrogen remains bonded to hydrogen in the form of ammonia and is unavailable for large-scale chemical synthesis of these materials.

A multitude of large, complex organic molecules must be forming continuously in the atmos-

phere of Titan. In the process, hydrogen is released and rapidly escapes, so that the reactions are not reversible and the hydrocarbon "sink" accumulates. Ultimately, these heavy molecules must precipitate to the surface, while the methane is renewed by slow diffusion upward from the lower atmosphere. The rate of diffusion is controlled by an atmospheric "cold trap" near the top of the troposphere, at a height of about 40 kilometers above the surface, where the temperature drops to -200 °C. Thick clouds of frozen methane probably exist in the troposphere, possibly extending down to the surface.

Two additional gases are present in the lower atmosphere. The IRIS measured a hydrogen abundance of 0.2 percent. With this excess of hydrogen, no free oxygen or oxygen-rich compounds are expected. The oxygen remains tightly locked in the interior in the form of frozen water, unable to participate in the blending of Titan's organic soup. In addition, the radio occultation observations, considered in conjunction with the IRIS, indicate that the average molecular weight in the lower atmosphere is slightly but significantly higher than that expected for nitrogen and the minor constituents identified. The most likely heavy gas is inert argon, which is also present in the atmospheres of Venus, Earth, and Mars. Perhaps 5 percent of the atmosphere of Titan is composed of this gas.

The atmospheric pressure at the surface of Titan is 1.6 bars, higher than that of any inner planet except Venus. The *amount* of gas is still greater, since it takes more gas to exert a given pressure in the low gravity of this satellite. Titan has about ten times more gas above each square meter of surface as does Earth.

The Surface

What is the surface of Titan like? One clue is provided by the amount of nitrogen in the atmosphere. Today there are about 200 atoms of nitrogen for every atom of carbon, since the methane amounts to only about 1 percent of the atmosphere. If the original amounts of methane and ammonia are comparable (as calculations predict) and both are fully outgassed from the interior, there must be a lot of missing methane on the surface—enough to form a methane sea about 1 kilometer thick. The surface temperature is near the value (-182 °C) at which methane can be either solid or liquid, so we can imagine a situation rather like that on Earth, but with methane playing the role of water: oceans of methane near the equator with polar caps of frozen methane ice. In addition, there is the constant rain of organics from the upper atmosphere, which calculations show could have contributed a 100-meter-thick layer of tar-like materials. Add to this an unknown but possibly active geology, and you have a portrait of a truly remarkable world!

Most of the sunlight striking Titan is absorbed in the high layers of photochemical haze and smog about 200 kilometers above the surface. Only a small percentage reaches the tropospheric methane clouds, and still less is absorbed at the surface, which must be a pretty dark and gloomy place. The maximum variation in surface temperature detected by the IRIS was 3 °C. Any diurnal or seasonal weather variations are further suppressed by the great mass of the lower atmosphere, which can hardly respond at all to the changing amounts of sunlight—rather like the thick atmosphere of Venus or the ocean depths on Earth. The weather is largely confined to the middle atmosphere, and even here the response is primarily to seasonal (30-year) variations rather than to diurnal (16-day) ones. Scientists believe the asymmetry in brightness between the northern and southern hemispheres seen in the Voyager images is a manifestation of these seasonal changes. Although Voyager arrived near the spring equinox, the apparent season was midwinter in the north and midsummer in the south, because of the long thermal lag in the atmospheric responses (just as terrestrial seasons lag by one to two months). Long-term variations in the brightness of Titan have been detected from Earth, and it is now believed that these are indications of seasonally changing weather on the satellite.

In summary, Voyager found Titan to be a fascinating place. It is, as Von Eshleman said, ''a terrestrial planet in deep freeze,'' in many ways more like the Earth than any other planetary body in the solar system. In addition, the unique conditions that cause the production of large quantities of organic materials and their accumulation on the surface make Titan the most interesting place in the solar system to study the processes of prebiotic organic chemistry that ultimately gave rise to life on Earth some 4 billion years ago.

The Magnetosphere: Twixt Earth and Jupiter

A planetary magnetosphere is formed when the outward flowing charged particles of the solar wind interact with the intrinsic magnetic field of a planet. Because these particles are charged, they are deflected by magnetic forces, and a complex series of plasma processes begins. (A plasma is any gas in which the particles are charged, rather than electrically neutral.) First, there develops a shock front, called the bow shock, where the supersonic solar wind first senses the planetary field and slows down to subsonic speeds. Then comes the magnetopause, the formal boundary of the magnetosphere. Inside the magnetopause, the planetary magnetic field dominates. Facing into the solar wind, the magnetosphere is pushed back against the planet, while in the downstream direction it can form a long, comet-like tail.

Inside the magnetosphere of a planet the charged particles are trapped by the magnetic field, and they tend to spiral back and forth along magnetic field lines, forming charged particle "belts," such as the Van Allen belts surrounding Earth. In the case of Earth, most of the particles in the belts arrive in the solar wind, although some also come from the upper atmosphere of Earth. For Jupiter, the situation is reversed: the particle population is dominated by material ejected from the volcanoes of Io, with solar wind contributions relatively minor. Saturn has a magnetosphere between these two extremes, with both internal and external sources playing a role. The primary internal sources of charged particles appear to be the atmosphere of Titan and the icy ring and satellite surfaces.

The Planetary Magnetic Field

In order to have a magnetosphere, there must be an intrinsic planetary magnetic field. Although the processes that generate such fields are not well understood, scientists generally believe that motions induced in the metallic core of a rotating

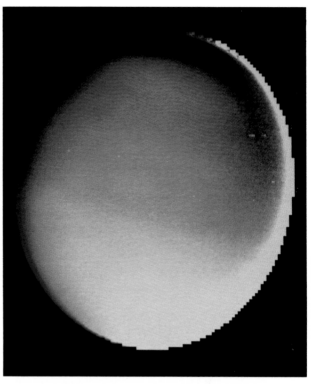

Although Titan is generally shrouded by opaque haze and clouds, some structure can be brought out by special image-processing techniques. In this Voyager 1 view, it is possible to see very faint banded structure in the northern hemisphere in addition to the more pronounced brightness difference between the north and the south halves of the satellite. (260-1166)

The magnetosphere of Saturn is a huge region within which charged particles (primarily protons and electrons) are trapped by the magnetic field of the planet. In this sketch two areas of primary interest are noted: the radiation belts with maximum intensity near the orbits of Mimas, Enceladus, Tethys, and Dione, and the large toroidal cloud of neutral hydrogen that originates at Titan and stretches inward approximately to the orbit of Rhea. The positions of the bow shocks and magnetopause are variable, depending on the pressure of the solar wind, but they are generally outside the orbit of Titan.

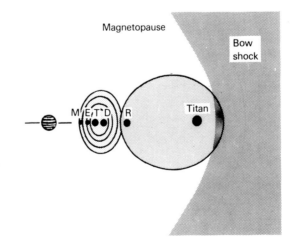

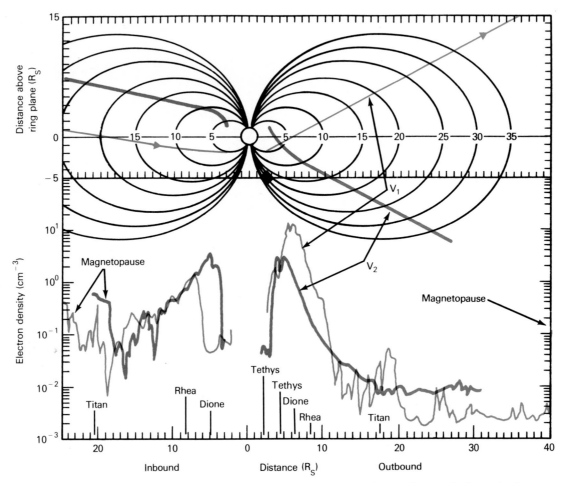

The density of plasma in the inner magnetosphere is affected by the satellites, which are both sources and sinks of energetic charged particles. In the upper part of the figure we see the regions of the magnetosphere sampled by the two Voyager spacecraft on their different trajectories through the system. At the bottom electron measurements with the plasma particle detector are shown for the Voyager 1 and Voyager 2 encounters.

planet provide the source. Saturn has both a metallic hydrogen core and rapid rotation, so it is not surprising that its field is second only to that of Jupiter among the planets we have visited with spacecraft. Although the intrinsic field is much larger than that of Earth, the actual surface fields (0.2 gauss at the equator) are a little smaller than our own, because of the larger distance of the surface from the interior source.

On the other two planets with well-observed magnetic fields, Earth and Jupiter, the alignment of the magnetic poles is considerably different from the rotational poles—they are tilted at an angle and offset from the center of the planet. It was therefore with great surprise that the Pioneer Saturn investigators found that the magnetic axis of Saturn was aligned almost exactly with the rotational axis. This alignment was confirmed by Voyager: the relative tilt of the two axes is only 0.7 degree, and there is no measureable offset at all. The resulting external magnetic field is almost perfectly symmetrical around Saturn, with none of the wobbly characteristics of Jupiter and Earth. This discovery has discomfitted theorists, who had believed before that magnetic tilt and offset were necessary for the generation of a large planetary field.

Geography of the Magnetosphere

Although the magnetic field of Saturn is not a great deal smaller than that of Jupiter, the number of charged particles is very much smaller. Roughly, Saturn has a Jovian-type field with Earth-like radiation belts. The primary reasons for this difference are (1) the absence at Saturn of a huge source such as the Io volcanoes, which pour about a ton of material into the magnetosphere each second, and (2) the presence of the rings, which absorb charged particles and effectively clean up the inner magnetosphere, where one would otherwise expect the highest intensity radiation belts.

Moving outward from Saturn, there are almost no charged particles trapped in the regions of the magnetic field that intersect the rings. At about $2.5\ R_S$, the charged particle population begins to rise rapidly, although considerable variations are caused by the absorption of particles by individual satellites and by the tenuous E Ring. Maximum intensities for electrons and most ions appear to be between the orbits of Tethys and Rhea—between roughly 5 and $10\ R_S$.

Within this inner magnetosphere, the charged particles are tightly coupled to the rapidly spinning magnetic field, which shares the rotation of the planet. The result is a plasma sheet of co-rotating particles, which form a sort of ring current girding the planet near its equatorial plane. The central plasma sheet, between 4 and $7\ R_S$, is about $1\ R_S$ thick and has electron densities of about ten per cubic centimeter. Farther out, a more diffuse plasma sheet is about twice as thick, extending from a sharp inner edge at $7\ R_S$ out toward an indistinct outer boundary beyond $15\ R_S$. Here the density is lower, amounting to about one electron per cubic centimeter.

From the orbit of Rhea out to beyond Titan, a large torus of neutral hydrogen envelops the Saturn system. This gas cloud is composed primarily of the hydrogen atoms that are produced from the photochemical breakdown of methane and then escape from the atmosphere of Titan.

Interaction between the neutral gas and co-rotating magnetospheric particles knocks apart the protons and electrons of the hydrogen atoms, providing another source of charged particles, estimated at about 10^{24} ions per second.

Beyond the orbit of Titan, the magnetosphere is disordered and subject to the changing pressure of the solar wind. When external pressures are low, the magnetosphere can inflate and expand out to $30\ R_S$ or beyond. But high solar wind pressures can quickly compress it, sometimes forcing the magnetopause to collapse to inside the orbit of Titan at $20\ R_S$.

Pointing away from the Sun, the magnetosphere is drawn out into a long tail that can extend outward for hundreds of millions of kilometers. Because of this ''downwind'' extension, the Voyager spacecraft spent more time in the magnetosphere after encounter than before, and the outbound times of crossing the magnetopause and the bow shock were difficult to predict.

Satellite Interactions

Titan, as an object of planetary dimensions, has a major impact on the magnetosphere near its orbit. In many ways, the interaction of Titan with the co-rotating ions is similar to that of a planet with the solar wind. But, since Titan has no intrinsic magnetic field, this interaction is more like that of Venus or Mars than that of Earth or Jupiter.

To the surprise of many Voyager scientists, there was no conventional bow shock where Titan impeded the flow of the magnetospheric particles sweeping toward it. In addition, Titan proved to have little or no ionosphere of its own. In these respects the interaction was unique and therefore of great interest to plasma physicists.

Directly behind Titan, the plasma stream slows down and forms a higher-density wake. There is also a small region from which higher-energy electrons are completely absent. In this region, atoms of both nitrogen and hydrogen can escape directly from the atmosphere and can be injected into the Saturnian magnetosphere. Initially, the plasma emitted by Titan is confined to a long and narrow wake in the magnetospheric flow that can be compared to the plume from a smokestack in

The Satellites of Saturn

Name	Distance from Saturn (R_S)	Orbital Period (hr)	Diameter (km)	Mass (10^{23} g)	Density (g/cm^2)	Albedo	Best Resolution (km)	Voyager Spacecraft
1980S28	2.28	14.4	30	—	—	0.4	13	1
1980S27	2.31	14.7	100	—	—	0.6	7	2
1980S26	2.35	15.1	90	—	—	0.6	8	2
1980S3	2.51	16.7	120	—	—	0.5	3	1
1980S1	2.51	16.7	200	—	—	0.5	6	1
Mimas	3.08	22.6	392	0.45	1.4	0.7	2	1
Enceladus	3.95	32.9	500	0.84	1.2	1.0	2	2
Tethys	4.88	45.3	1060	7.6	1.2	0.8	2	2
1980S13	4.88	45.3	30	—	—	0.6	12	2
1980S25	4.88	45.3	25	—	—	0.8	5	2
Dione	6.26	65.7	1120	10.5	1.4	0.6	3	1
1980S6	6.26	65.7	35	—	—	0.5	6	2
Rhea	8.74	108	1530	25	1.3	0.6	1	1
Titan	20.3	383	5150	1346	1.9	0.2	1	1
Hyperion	24.6	511	300	—	—	0.3	9	2
Iapetus	59.0	1904	1460	19	1.2	0.5, 0.05	17	2
Phoebe	215	13 211	220	—	—	0.06	38	2

the wind. The Titan plasma plume may be hundreds of thousands of kilometers long before it blends into the rest of the magnetosphere.

Major effects in the inner magnetosphere are produced by the absorption of electrons and ions by Rhea, Dione, and Tethys, all of which orbit Saturn in the densest parts of the magnetosphere. Where these edges are carved out in the particle populations, plasma instabilities can arise, leading to the generation of plasma waves and low-frequency radio emission. These "tones," produced by the satellite-magnetospheric interaction, are a unique feature of the Saturn system. Apparently, in addition, Dione manages to modulate the pulsating radio emission from Saturn, but how the effect is propagated from the satellite to the planet remains unknown.

The Icy Satellites

The satellites of Saturn form a diverse and remarkable ensemble of worlds; seventeen satellites have been identified, up from nine just a few years ago. Titan, of course, is in a class by itself. The other six major satellites have much in common, all being of intermediate size (400 to 1500 kilometers in diameter) and composed primarily of water ice. Ten smaller objects may include both captured asteroids and fragments from intersatellite collisions. In this section we consider the six major icy satellites, all larger than Jupiter's Amalthea and most of the asteroids, yet clearly not of planetary dimensions.

The six icy objects are, moving outward from the planet, Mimas, Enceladus, Tethys, Dione,

The Small Satellites of Saturn

Name	Informal Name	Distance from Saturn (R_S)	Orbital Period (hr)	Dimensions (km)
1980S28	A Ring Shepherd	2.276	14.45	20 × 40 × ?
1980S27	F Ring Shepherd	2.310	14.71	140 × 100 × 80
1980S26	F Ring Shepherd	2.349	15.09	110 × 90 × 70
1980S3	Co-orbital	2.510	16.66	140 × 120 × 100
1980S1	Co-orbital	2.511	16.67	220 × 200 × 160
1980S13	Tethys Lagrangian	4.884	45.31	34 × 28 × 26
1980S25	Tethys Lagrangian	4.884	45.31	34 × 22 × 22
1980S6	Dione Lagrangian	6.256	65.69	36 × 32 × 30
Hyperion	—	24.55	510.7	410 × 260 × 220
Phoebe	—	215	13 211	220 × 220 × 220

Rhea, and Iapetus. All have been studied by astronomers for many years; indeed, it is Earth-based spectroscopy that established that water ice was the dominant material on their surfaces. All are in regular orbits: nearly circular and confined to the equatorial plane of Saturn. The inner five occupy adjacent orbits, while Iapetus is much farther out, beyond Titan and Hyperion, in a highly inclined orbit 59.3 R_S (3.5 million kilometers) from Saturn. In terms of size, the six satellites divide nicely into three groups of two each: Mimas and Enceladus (400 to 500 kilometers in diameter), Tethys and Dione (about 1000 kilometers), and Rhea and Iapetus (about 1500 kilometers). As the primary bodies in Saturn's miniature planetary system, we look to these satellites to tell us about the formation and evolution of the Saturn system.

Mimas

Mimas, with its diameter of just under 400 kilometers, is the smallest and innermost of the classically known satellites of Saturn, circling the planet in less than 22 hours. Because of its proximity to Saturn, it is very difficult to study telescopically from Earth. However, Voyager 1 came within 88 000 kilometers of Mimas, providing images with resolutions as high as 2 kilometers.

The most striking surface feature of Mimas is a giant crater (tentatively named Arthur for the legendary English King Arthur) 130 kilometers in diameter located near the center of the leading hemisphere (longitude 100°, latitude 0°). The floor of Arthur is as much as 10 kilometers deep, and a large central mountain rises to a height of 6 kilometers from the crater floor. This crater, about one-third the diameter of the satellite, was produced by impact with a body about 10 kilometers across—very nearly as large an impact as could occur without breaking Mimas apart.

The surface of Mimas shows the scars of repeated impact cratering. These craters, which are also named for figures from the legend of King Arthur, are packed shoulder to shoulder; addi-

The large, icy satellites of Saturn form a new class of objects never observed before Voyager's encounters with the Saturn system. Here we see them together in a family portrait to correct relative size and with approximately correct color and brightness differences. They are shown from upper left to lower right in order of distance from Saturn: Mimas, Enceladus, Tethys, Dione, Rhea, and Iapetus. (260-1500)

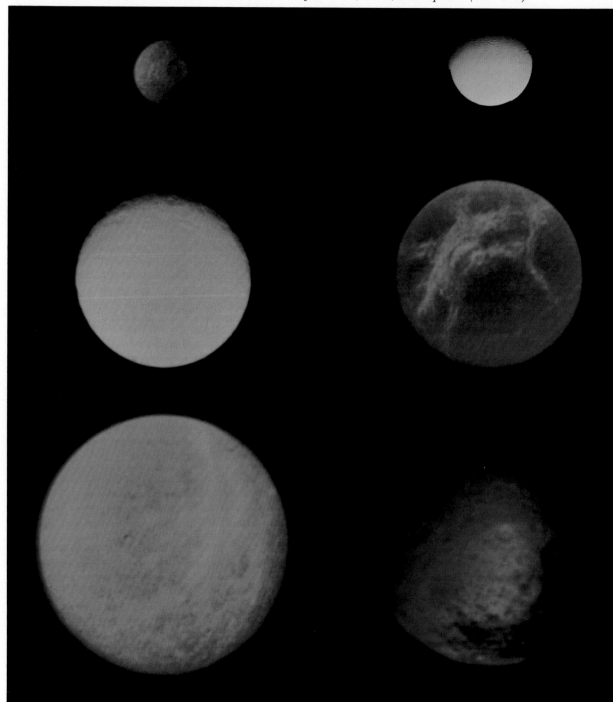

tional impacts cannot change the number of craters, since an old crater will necessarily be destroyed for each new one created. Although Mimas is composed primarily of ice, the craters look very much like those formed in the rocky crust of the Moon. In fact, the Mimas craters tend to be even sharper and deeper, a natural result of the low surface gravity on this small object.

In addition to the craters, which are of external origin, the surface of Mimas shows a few indications of internal activity in the form of grooves up to about 100 kilometers long, 10 kilometers wide, and 1 to 2 kilometers deep. Quite possibly these represent cracks produced at the time of the impact that created the giant crater.

Mimas has a density of about 1.3 grams per cubic centimeter, fairly typical of the icy satellites of Saturn. Pure ice would have a density of a little less than 1.0 grams per cubic centimeter; thus scientists infer that some fraction of the internal material of the satellite is composed of rock as well as ice. With its small size, Mimas is expected to be frozen all the way through, and probably not much of excitement has happened there since the crater Arthur was formed billions of years ago.

This highest-resolution color view of Mimas shows craters as small as about 2 kilometers across. This part of the satellite is densely covered with small craters, but shows no features to rival the giant crater Arthur. (P-23112)

Mimas, the innermost of the large, icy satellites of Saturn, has a diameter just under 400 kilometers. This picture, with a resolution of about 8 kilometers, shows the Saturn-facing hemisphere dominated by the giant crater Arthur. (P-23210)

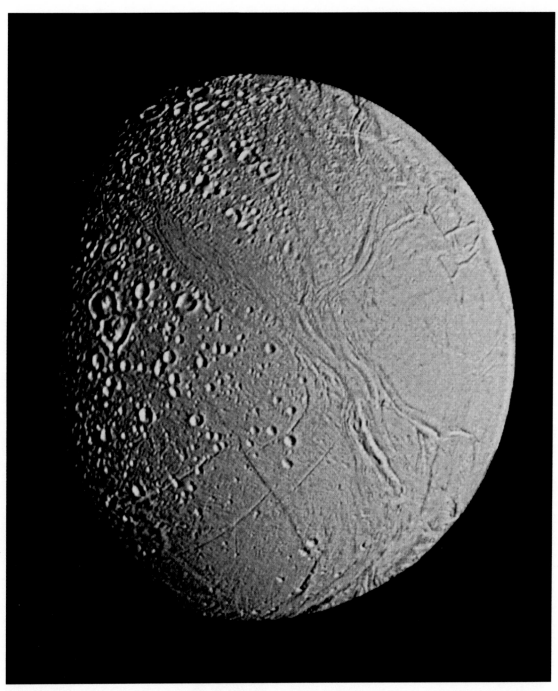

Enceladus is one of the most remarkable of the satellites of Saturn. In spite of its small size (about 500 kilometers in diameter), the surface of Enceladus shows signs of extensive and fairly recent geological activity. This highest-resolution Voyager 2 mosaic of Enceladus has a resolution of about 2 kilometers. Some regions of the surface show impact craters up to 35 kilometers in diameter, while other areas are smooth and uncratered, suggesting that they have been resurfaced within the past 100 million years. (P-24308)

Enceladus

Mimas and Enceladus form a pair; before the spacecraft encounters, scientists expected that the two might be similar. They could hardly have been more wrong! Although Mimas is basically the sort of inactive, heavily cratered object expected before Voyager, Enceladus turns out to be one of the strangest and most enigmatic objects in the outer solar system.

Voyager 2 came within less than 100 000 kilometers of Enceladus; although the highest resolution images were lost because of the scan platform failure, excellent imaging was obtained a few hours earlier at a resolution of 2 kilometers. The surface revealed in these images was remarkable for its youth and diversity, indicating a long history of geological activity.

Other observations had already singled out Enceladus from among its brother satellites. First, its surface is extraordinarily bright, reflecting more than 90 percent of the incident sunlight. To achieve this high reflectivity, which exceeds that of new-fallen snow, the surface must be composed of extremely pure ice, without the contaminating dust or rock that darkens the other icy satellites. This satellite is also cooler than the others; on Voyager 2, the IRIS measured an average day-side temperature of -200 °C. Enceladus appears to be associated with the tenuous E Ring of Saturn, which has a peak in brightness near the orbit of the satellite. Several researchers have suggested that Enceladus might be the origin of the E Ring particles, which could have been ejected in a major impact or, even more exciting, resulted from the eruption of some sort of water volcanoes on the satellite.

It is unfortunate that we do not have a good value for the mass, and therefore the density, of Enceladus. It is too small to have exerted a measurable gravitational tug on passing spacecraft, and Earth-based measurements have established only that its density is low, like the other satellites, but with the precise value indeterminate. Thus we cannot say whether Enceladus is compositionally different from Mimas.

As seen in the Voyager pictures, the surface of Enceladus can be divided into several provinces of different geological history. Parts of the satellite show impact craters up to 35 kilometers in diameter, but there are no larger craters, and none of the craters are really densely packed. Even the most heavily cratered regions probably have not accumulated enough impacts to date back to the period of heavy bombardment recorded on the surface of Mimas. But other areas have fewer craters, and broad swaths of the surface have none visible at all. Apparently, there are mechanisms at work to resurface parts of the satellite, obliterating old cratered terrain. There have clearly been several such resurfacing events, with the most recent (representing the uncratered plains) having taken place since the age of the dinosaurs—just yesterday, geologically speaking. Even in the older, cratered terrain, the craters have been noticeably altered by flow and relaxation of the crust, indicating that the mantle underneath has remained plastic or even liquid to within 10 or 20 kilometers of the surface.

Voyager did not catch any ice volcanoes in the act of erupting. Indeed, no obviously volcanic landforms were seen on the surface, although the crater-free areas show undulating ridges that look like flow marks from ancient outbursts of liquid water, and one long mountain that could be of volcanic origin. But something like volcanic activity must take place from time to time. The variety of surface ages clearly suggests a continuing internal process, not a single discrete event, as might have resulted from a random catastrophe such as the impact of a large comet.

Unexpected though it may be, one must conclude from the Voyager data that some sort of "heat engine" has kept Enceladus molten and active through much of its lifetime. Primordial heat cannot do the trick, since Enceladus would cool and freeze solid on time scales of a few hundred million years at most. Nor is radioactive heating likely, unless this satellite has many times its fair share of uranium or other radioactive elements. The most plausible idea, that Enceladus is heated by tidal stresses induced by an orbital resonance with Dione, has not been worked out quantitatively. But whether or not theorists are prepared to explain the origin of this internal heat, Voyager scientists believe the empirical evidence proves a continuing geological activity of some sort, probably extending to the present day. Enceladus, like Io in the Jovian system, is of tremendous interest because its level of activity greatly exceeds that of its neighbors.

Tethys

With Tethys, we step up in size to objects about a thousand kilometers in diameter. Voyager 1 came within 416 000 kilometers and Voyager 2 within just 93 000 kilometers. When the scan platform failed, the highest-resolution images were lost, together with an opportunity for the IRIS to measure the cooling of the surface as Tethys passed into the shadow of Saturn; the best resolution, obtained from a distance of about a quarter of a million kilometers, was 5 kilometers.

The surface of Tethys has been molded primarily by impact cratering; generally, the craters are as densely packed as on Mimas, indicating a surface of great antiquity. One crater, probably to be named Odysseus, is 400 kilometers across—larger than the diameter of Mimas! Unlike the giant crater Arthur on Mimas, Odysseus has been degraded by subsequent adjustment of the crust, indicating that Tethys is more plastic than Mimas. This difference is primarily the result of Tethys' greater size and higher surface gravity; only the smallest objects can depart very much from a smooth, spherical shape.

The most dramatic geological feature on Tethys is an immense, 2000-kilometer-long complex of valleys or troughs, Ithaca Chasma, that stretches three-quarters of the way around the satellite. The width of the valley complex is about 100 kilometers and its depth is several kilometers, making it comparable in dimensions (although not in detailed appearance) to the great Valles Marineris on Mars. Possibly Ithaca Chasma is a crack produced by the same impact that made the giant crater Odysseus, but more likely it is the product of simple expansion of the satellite as its initially liquid water interior gradually cooled and expanded as it froze.

One other peculiarity of Tethys deserves mention. Parts of the surface are darker than others,

The giant crater Odysseus on Tethys is the largest impact structure observed in the Saturn system. This specially processed Voyager 2 image has a resolution of about 15 kilometers. Odysseus is about 400 kilometers across, but not very deep; the crater has been flattened by the flow of softer ice and no longer shows the deep bowl shape characteristic of fresh craters. (P-24066)

with relatively sharp, linear boundaries setting off the dark regions. Where one of these boundaries transects a large crater near longitude 250°, it appears to have produced local brightness or albedo variations that follow the circular contour. At first glance, these markings appear to be painted onto the surface as if from an external source. Brightness boundaries may also be associated with regions of differing crater densities. None of these enigmatic features has so far been explained by Voyager scientists.

Dione

Dione may be a twin of Tethys in size, but it is not an identical twin. The density of Dione is 1.4 grams per cubic centimeter, highest of the icy

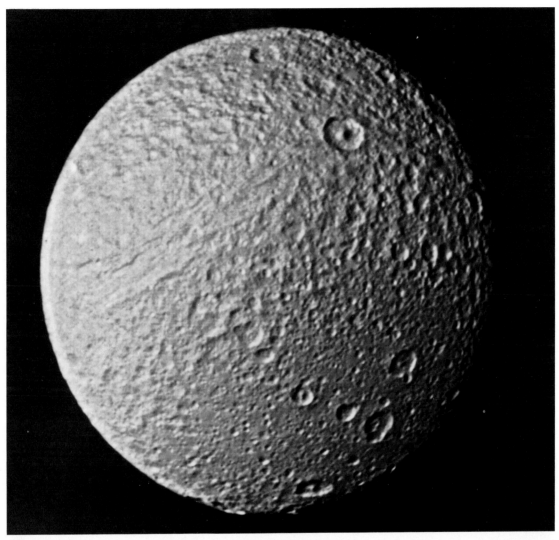

The heavily cratered surface of Tethys is shown in this specially processed image with a resolution of about 5 kilometers. A boundary between heavily cratered regions (top right) and more lightly cratered regions (bottom right) is evidence for a period of internal activity early in Tethys' history. The large crater in the upper right lies almost on the huge trench system, Ithaca Chasma, that girdles nearly three-quarters of the circumference of the satellite. (P-24065)

satellites. Presumably, Dione has a somewhat larger fraction of rocky materials and a correspondingly greater source of radiogenic heat. Dione also apparently has an important but poorly understood interaction with the magnetosphere of Saturn that causes a modulation of radio emission from the planet with the satellite's orbital period of 2.7 days.

As seen at low resolution, Dione exhibits a greater variety of surface brightness than do the inner satellites. Its trailing hemisphere is relatively dark and covered by a network of broad, wispy bright markings. The heavily cratered leading hemisphere, in contrast, looks much like the surface of Tethys. Where the bright wispy lines have been seen at high resolution, they appear to

Dione, seen here against the disk of Saturn, is a bright, white, icy object like the other inner satellites. There is a difference in character between its leading and trailing hemispheres; the trailing side, seen on the left in this image, shows a pattern of bright wispy streaks against a darker background. (P-23215)

A closer look at the trailing hemisphere of Dione shows considerable detail in the wispy streaks, as well as the underlying presence of craters. The streaks are thought to be deposits of ice that escaped along a system of planet-wide cracks early in the evolution of Dione. (P-23269)

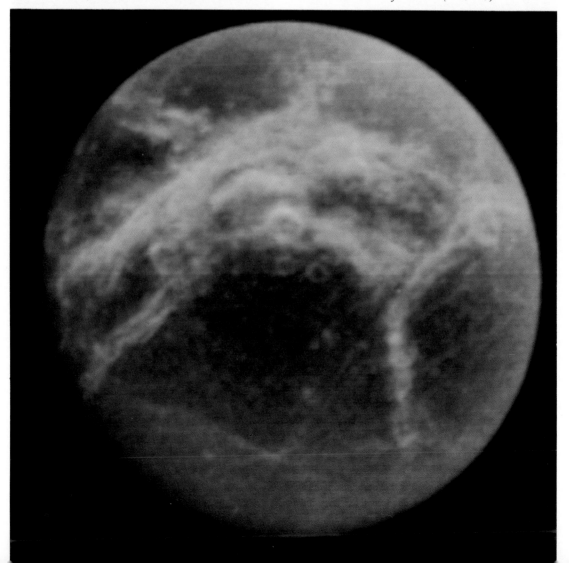

be associated with troughs or valleys. Although the origin of these features remains a matter of dispute, it is thought by many that they are deposits of fresh ice produced by ancient outgassing of interior water (and possibly methane) along these troughs or cracks.

Even the leading side of Dione shows a variety of geological terrain. The crater densities differ considerably, indicating several periods when resurfacing events took place during the first billion years of its history. It is possible that Dione has been more geologically active than its twin, Tethys, as a consequence of the slightly greater supply of radioactivity in its core.

Rhea

Rhea is the largest of the inner satellites, 1500 kilometers in diameter. However, it shows less

Voyager 1 obtained color images of Dione with a resolution of about 3 kilometers. This view of the heavily cratered leading face shows terrain with different densities of craters, indicating that there have been episodes of surface renewal since the period of heavy bombardment. Also visible is one large, slightly curvilinear trough or valley and several thin white streaks, apparently extending around from the trailing hemisphere. (P-23113)

geological activity than the smaller bodies Dione, Tethys, and, of course, Enceladus, proving that other effects dominate simple size in driving internal activity. Voyager 1 came within 74 000 kilometers of Rhea, the closest encounter of either spacecraft with an icy Saturn satellite, providing images of the leading hemisphere in the north polar regions at resolutions of about 1 kilometer.

During the Voyager approach, Rhea showed the same sort of division as Dione between a bright, bland leading hemisphere and a contrasting trailing hemisphere with bright streaks superimposed on a darker background. Geologist Gene Shoemaker suggests that the streaks were originally formed all over these satellites as part of an episode of internal activity early in their history. Subsequently, the leading hemispheres received so many meteoric impacts that the surface was pulverized and "gardened," while the streaks

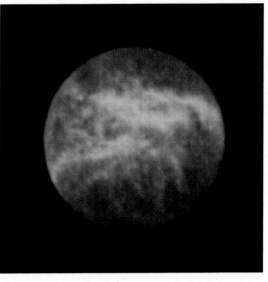

The trailing side of Rhea, like that of Dione, exhibits wispy terrain, with a complex pattern of bright markings superimposed on the underlying cratered surface. In this Voyager 1 view, the color differences have been exaggerated to bring out details in the bright streaks. (P-23093)

The best color picture of Rhea, taken by Voyager 1, has a resolution of about 3 kilometers, similar to that of the best telescopic views of the Moon from Earth. The surface is heavily cratered. The light-colored walls on a few of the craters may represent relatively fresh ice exposed at the surface, perhaps as the result of landslides on steep slopes. (P-23208)

Seen at close range, the surface of Rhea is dominated by impact craters. This Voyager 1 north polar mosaic has a resolution of about 1 kilometer and has been interpreted as indicating two populations of impacting bodies in the ancient past. (P-23177)

saturated with smaller craters, lack the big ones. This and other data led Voyager scientists to suggest that there have been two distinct populations of impacting projectiles. One population includes the original materials from which the system formed. The second population, which lacks the large objects, may be made of debris from later collisions within the Saturn system, perhaps associated with the formation of the rings or the break-up of one or more small satellites.

Rhea was also observed by the Voyager 1 IRIS, which measured the surface temperature in bright sunlight and when the satellite was eclipsed by Saturn. Under the full illumination of the Sun (which is nearly a hundred times weaker than at Earth), the temperature was – 174 °C. As the shadow crossed Rhea, its surface did not cool uniformly; some parts stabilized at about – 200 °C, while other regions cooled an additional 20 °C or more. Such behavior is typical of a heterogeneous surface consisting of both dense ice and lighter frost.

Iapetus

The outermost of the large icy satellites of Saturn is Iapetus, which is nearly the twin of Rhea, 1460 kilometers in diameter. Based on Voyager 2 measurements, however, Iapetus does differ significantly from Rhea in density, suggesting a smaller allotment of rocky materials. It is also possible that, like Titan, Iapetus formed with some methane and ammonia ice in its interior. These volatile ices probably never condensed close to Saturn, where the temperatures were higher than in the outer parts of the protoplanetary nebula.

Since its discovery, Iapetus has been known to be unusual, with a dark leading hemisphere and a bright trailing hemisphere. Voyager images further illustrate its bizarre nature. Most of the surface is bright and apparently consists of ordinary

were preserved on the more protected trailing side.

In the highest-resolution Voyager pictures, the crater-packed surface of Rhea resembles the highlands of the Moon, except that the material is brilliant white ice rather than dark brownish rock. There are visible differences, however, that are of great interest to geologists. In some sections, there are many large craters (more than 50 kilometers in diameter), while other regions, equally

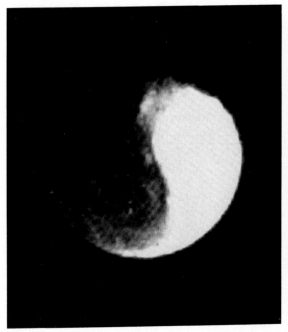 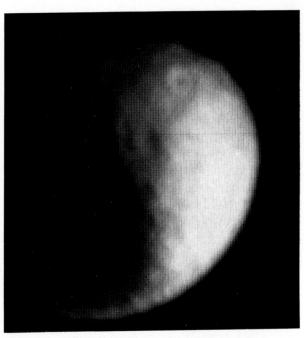

The extraordinary contrast between the dark leading and bright trailing hemispheres of Iapetus makes this satellite unique. These Voyager 1 views of the border between the light and dark hemispheres differ only in their level of exposure. One or two prominent craters are visible near the border at this resolution (about 50 kilometers). (260-1137A and 260-1137B)

water ice, just like Rhea. But the leading face (except near the poles) is black, as black as tar or asphalt. The dark oval spot on the leading side is less than one-tenth as bright as the rest of the satellite. Presumably, the dark face represents a relatively thin coating on a basically icy satellite, although this is a conclusion based on the indirect evidence of the low overall density of Iapetus, not on direct observations. In particular, there are no white spots or bright ray craters on the dark hemisphere, as would be expected if occasional meteoric impacts punched through a thin surface layer of black material. The dark material is either thick or it is constantly renewed to cover up bright impact ejecta.

If the black material is just a coating of strange composition, we can ask whether it is of internal or external origin. The fact that it is distributed so uniformly on one hemisphere and oriented so precisely toward the direction of motion cries out for an external origin, perhaps in the form of dust drifting inward from the outer satellite, Phoebe.

(Phoebe, however, has a slightly different color from the dark side of Iapetus.) Such an origin would also explain the ability of the dark material to renew itself. But the best Voyager images also reveal convincing evidence that dark material on the trailing side is concentrated in crater floors, as if it had been generated from inside. Thus, a number of Voyager scientists are convinced that the black material has an internal origin, and they suggest that it may have been the product of eruptions of methane from the interior. According to this theory, Iapetus is unique in having the black coating because it is the only icy satellite that included methane in its original inventory of materials.

Even after the Voyager 2 flyby, which yielded pictures of Iapetus with a resolution better than 20 kilometers, the basic question of the origin of its black coating remains open. Perhaps further study of Voyager data will lead to a scientific consensus, or perhaps this strange object will remain an enigma of the Saturn satellite system.

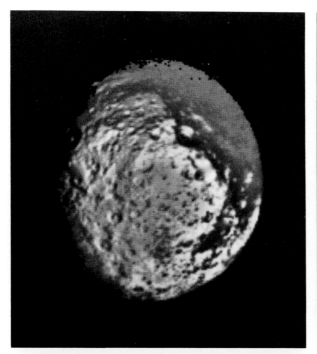

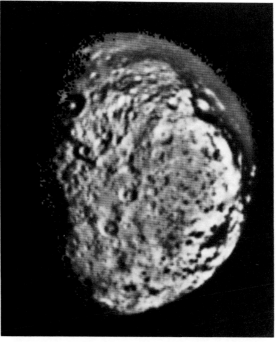

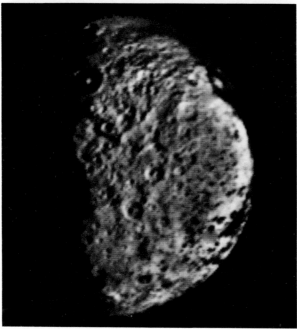

These three Voyager 2 views of Iapetus are the best pictures of this strange world. The resolution goes from 22 to 18 kilometers as the spacecraft moves into the bright trailing hemisphere and up over the north pole of the satellite. The boundary between light and dark is ragged, with dark material extending into the trailing hemisphere, particularly in crater floors. The bright icy surface near the north pole is heavily cratered and looks much like the surface of Rhea. (260-1476, 260-1477, 260-1478)

The Small Satellites

Ten small satellites of Saturn are known; they range in size from Hyperion (300 kilometers across) down to the A Ring shepherd, only about 30 kilometers in diameter. Presumably, there are undiscovered smaller objects, although a concerted search by Voyager 2 failed to reveal any. Since objects smaller than about 400 kilometers in diameter lack the gravitational pull to force themselves into a spherical shape, irregular profiles that result from impacts and fragmentation are preserved. It is these strange shapes that cause the small Saturn satellites to be irreverently referred to as "rocks" in spite of their substantial size and the fact that they are mostly of icy, rather than rocky, composition.

None of the small satellites has been the subject of much telescopic study, and even with Voyager little could be accomplished beyond imaging. In particular, no masses are known for these satellites. The absence of any idea as to their densities makes statements about their bulk composition purely speculative.

One of the most interesting aspects of the small satellites is their orbits. Nearly every one of them has an orbit that is remarkable in some way. Phoebe moves around Saturn in a backward, or retrograde, sense. The co-orbitals, 1980S1 and 1980S3, share the same orbit, as their nickname implies. And three others share orbits with Dione or Tethys, oscillating about the stable Lagrangian points in their orbits. In addition, the ring-skimming objects 1980S26, 1980S27, and 1980S28, all discovered by Voyager 1, are believed to play a critical role in establishing the outer dimensions of the Saturn ring system.

Phoebe

The outermost satellite of Saturn is Phoebe, circling the planet in a retrograde orbit at a distance of more than 10 million kilometers in a period of 406 days. Voyager 2, flying within 1.5 million kilometers, found a nearly spherical object with a diameter of 200 kilometers and a very dark surface, rotating with a period of 9 hours. With a reflectivity of less than 5 percent, Phoebe resembles very closely the common class of dark, carbonaceous asteroids. These asteroids are thought to be chemically very primitive, composed of the original solids that condensed out of the solar nebula. Being so small, they never heated up to modify their original composition. Perhaps Phoebe is just such a primitive object, the first ever photographed by a spacecraft. In addition, Phoebe may be the source of the dark material deposited on the leading face of Iapetus.

Hyperion

Hyperion orbits between Iapetus and Titan, with a period of 22 days. Voyager 2 came within 500 000 kilometers, yielding images with a resolution of about 10 kilometers. In addition, ground-based spectroscopy had shown that this too was an icy satellite, although perhaps a bit darker and dirtier than the large inner satellites.

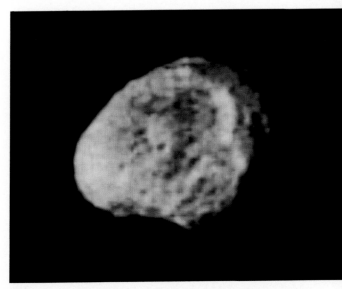

Although not much smaller than Mimas or Enceladus, Hyperion is a satellite with a much different character. Its irregular outline suggests that it has been subject to impact cratering and fragmentation. Hyperion appears to be composed primarily of water ice, although its reflectivity is substantially lower than that of the inner satellites, perhaps because it still retains the primordial dirty ice crust. (P-23936)

Hyperion is quite irregular in shape, with major dimensions of about 400 by 250 by 200 kilometers. Its battered shape is a testament to a history of impacts and fragmentation, in contrast to the serene sphericity of Phoebe. Even after Voyager, its exact rotation rate remains unknown; probably Hyperion always keeps the same face toward Saturn (as do all of the other satellites except Phoebe), but its irregular shape and the short period of time over which it was observed leave some question as to both its orientation and its rotation period.

The Lagrangian Satellites

In the eighteenth century, mathematicians determined that a small object could share an orbit with a large one if it stayed about 60 degrees away along the orbital arc, either leading or trailing. These stable areas for small satellites, which make equilateral triangles with the planet and the

The small satellites of Saturn tend to be irregular objects of apparently icy composition. This family portrait shows the eight small inner satellites, three of which were discovered by Voyager. They are, from left to right, the A Ring Shepherd (1980S28), the two F Ring Shepherds (1980S26 above and 1980S27 below), the two co-orbital satellites (1980S1 above and 1980S3 below), the two Tethys Lagrangian satellites (1980S25 above and 1980S13 below), and the Dione Lagrangian satellite (1980S6). (P-24061)

large satellite at the other two points, are called the Lagrangian points. The leading Lagrangian point is sometimes called L-4, and the trailing L-5. Until recently, the only known examples of objects in Lagrangian orbits were the so-called Trojan groups of asteroids in the L-4 and L-5 points of Jupiter's orbit.

Early in 1980, University of Arizona astronomers discovered a small satellite in the L-4 point of Dione's orbit. Subsequently, two similar-sized satellites were found sharing the orbit of Tethys, one in L-4 and one in L-5. All three of these Lagrangian satellites were targeted for study by Voyager 2 during its swing through the Saturn system.

The Lagrangians are irregular objects of apparently icy composition. The two Tethys companions (1980S13 and 1980S25) and Dione B (1980S6) are each 30 to 40 kilometers in diameter. All of them may be fragments of larger parent bodies. Voyager 2 searched the Lagrangian points of both Tethys and Dione for additional small satellites that might be trapped there, but none were found.

The Co-Orbital Satellites

Two satellites share nearly the same orbit, circling Saturn in just under 17 hours at a distance of 2.51 R_S. Both were first seen in 1966, at the time the rings were edge-on as seen from Earth, and again in 1980 under similar geometry. Pioneer Saturn nearly collided with one of them, and they were repeatedly photographed by both Voyagers. Officially, they are called 1980S1 and 1980S3; ultimately, they will be named as the tenth and eleventh satellites of Saturn.

The period of revolution of 1980S1 was 16.664 hours and that of 1980S3, 16.672 hours, both measured at the time of the Voyager 1 encounter. The slower object has an orbit just 50 kilometers larger than the faster one. About once every four years the inner one catches up with its slower-moving sibling, but, since the space between orbits is smaller than the objects, there is no room to pass. What happens is that, just short of a collision, the two satellites attract each other gravitationally and exchange orbits. They then slowly

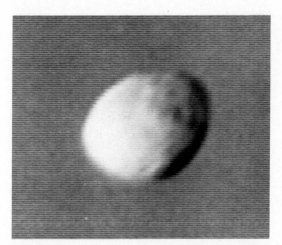

The smaller of Saturn's two co-orbital satellites, 1980S3, is seen here against the clouds of Saturn. The bright surface of this small irregular object suggests that it, like the large inner satellites, has a basically icy surface. (P-23351)

move apart in opposite directions, and the four-year cycle starts all over again. This strange orbital dance is unique, as far as we know, in the solar system.

Both co-orbital satellites are irregular objects, presumably icy in composition. Satellite 1980S1 has dimensions of 160 by 220 kilometers, while its smaller companion is about 100 by 140 kilometers. Each is heavily battered, and it seems likely that they are fragments of a larger parent body that was broken up by an impact early in Saturn's history, at a time when more debris was flying around to produce giant craters and disrupt an unlucky satellite or two.

The Shepherd Satellites

Objects 1980S26, 1980S27, and 1980S28 are called shepherds because of their presumed role in confining the ring particles to their proper orbits. The A Ring Shepherd, 1980S28, orbits just a few hundred kilometers from the outer edge of the A Ring, making it the innermost known satellite. Its orbital period is only 14.4 hours. The other two bracket the F Ring and may be responsible for the kinks and braids in that ring. These are nearly co-orbital, but their orbital separation (about 2000 kilometers) is much greater than

their diameters (about 200 kilometers), so they slip past each other about once each month with no difficulty.

The Remarkable Rings

Saturn's magnificent ring system is unique, with uncountable billions of icy particles in orbit around the planet. As revealed by Voyager, the rings are also almost unbelievably dynamic and complex. Almost anywhere in the ring system, at whatever scale the rings were observed, the intricate patterns of concentric features dazzled Voyager scientists and confused theorists who had the job of explaining the origin of this complexity. The rings of Saturn emerge from their scrutiny by the Voyager spacecraft as not only one of the most beautiful features in the heavens, but also one of the most scientifically challenging.

The main rings stretch from about 7000 kilometers above the atmosphere of the planet out to the F Ring, a total span of 74 000 kilometers. Within this vast region, the ring material is generally organized into narrow ringlets, individually less than 100 kilometers wide. Indeed, it appears probable that the typical width is much less than 100 kilometers, perhaps as small as 10 or even 1 kilometer. Generally speaking, however, there are not empty gaps between these ringlets, but only relative minima in the radial distribution of particles. At scales of less than 100 kilometers, it is probable that much of the structure is transitory, representing waves propagating through the ring material. A count of each ringlet would probably reveal tens of thousands, down to a 1-kilometer width.

A few wide gaps, nearly empty of particles, provide a natural separation into major areas of the rings. Other boundaries are provided by "edges," where the density of particles changes drastically. One of these edges is between the D and C Rings at 1.21 R_S from the center of Saturn; another divides the C and B Rings at 1.53 R_S. Within the C and D Rings, both of which are rather tenuous, there are several major gaps; in contrast, the dense B Ring is nearly devoid of gaps out to 1.95 R_S, its outer edge.

Between the B and A Rings lies the Cassini Division, a complex region of about 5000 kilometers

Voyager 1 obtained this wide-angle view of the crescent Saturn and its rings from a distance of about 1.5 million kilometers. A number of bright, forward-scattering features are particularly prominent in the C Ring and the F Ring, indicating the presence of small particles in these regions. The image of the planet is greatly overexposed. (P-23178)

across, containing several major gaps and hundreds of individual ring features. A bright region with many fine-scale wave patterns marks the inner edge of the A Ring, which continues out to $2.26 \, R_S$, where its outer edge is probably defined by the orbit of satellite 1980S28, the A Ring Shepherd. There are several gaps in the A Ring, the most prominent of which is called the Keeler Gap (or the Encke Gap).

Beyond the A Ring lies one more narrow ring, the F Ring, at $2.33 \, R_S$. The total width of the F Ring, which is confined between two shepherding satellites, is several hundred kilometers. Within this span, there are several major strands and as many as a hundred small features.

Far beyond the main rings are two additional rings of apparently different character, the G Ring at $2.8 \, R_S$ and the E Ring, stretching from 3.5 to $5.0 \, R_S$. Both are tenuous, and they appear to lack the fine-scale structure of the main rings. Apparently, the processes that produce intricate structure are confined to regions nearer the planet. The E Ring seems to be associated in some way with Enceladus.

The rings are composed predominantly, and perhaps nearly completely, of water ice, in particles that range from giant boulders to the finest dust. There are some differences in color from one region of the rings to another that may represent differences in bulk composition or may be more superficial in origin. The C Ring and the rings within the Cassini Division have similar colors, but even in the middle of the C Ring there are three ringlets with colors more representative of the dense B Ring. If these color variations represent real differences in composition, it appears that individual particles do not move from one ring to another, and that the major ring structures have remained stable since their formation.

The Voyager observations reveal a great deal about the sizes of ring particles, in spite of the fact that the individual particles are too small to be resolved. This information is derived from the way the rings reflect and scatter visible light and radio waves. As each spacecraft flew past Saturn, it measured the brightness of hundreds of ringlets from many angles, tracing out the distribution of scattered sunlight from each region. From these data it is easy to distinguish, for instance, very small particles (such as those in the F Ring or in the B Ring spokes) by their strong scattering in the forward direction. In a similar way, measurements of the scattering of the 3.6-centimeter and 13-centimeter wavelength radio signals from the spacecraft are particularly useful for detecting the presence of large particles (a meter or more in diameter).

As a result of the Voyager measurements, we now know that there are particles of many sizes in the rings, ranging from submicrometer to boul-

Possible variations in chemical composition from one part of Saturn's ring system to another are visible in this Voyager 2 picture as subtle color variations that can be recorded with special computer-processing techniques. This highly enhanced color view with a resolution of about 20 kilometers shows the blue color of the C Ring and Cassini Division and fainter differences in the colors within the B Ring and the A Ring. (P-23953)

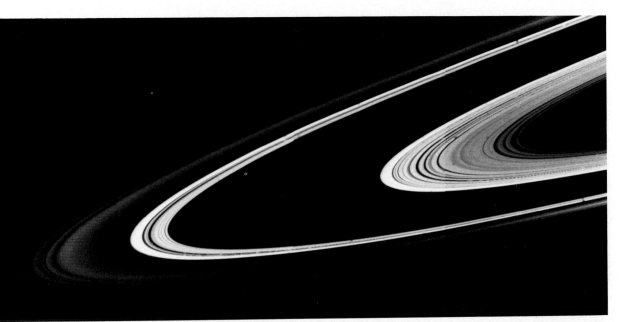

When seen from the unlit side, the rings of Saturn present a much different appearance from that familiar to telescopic observers. Relatively opaque areas like the B Ring turn black, while lightly populated zones, such as the C Ring and the Cassini Division, prove to be excellent diffuse transmitters of sunlight. The A Ring, with intermediate opacity, is at an intermediate level of brightness. (260-1148)

The Rings of Saturn

Feature	Distance from Center of Saturn (km)	Distance from Center of Saturn (R_S)	Period (hr)
Cloud tops	60 330	1.00	10.66
D Ring inner edge	67 000	1.11	4.91
C Ring inner edge	73 200	1.21	5.61
B Ring inner edge	92 200	1.53	7.93
B Ring outer edge	117 500	1.95	11.41
Cassini Division (middle)	119 000	1.98	11.75
A Ring inner edge	121 000	2.01	11.93
Keeler (Encke) Gap	133 500	2.21	13.82
A Ring outer edge	136 200	2.26	14.24
F Ring	140 600	2.33	14.94
G Ring	170 000	2.8	19.9
E Ring (middle)	230 000	3.8	31.3

ders 10 meters or more across. In addition, it is clear that different parts of the rings are dominated by different particle sizes; for instance, the F Ring is mostly made up of small particles, while in the Cassini Division submicrometer particles are almost entirely absent, and many particles are tens of meters in diameter. These results reinforce the conclusion from color differences that the physical nature of the rings is highly variable with position.

The Voyager ultraviolet spectrometer detected the glow of atomic hydrogen from the region of the rings. From these data scientists infer the presence of a tenuous water and hydrogen atmosphere around the rings, maintained by the slow release of water vapor from the icy ring particles. Ring temperatures have also been measured, from the ground and from spacecraft: They range from a high near −180 °C to values in the shadow of the planet that are lower than −200 °C.

We now look at the rings in more detail, proceeding outward from Saturn.

The D Ring

Between the classically known rings and the top of Saturn's atmosphere are a number of very thin

These Voyager 1 views show the unlit side of the rings in false color, which is used to bring out detail in the very dark B Ring. The upper picture shows the Cassini Division (bright), the A Ring, and the F Ring; below are the B and C Rings. (P-23207 and P-23111)

When the rings are viewed against the planet, additional information can be obtained from a study of how they block light coming from behind. The B Ring is largely opaque, while the edge of Saturn can be seen through the C and A Rings. This Voyager 2 image has a resolution of 60 kilometers. (P-23931)

ringlets discovered by Voyager. Collectively called the D Ring, these ringlets appear to be as intricate in structure as the more dense regions farther out.

The C Ring

The tenuous C Ring is faintly visible through even a rather small telescope. We do not understand the reason for its boundaries: neither the sharp inner edge at 73 000 kilometers from the center of Saturn nor the steep transition to the dense B Ring at 92 000 kilometers. Within its 19 000-kilometer breadth, the C Ring displays a regular ordering of alternating light and dark bands. There are two prominent gaps, one at 77 300 kilometers (about 200 kilometers wide) and one at 87 000 kilometers (about 300 kilometers wide). The outer gap contains a narrow, dense, eccentric (noncircular) bright ring. This eccentric ring varies in width; it is about 90 kilometers wide where it is farthest from Saturn and only 35 kilometers wide at its closest point. Although the cause of this and the few other eccentric rings is not well understood, one popular theory suggests that there is a small satellite embedded within the bright ring. Another theory is that the ring is confined between two shepherding satellites, but no such small objects were detected by Voyager 1 or Voyager 2.

The C Ring is deficient in very small particles, compared to other parts of the rings. The particle diameter inferred from the radio occultation was about 2 meters. However, the radio signals are especially sensitive to *large* particles, so we should not infer from these results that most of the C Ring particles are 2 meters across. In fact, for a typical *distribution* of sizes, there might be 10 one-meter particles and 10 000 ten-centimeter particles for each two-meter particle. Such a distribution would be consistent with the radio observations and other data on the likely sizes of such an ensemble of particles.

The B Ring

From a distant perspective, the B Ring is the dominant feature of the Saturnian ring system. It is brighter than all the other rings combined, and it presumably contains most of the ring mass. It is also the only part of the ring that is opaque over most of its width, casting a black shadow on the planet. From the dark side, the B Ring is so opaque that it can hardly be seen at all.

The B Ring has the most extensive and uniform small-scale structure in the ring system. Seen at resolutions of about 100 kilometers, its surface resembles a grooved phonograph record. At the highest resolution obtained by Voyager 2, a much more intricate structure, consisting of thousands of ringlets, is apparent. Much of this structure at scales of tens of kilometers or smaller exhibits the regular patterns that scientists attribute to waves propagating through a resisting medium. This pattern is not static, but changes from place to place and time to time.

On a broader scale, the B Ring can be divided into four radial zones of roughly equal width that show evidence of different particle size distributions, with very small particles more prevalent in some areas than others. Since the B Ring was opaque to radio signals as well as visible light, we have no indication of the upper limits to the particle sizes, nor is there an estimate of the total mass of material in the B Ring. Ground-based measurements set an upper limit of about 2 kilometers to its thickness, and the high radar reflectivity of the rings suggests a great many particles in the large snowball size range, from 10 centimeters to 1 meter in diameter.

Perhaps the most enigmatic feature of the B Ring discovered by Voyager was the dark radial spokes. These features are dark only when viewed in backscattered light (with the Sun behind the camera); as seen in forward scattering (looking toward the Sun), they are brighter than the surrounding part of the B Ring. This behavior is characteristic of very small particles and has led to

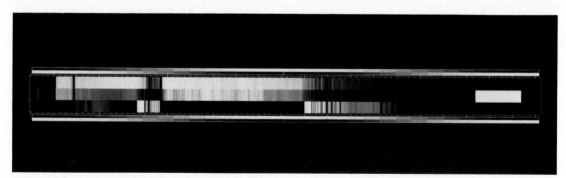

The more ways we look at the rings, the more chance we have of understanding their complex structure. Here we see three radial profiles, each with a different geometry. At the top is the normal view in backscattered light; in the middle is the appearance from the unlit side dominated by diffusely transmitted sunlight; at the bottom is the forward-scattering view of the illuminated side of the rings. Clearly, the individual ringlets display a wide variety of light-scattering properties. (260-1177)

the suggestion that the spokes are regions in which clouds of fine particles are levitated above this ring. The degree of levitation need be only tens of meters to produce the observed effects.

The spokes have typical lengths of about 10 000 kilometers and widths ranging from 100 to 1000 kilometers. They are formed pointing radially outward from Saturn in the densest part of the B Ring, between 105 000 and about 115 000 kilometers from the center of the planet. Spokes can form at any place around the circumference of the ring, although they generally appear more prominent on the leading side of the rings. Voyager 2

photographed the formation of a number of spokes. Several of these appeared to begin as thin lines and then to widen into a wedge shape over a period of tens of minutes. Once they have formed, the spokes can survive only a few hours before they are pulled apart, since the inner parts of the ring orbit the planet more rapidly than the outer parts. As far as can be measured, the shearing of the spokes indicates that the individual particles are moving in normal orbits under the gravitational attraction of Saturn.

The origin of the spokes remains a mystery. The most plausible theory is that the clouds of fine particles are levitated by electrostatic forces, perhaps related to the huge electrical discharges detected by the Planetary Radio Astronomy instruments on both Voyager spacecraft. Just how this

Inside the C Ring lies additional very faint material which is collectively termed the D Ring. This wide-angle Voyager 2 view, taken from a distance of 200 000 kilometers, includes the Sun's shadow cast across the ring. Even in this tenuous region, the ring clearly possesses a great deal of fine structural detail. (P-23967)

The dramatic change in appearance of the rings when viewed from their lit and unlit sides is shown in this Voyager 1 view of the C Ring obtained at a resolution of about 50 kilometers. The upper part shows the C Ring in forward-scattered light, the lower part in diffusely transmitted light. Some of the brightest ringlets in the upper part are invisible below because they are too opaque to transmit much light. (P-23354)

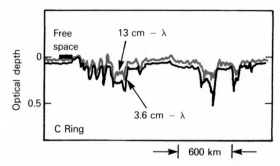

One way of determining the size of the ring particles as well as their distribution is by measuring their opacity to microwaves. Here we see plots of the opacity of a part of the C Ring to the two wavelengths of the Voyager 1 radio telemetry system. In regions where the red and yellow curves differ, there are many particles in the 10-centimeter size range. (260-1309)

happens, or what triggers the formation of a particular spoke, remains unclear, however. Although the magnetic field of Saturn may be responsible for the creation of a spoke, their dynamics follow the ordinary rules of gravitational motions once they are formed.

The Cassini Division

The inner or B Ring edge of the Cassini Division is a sharp discontinuity located at the 2 to 1 orbital resonance with Mimas, where a ring particle will orbit Saturn exactly twice for each orbit of Mimas. This boundary is eccentric, being in some places about 70 kilometers closer to Saturn than in others. It is unique in that, although the shape of the boundary is elliptical, the center of the planet is not at one focus of the ellipse but rather at its center. This remarkable shape is taken as strong evidence that the boundary is indeed created and controlled by the Mimas resonance. About 100 kilometers outside this boundary lies a thin, dense, eccentric ring of the "normal" kind, with Saturn at one focus. This ring is another candidate for a feature controlled dynamically by one or more embedded satellites.

The interior of the Cassini Division, once thought to be nearly devoid of matter, is seen in Voyager images to consist of a regular sequence of bright and dark features. Between the ringlets, each a few hundred kilometers across, lie empty gaps. Before Voyager 2, it seemed extremely likely that these gaps were cleared of particles by embedded satellites 10 to 30 kilometers in diameter. Although no such objects were detected, some dynamic process involving perhaps smaller embedded "moonlets" is still favored by many to explain this structure.

At the outer edge of the Division is a band about 1400 kilometers wide that contains many evenly spaced wave-like features. Theorists believe these regular undulations represent a propagating spiral "density wave" and from its properties conclude that the amount of material present is 16 grams per square centimeter of area—the only estimate we have of the actual mass of material in a part of the rings. With this value, the total mass of the 1400-kilometer-wide band would be 10^{20} grams, or about 0.3 percent of the mass of Mimas. The particle sizes resemble those of the C Ring, although the upper range of particles is larger: 8 meters, as opposed to 2 meters for the C Ring.

The A Ring

The inner edge of the A Ring is as abrupt as the B Ring/C Ring boundary and as opaque as any region of the B Ring. Most of the A Ring, however, is more transparent. In the inner three-quarters of the ring, the structure is fairly regular and has a smaller amplitude than in most other parts of the ring system. Particle sizes span a broad range, from characteristic sizes of about 10 meters to an abundance of micrometer-sized dust grains. The edges of the ring and its gaps are remarkably sharp, even at the kilometer scale probed by the Voyager 1 radio observations and the hundred-meter scale probed by the Voyager 2 photopolarimeter occultation. Just beyond the A Ring orbits the small shepherd satellite, 1980S28, which may be responsible for its sharp outer boundary.

The dark spokes in the B Ring of Saturn can be seen in this Voyager 2 picture, part of one of the spoke time-lapse movies used to study the formation and development of these strange and transient markings. (260-1505)

After the spacecraft passed Saturn and were able to view the B Ring in forward-scattered light, the dark spokes were seen as bright streaks, indicating that the spokes were caused by particles no larger than the wavelength of light. (260-1176)

Most of the structure of the A Ring is present in its outer part. Here there are several gaps, the most prominent of which is the Keeler Gap, 270 kilometers across. A series of ringlets outside this gap demonstrates a clear resonance pattern. The brightest part of the ring is an outer band a few hundred kilometers wide, separated from the rest of the ring by a 50-kilometer-wide gap. At the

One of the most remarkable discoveries of Voyager 2 was the dynamic nature of the small-scale structure in the B Ring. Here we see four pictures of the outer part of the B Ring and the inner part of the Cassini Division. In addition to the presence of several eccentric rings, including the outer edge of the B Ring, we see that on a small scale there is very poor correspondence from one image to another in the B Ring. (260-1473)

This detailed mosaic of the underside of the Cassini Division was obtained by Voyager 1 with a resolution of about 10 kilometers. The classical Cassini Division appears here to the right of center as five bright rings with substantial black gaps on either side. The inner edge of the A Ring, to the left of center, is the brightest part of this image. The fine-scale wave structure in this region has been interpreted as being the result of gravitational density waves. (260-1129)

The Voyager 2 photopolarimeter provided a new way to observe the rings at higher resolution than can be obtained by direct imaging. Here we see three presentations of the opacity of the Keeler Gap in the A Ring, produced by measuring the variations in brightness of the star δ Scorpii as it blinked behind the rings. The highest resolution obtained in this occultation observation was about 100 meters.

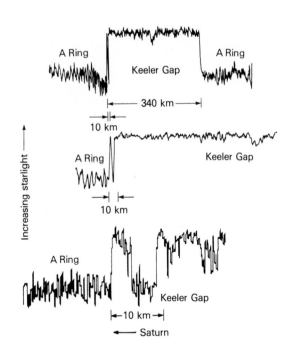

outer edge, the photopolarimeter on Voyager 2 determined an upper limit for the ring thickness of less than 300 meters.

The Keeler Gap, sometimes called the Encke Division, contains a pair of extraordinary ringlets that are both *discontinuous* and *kinky*. A few other ringlets are clumpy, but these are the only ones known that apparently consist of only short arcs. The kinks, of unknown origin, are spaced a few hundred kilometers apart. The high-resolution

179

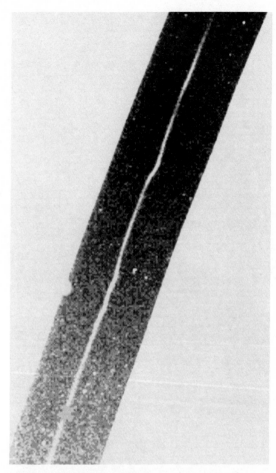

Within the Keeler Gap lie at least two discontinuous ringlets. This Voyager 2 picture, with a resolution of about 10 kilometers, shows one of these rings to be kinky. The kinks are spaced about 700 kilometers apart, approximately ten times more closely than the F Ring kinks photographed by Voyager 1. (260-1305)

profile of the Keeler Gap obtained by the photopolarimeter showed more than a dozen very faint features less than a kilometer wide, as well as one of the two kinky rings. Moonlets within the gap have been suggested as the cause of this structure, but none was seen by the Voyager cameras.

The F Ring

Like a thin pencil line circumscribing the main rings, the F Ring orbits Saturn at a distance of 2.33 R_S, or 140 600 kilometers. Discovered by Pioneer Saturn, the F Ring, which is slightly eccentric, is gravitationally confined between the two shepherd satellites, 1980S26 and 1980S27. Each of these satellites is also in a slightly eccentric orbit, and at times the inner shepherd can approach within grazing distance of the ring.

The total width of the F Ring is several hundred kilometers. Within this span are several perhaps discontinuous strands each less than 25 kilometers across; Voyager 2 photographed as many as five in one image. Still greater complexity was revealed by the photopolarimeter trace, which resolved the brightest of these strands into many additional components. At moderate resolutions the F Ring appears clumpy, and at the highest resolution Voyager 1 photographed kinks and apparent intertwining of strands, with the kinks spaced about 7000 kilometers apart, ten times the scale of the kinky ring in the Keeler Gap. Voyager 2 also obtained one photograph showing a twist or braid in the F Ring, but in most of the Voyager 2 images the ring consisted of single or multiple parallel strands without the peculiar structure discovered by Voyager 1.

The cause of the F Ring kinks and braids remains one of the big mysteries of the Saturn system. It has been suggested that the complex gravitational pulls of the eccentric shepherding satellites can separate the strands and set up gravitational waves that might propagate through the rings, but the number of observations is too small for a convincing test of these ideas.

Origin of the System

One of the main reasons scientists study the planets is to learn about the origin and evolution of the entire solar system. The Earth, as an extremely active planet geologically, has pretty well erased the evidence of its birth and early history. Also, of course, any one planet is the product of local conditions that might not be representative of the system as a whole. Only by exploring other worlds and comparing them can we gain a perspective on Earth and its place in the solar system.

At the time of a spacecraft encounter, the primary emphasis is on exploration. New worlds

One of the most exciting discoveries of Voyager was the presence of wave patterns in the rings. In this pseudo-image generated from the photopolarimeter occultation trace, we see the outer part of the A Ring, including a narrow 50-kilometer gap, at a resolution of about 1 kilometer. False color is used to enhance the visibility of the wave patterns. (260-1459AC)

present themselves, often in dazzling and unexpected forms. Only later will all the data be sifted and analyzed, and attempts made to answer the more fundamental questions of origins and evolution. In the case of Saturn, this kind of synthesis has hardly begun.

It is probable that the planet and its entourage formed together, accreting from solids that condensed as the proto-Saturn nebula cooled about 4.6 billion years ago. The central mass, which was to become Saturn, had sufficient gravity to hold onto the light gases, hydrogen and helium, as well as denser solid grains. As it formed, it also grew quite hot, perhaps hot enough to evaporate the grains of ice and other solids in its vicinity. Initially, the accretion of satellite bodies could probably take place only a great distance from the highly luminous planet.

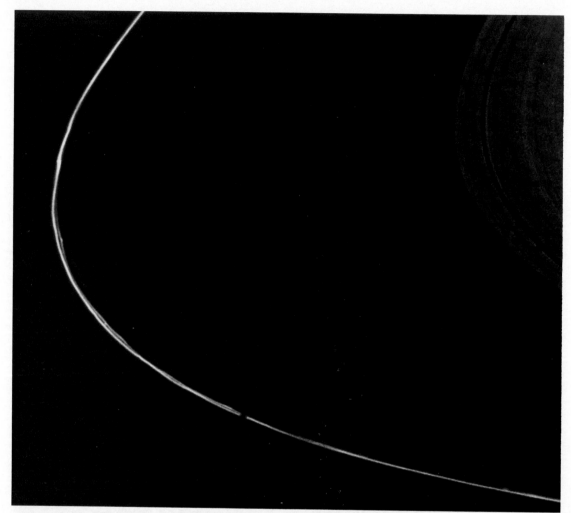

One section of the F Ring viewed by Voyager 1 showed a spectacular variety of kinks, strands, and apparent braids. Also visible in this view, taken from underneath the rings, is the outer part of the A Ring faintly illuminated by diffusely transmitted sunlight. (260-1174)

We do not really know how the satellites formed. Perhaps each grew in essentially its present orbit by attracting the fine dust and small particles that were formed there as the nebula cooled. Or perhaps an intermediate generation of planetesimals, perhaps one or several hundred kilometers in diameter, were formed. Subsequently, collisions between these planetesimals could have fragmented some and led to coalescence and growth of others. It is possible that the rings were formed by the break-up of one or more of these parent bodies, and the small, irregularly shaped satellites might have had a similar origin. It is also possible, but not likely, that the rings are of a more recent origin.

One important question about the satellites concerns their initial chemical composition. Was any substantial amount of methane or ammonia included in their inventory? Apparently, the answer is yes for Titan, but how about the smaller bodies? Is the black face of Iapetus somehow related to its initial composition? Do the wispy

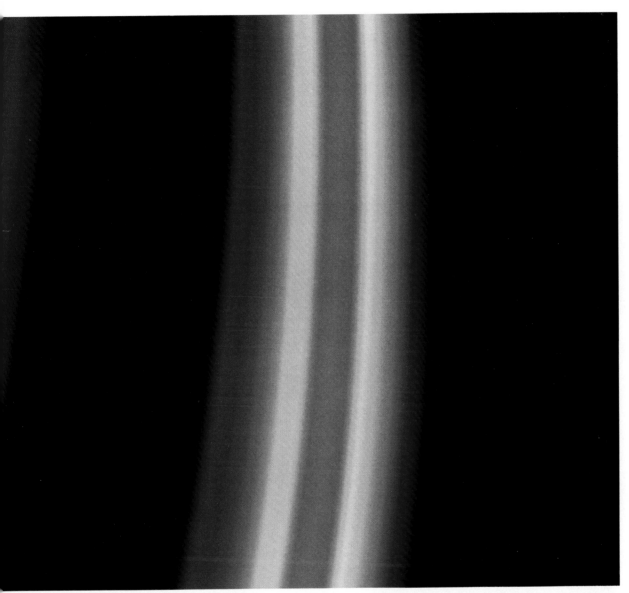

The innermost core of the bright central strand of the F Ring has structure detected by the photo-polarimeter occultation measurements. In this false-color pseudo-image the resolution is a few hundred meters. This image covers only the brightest part of the F Ring pseudo-image (P-23966) shown on page 128. (260-1458BC)

streaks on Rhea and Dione represent methane outgassing, or were they produced by higher-temperature eruptions of water or steam? And what about Enceladus—what is the origin of its continuing high level of geologic activity? Is it tidal heating, or is it related to composition?

These are just a few of the questions raised by Voyager data. Equally challenging are the dynamic problems associated with the rings. A few years ago, some scientists felt they understood the rings pretty well; today there is a more modest and realistic view. Many believe that an understanding of the ring dynamics today will lead to a better appreciation of the conditions in the early solar nebula and the associated rings of particles from which the planets formed.

Science always represents a quest for understanding. There are no final answers, only better approximations to comprehending the complexities of nature. Voyager provided a wealth of new discoveries and information, but it will require a great deal of study and analysis to incorporate the new data into an improved perspective on the universe and our place within it.

The parting view of Saturn from Voyager 2 as it sped toward its 1986 encounter with Uranus showed the dark south side of the rings, unlike the Voyager 1 perspective (P-23254) of the bright northern side shown on page 95. (P-24368)

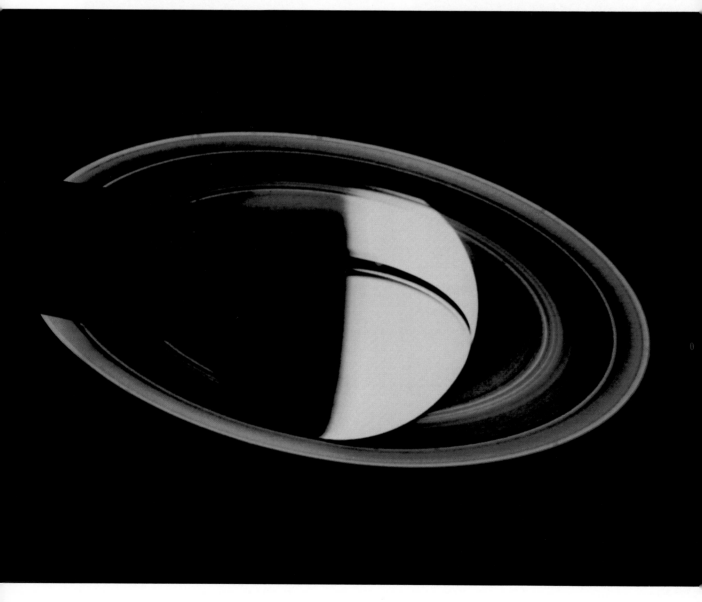

APPENDIX A

Voyager Science Teams

Cosmic Ray

Rochus E. Vogt, California Institute of Technology, Principal Investigator
J. Randy Jokipii, University of Arizona
Frank B. McDonald, Goddard Space Flight Center
Edward C. Stone, California Institute of Technology
James H. Trainor, Goddard Space Flight Center
William R. Webber, University of New Hampshire
Al W. Schardt, Goddard Space Flight Center

Infrared Interferometry and Spectrometry

Rudolph A. Hanel, Goddard Space Flight Center, Principal Investigator
Barney Conrath, Goddard Space Flight Center
Dale Cruikshank, University of Hawaii
F. Michael Flasar, Goddard Space Flight Center
Daniel Gautier, Observatoire de Paris, France
Peter Gierasch, Cornell University
Shailendra Kumar, University of Southern California
Virgil Kunde, Goddard Space Flight Center
William Maguire, Goddard Space Flight Center
John Pearl, Goddard Space Flight Center
Joseph Pirraglia, Goddard Space Flight Center
Cyril Ponnamperuma, University of Maryland
Robert Samuelson, Goddard Space Flight Center

Imaging Science

Bradford A. Smith, University of Arizona, Team Leader
Geoffrey Briggs, NASA Headquarters

Allan F. Cook II, Center for Astrophysics
G. Edward Danielson, California Institute of Technology
Merton E. Davies, Rand Corp.
Gary E. Hunt, University College, London
Torrence V. Johnson, Jet Propulsion Laboratory
Harold Masursky, U.S. Geological Survey
Tobias Owen, State University of New York, Stony Brook
Carl Sagan, Cornell University
Laurence Soderblom, U.S. Geological Survey, Deputy Team Leader
Verner E. Suomi, University of Wisconsin
Reta Beebe, New Mexico State University
Joseph Boyce, NASA Headquarters
Anne Bunker, Jet Propulsion Laboratory
Michael Carr, U.S. Geological Survey
Steward A. Collins, Jet Propulsion Laboratory
Jeffrey Cuzzi, Ames Research Center
Candice J. Hansen, Jet Propulsion Laboratory
Andrew Ingersoll, California Institute of Technology
John McCauley, U.S. Geological Survey
Jimmy L. Mitchell, Jet Propulsion Laboratory
David Morrison, University of Hawaii
James B. Pollack, Ames Research Center
Eugene Shoemaker, California Institute of Technology, U.S. Geological Survey
Robert Strom, University of Arizona
Richard Terrile, Jet Propulsion Laboratory
Joseph Veverka, Cornell University

Low Energy Charged Particles

S. M. (Tom) Krimigis, Johns Hopkins University, Principal Investigator

Thomas P. Armstrong, University of Kansas
W. Ian Axford, Max-Planck-Institut fur
Aeronomie
Carl O. Bostrom, Johns Hopkins University
Chang-yun Fan, University of Arizona
George Gloeckler, University of Maryland
Ed Keath, Johns Hopkins University
Louis J. Lanzerotti, Bell Laboratories

Plasma Science

Herbert S. Bridge, Massachusetts Institute of
Technology, Principal Investigator
John W. Belcher, Massachusetts Institute of
Technology
Len F. Burlaga, Goddard Space Flight Center
Chistoph K. Goertz, Max-Planck-Institut fur
Aeronomie
Richard E. Hartle, Goddard Space Flight Center
Art J. Hundhausen, High Altitude Observatory
Alan J. Lazarus, Massachusetts Institute of
Technology
Keith Ogilvie, Goddard Space Flight Center
Stanislaw Olbert, Massachusetts Institute of
Technology
Jack D. Scudder, Goddard Space Flight Center
George L. Siscoe, University of California,
Los Angeles
James D. Sullivan, Massachusetts Institute of
Technology
Vytenis M. Vasyliunas, Max-Planck-Institut fur
Aeronomie

Magnetic Fields

Norman F. Ness, Goddard Space Flight Center,
Principal Investigator
Mario F. Acuna, Goddard Space Flight Center
Ken W. Behannon, Goddard Space Flight
Center
Len F. Burlaga, Goddard Space Flight Center
Ron P. Lepping, Goddard Space Flight Center
Fritz M. Neubauer, Der Technischen Universitat
Braunschweig

Photopolarimetry

Arthur L. Lane, Jet Propulsion Laboratory,
Principal Investigator

David Coffeen, Goddard Institute for Space
Studies
Larry Esposito, University of Colorado
James E. Hansen, Goddard Institute for Space
Studies
Charles W. Hord, University of Colorado
Makiko Sato, Goddard Institute for Space
Studies
Robert West, University of Colorado
Richard B. Pomphrey, Jet Propulsion Laboratory
Robert M. Nelson, Jet Propulsion Laboratory

Planetary Radio Astronomy

James W. Warwick, Radiophysics, Inc.,
Principal Investigator
Joseph K. Alexander, Goddard Space Flight
Center
Andre Boischot, Observatoire de Paris
Walter E. Brown Jr., Jet Propulsion Laboratory
Thomas D. Carr, University of Florida
Samuel Gulkis, Jet Propulsion Laboratory
Fred T. Haddock, University of Michigan
Christopher C. Harvey, Observatoire de Paris
Michael L. Kaiser, Goddard Space Flight Center
Yolande Leblanc, Observatoire de Paris
Jeffrey B. Pearce, Radiophysics, Inc.
Robert G. Peltzer, Martin Marietta Corp.
Roger Phillips, Jet Propulsion Laboratory
Anthony C. Riddle, University of Colorado
David H. Staelin, Massachusetts Institute of
Technology

Plasma Wave

Frederick L. Scarf, TRW Defense and Space
Systems Group, Principal Investigator
Donald A. Gurnett, University of Iowa
William Kurth, University of Iowa

Radio Science

G. Len Tyler, Stanford University, Team
Leader
John D. Anderson, Jet Propulsion Laboratory
Thomas A. Croft, SRI International
Von R. Eshleman, Stanford University
Gerald S. Levy, Jet Propulsion Laboratory
Gunnar F. Lindal, Jet Propulsion Laboratory
Gordon E. Wood, Jet Propulsion Laboratory

Ultraviolet Spectroscopy

A. Lyle Broadfoot, University of Southern
California, Principal Investigator
Sushil K. Atreya, University of Michigan
Michael J. S. Belton, Kitt Peak National
Observatory
Jean L. Bertaux, Service d'Aeronomie du CNRS
Jacques E. Blamont, Jet Propulsion Laboratory,
Centre National d'Etudes Spatiales

Alexander Dalgarno, Harvard College Observatory
Thomas M. Donahue, University of Michigan
Richard Goody, Harvard University
John C. McConnell, York University
Michael B. McElroy, Harvard University
H. Warren Moos, Johns Hopkins University
Bill R. Sandel, University of Southern California
Donald E. Shemansky, University of Southern
California
Darrell F. Strobel, Naval Research Laboratory

187

APPENDIX B

Voyager Management Teams

NASA Office of Space Science

Andrew J. Stofan, Associate Administrator for Space Science (Acting)

Adrienne F. Timothy, Assistant Associate Administrator for Space Science (V1)

Jeffrey D. Rosendahl, Assistant Associate Administrator for Space Science (Acting) (V2)

Angelo Guastaferro, Director, Solar System Exploration Division (V1)

Daniel H. Herman, Director, Solar System Exploration Division (Acting) (V2)

Geoffrey A. Briggs, Deputy Director, Solar System Exploration Division

C. Howard Robins, Manager, Solar System Mission Operations

Frank A. Carr, Program Manager (Acting)

Milton A. Mitz, Program Scientist

NASA Office of Space Tracking and Data Systems

Robert E. Smylie, Associate Administrator for Space Tracking and Data Systems

Charles A. Taylor, Director, Network Systems Division

Norman Pozinsky, Deputy Director, Network Systems Division

Richard Green, Program Manager, Deep Space Network

Harold G. Kimball, Director, Communications and Data Systems Division

Jet Propulsion Laboratory

Bruce C. Murray, Director

Gen. Charles A. Terhune, Jr., Deputy Director

Robert J. Parks, Associate Director for Flight Projects

Raymond Heacock, Project Manager (V1)

Esker K. Davis, Deputy Project Manager (V1), Project Manager (V2)

Richard P. Laeser, Deputy Project Manager (V2), Mission Director

George P. Textor, Deputy Mission Director

Richard P. Rudd, Deputy Mission Director

Charles E. Kohlhase, Manager, Mission Planning Office

Robert G. Polansky, Manager, Ground Data Systems

Marvin R. Traxler, Manager, Tracking and Data Systems

Charles H. Stembridge, Manager, Flight Science Office

Ellis D. Miner, Assistant Project Scientist for Saturn

Edward L. McKinley, Manager, Flight Engineering Office

Douglas G. Griffith, Manager, Flight Operations Office

California Institute of Technology

Edward C. Stone, Project Scientist

APPENDIX C

Pictorial Maps of the Saturnian Satellites

These maps were prepared for the Voyager Imaging Team by the U.S. Geological Survey in cooperation with the Jet Propulsion Laboratory, California Institute of Technology and the National Aeronautics and Space Administration. Copies are available from Branch of Distribution, U.S. Geological Survey, 1200 South Eads Street, Arlington, VA 22202, and Branch of Distribution, U.S. Geological Survey, Box 25286, Federal Center, Denver, CO 80225.

Preliminary Pictorial Map of Rhea

Atlas of the Saturnian Satellites
1:10,000,000 Topographic Series
Sr 10M 2AN, 1981

This map was compiled from Voyager 1 and 2 pictures of Rhea. Map controls are based on the known position and orientation of the satellite with respect to the spacecraft at the time each picture was taken. A scaled grid, showing a perspective view of meridians and parallels, was superimposed over each picture. Map details were manually transferred, grid cell by grid cell, from the perspective view to Mercator and polar stereographic projections. Relative accuracy of feature placement is probably within 70 kilometers over 66 percent of the map area.

All landforms are shown as if illuminated from the west, regardless of their illumination on the photographic source material. Albedo markings visible on the Voyager pictures are also shown. It was not always possible to make distinctions between albedo and relief, either in interpretation or in portrayal. Extreme variation in image resolution precluded consistent interpretation of the pictures. Consistent portrayal was complicated by such phenomena as dark albedo deposits covering sunlit crater walls.

Names of features shown are provisional. The map projection is based on a sphere with a diameter of 1530 kilometers. The Mercator and polar stereographic projections have common scales at ± 56°. Airbrush representation was made by Jay L. Inge. Grid, data preparation, and preliminary image processing were done by K. F. Mullins, Christopher Isbell, E. M. Lee, H. F. Morgan, and B. A. Skiff. The work was directed by R. M. Batson.

Sr 10M 2AN: Abbreviation for Saturn; satellite Rhea; 1:10,000,000 series; second edition; A, shaded relief and markings; N, feature names.

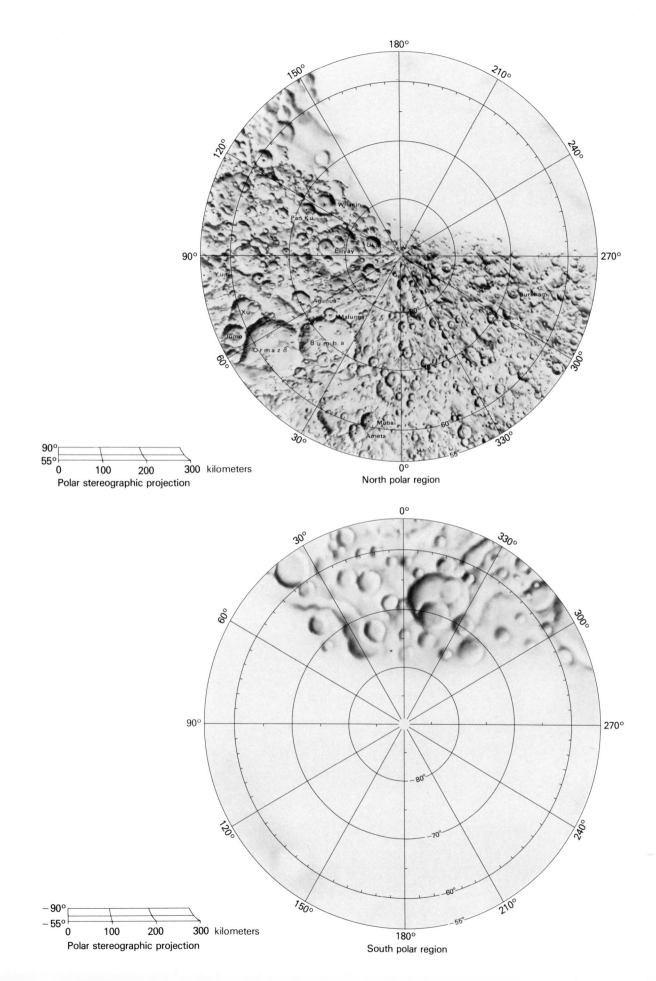

180°

150°   210°

120°   240°

90°   270°

Whanin
Pan Ku
Ukko
Ellyay   Burkham
Yuri
Agunua
Xu   Mafunga
Jumo   B u m b a
O r m a z d

60°   300°

30°   330°

Mubai
Ameta
0°

North polar region

90°
55°
0   100   200   300   kilometers
Polar stereographic projection

0°

30°   330°

60°   300°

90°   270°

120°   240°

150°   210°

180°

South polar region

−90°
−55°
0   100   200   300   kilometers
Polar stereographic projection

Rhea

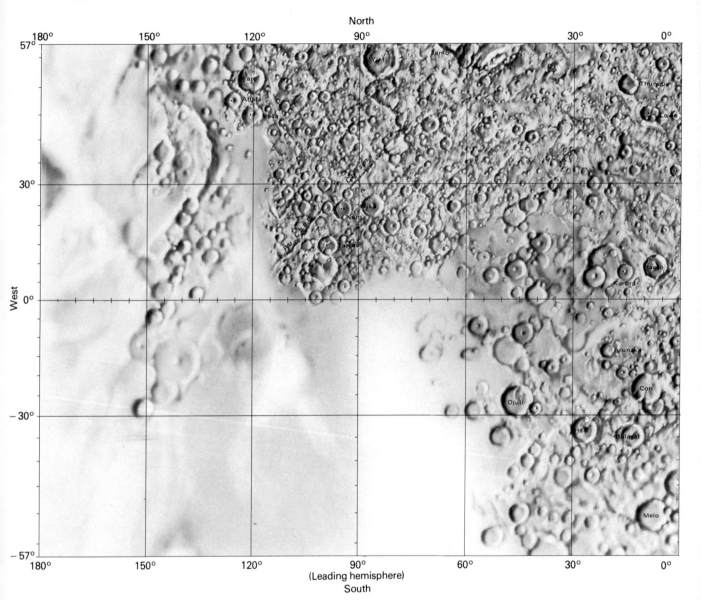

180° 150° 120° 90° 30° 0°

57°

30°

West 0°

-30°

-57°

180° 150° 120° 90° 60° 30° 0°

(Leading hemisphere)
South

Yu-ti   Jumo

Faro   Thunupa
Atida   Lowa
Iraca

Chasma

Pu Chou   Djika   Haoso
Num   Karora
Taaroa

Arunaka

Con

Djuli

Haik   Bulagat

Melo

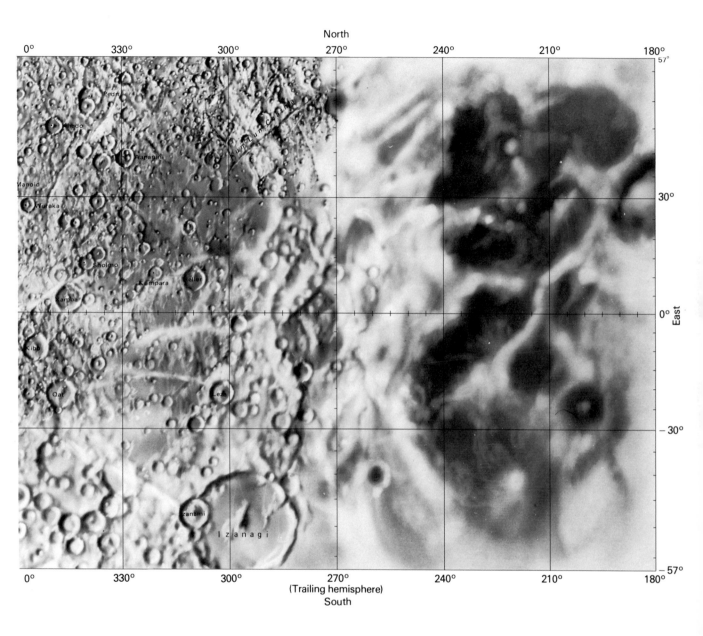

0°   330°   300°   270°   240°   210°   180°
57°
30°
0° East
−30°
−57°

(Trailing hemisphere)
South

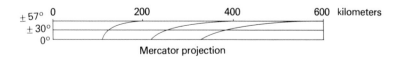

±57°   0   200   400   600   kilometers
±30°
0°
Mercator projection

Preliminary Pictorial Map of Mimas

Atlas of the Saturnian Satellites
1:5,000,000 Topographic Series
Sm 5M 2AN, 1981

This map was compiled from Voyager 1 and 2 pictures of Mimas. Map controls are based on the known position and orientation of the satellite with respect to the spacecraft at the time each picture was taken. A scaled grid, showing a perspective view of meridians and parallels, was superimposed over each picture. Map details were manually transferred, grid cell by grid cell, from the perspective view to Mercator and polar stereographic projections. Relative accuracy of feature placement is probably within 20 kilometers over 66 percent of the map area.

All landforms are shown as if illuminated from the west, regardless of their illumination on the photographic source material. Albedo markings visible on the Voyager pictures are also shown. It was not always possible to make distinctions between albedo and relief, either in interpretation or in portrayal. Extreme variation in image resolution precluded consistent interpretation of the pictures. Consistent portrayal was complicated by such phenomena as dark albedo deposits covering sunlit crater walls.

Names of features shown are provisional. The map projection is based on a sphere with a diameter of 392 kilometers. The Mercator and polar stereographic projections have common scales at $-56°$. Airbrush representation was made by Jay L. Inge. Grid, data preparation, and preliminary image processing were done by K. F. Mullins, Christopher Isbell, E. M. Lee, H. F. Morgan, and B. A. Skiff. The work was directed by R. M. Batson.

Sm 5M 2AN: Abbreviation for Saturn; satellite Mimas; 1:5,000,000 series; second edition; A, shaded relief and markings; N, feature names.

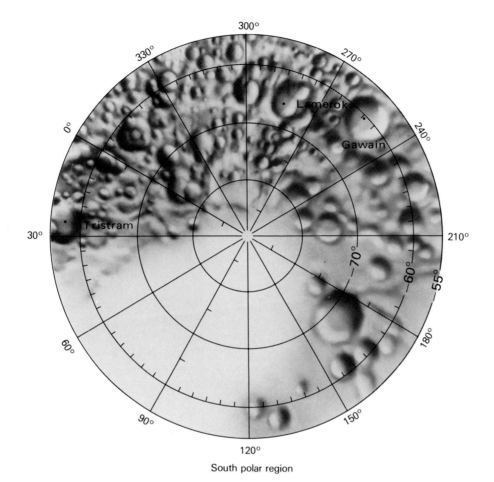

300°

330°   270°

0°   240°

                                    Lameroka

                                    Gawain

30°   210°

                                    70°
                                        60°
                                            55°
                                    180°
Tristram

60°

90°   150°

120°

South polar region

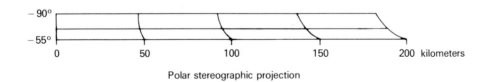

-90°

-55°

0   50   100   150   200 kilometers

Polar stereographic projection

197

Mimas

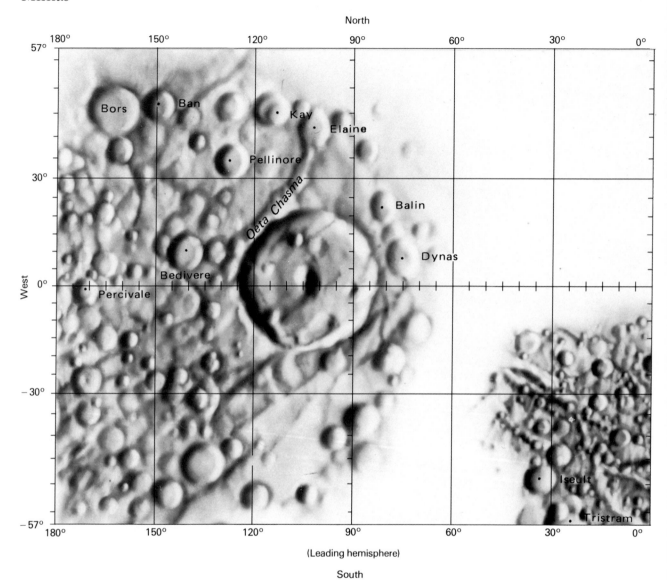

North

(Leading hemisphere)

South

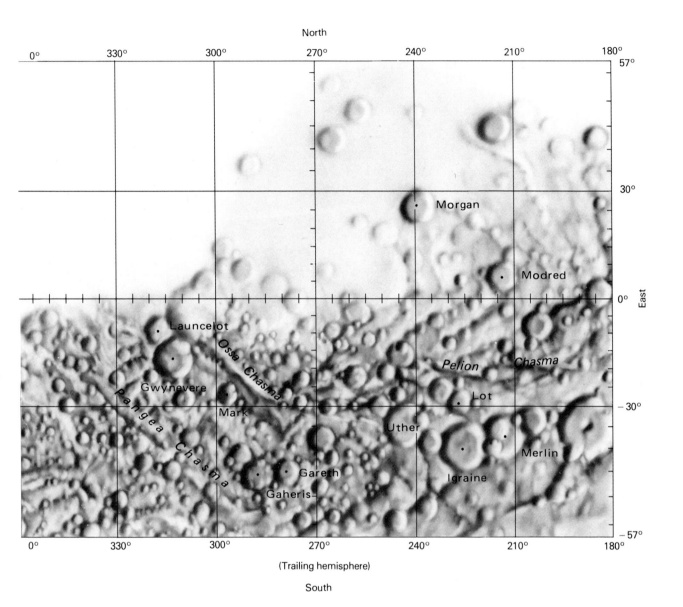

North

0°   330°   300°   270°   240°   210°   180°

57°

30°

Morgan

Modred

0°   East

Launcelot

Ossa Chasma

Pelion   Chasma

Gwynevere

Lot

Pangea Chasma

Mark

-30°

Uther

Merlin

Gareth

Igraine

Gaheris

-57°

0°   330°   300°   270°   240°   210°   180°

(Trailing hemisphere)

South

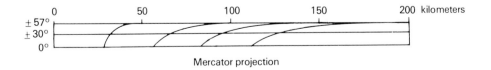

0   50   100   150   200 kilometers

±57°
±30°
0°

Mercator projection

199

Preliminary Pictorial Map of Tethys

Atlas of the Saturnian Satellites
1:10,000,000 Topographic Series
Ste 10M 2AN, 1981

This map was compiled from Voyager 1 and 2 pictures of Tethys. Map controls are based on the known position and orientation of the satellite with respect to the spacecraft at the time each picture was taken. A scaled grid, showing a perspective view of meridians and parallels, was superimposed over each picture. Map details were manually transferred, grid cell by grid cell, from the perspective view to Mercator and polar stereographic projections. Although relative accuracy of feature placement is probably within 50 kilometers over 66 percent of the map area, the tie between different views of the globe is extremely tenuous, and may be subject to interpretations other than the one shown here.

All landforms are shown as if illuminated from the west, regardless of their illumination on the photographic source material. Albedo markings visible on the Voyager pictures are also shown. It was not always possible to make distinctions between albedo and relief, either in interpretation or in portrayal. Extreme variation in image resolution precluded consistent interpretation of the pictures. Consistent portrayal was complicated by such phenomena as dark albedo deposits covering sunlit crater walls.

Names of features shown are provisional. The map projection is based on a sphere with a diameter of 1060 kilometers. The Mercator and polar stereographic projections have common scales at $\pm 56°$. Airbrush representation was made by Patricia M. Bridges. Grid, data preparation, and preliminary image processing were done by K. F. Mullins, Christopher Isbell, E. M. Lee, H. F. Morgan, and B. A. Skiff. The work was directed by R. M. Batson.

Ste 10M 2AN: Abbreviation for Saturn; satellite Tethys; 1:10,000,000 series; second edition; A, shaded relief and markings; N, feature names.

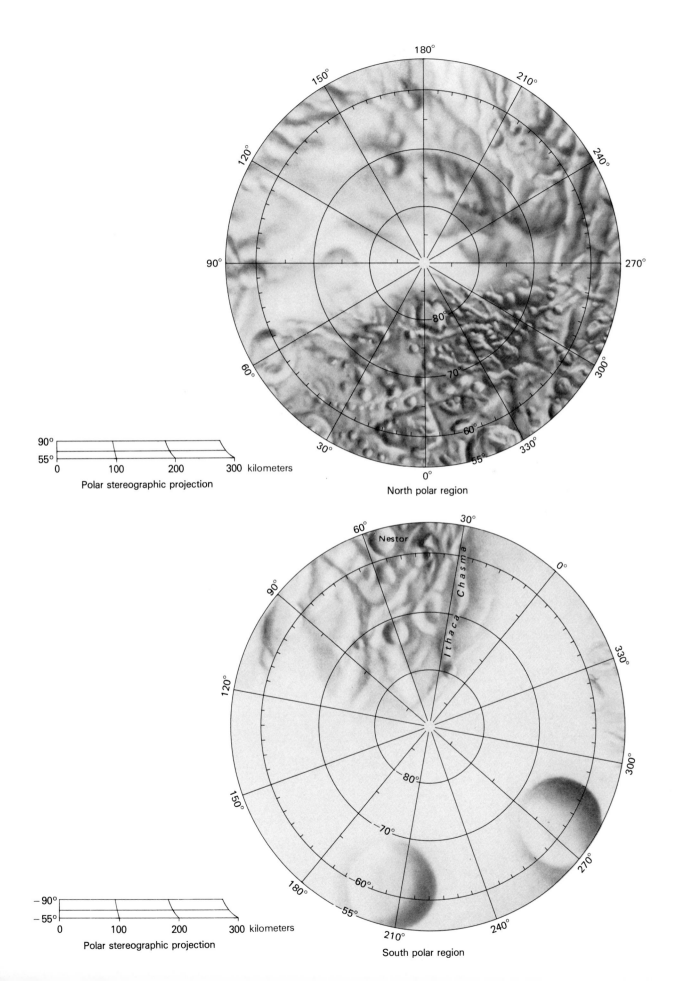

90°
55°
0   100   200   300 kilometers
Polar stereographic projection

North polar region

-90°
-55°
0   100   200   300 kilometers
Polar stereographic projection

South polar region

Tethys

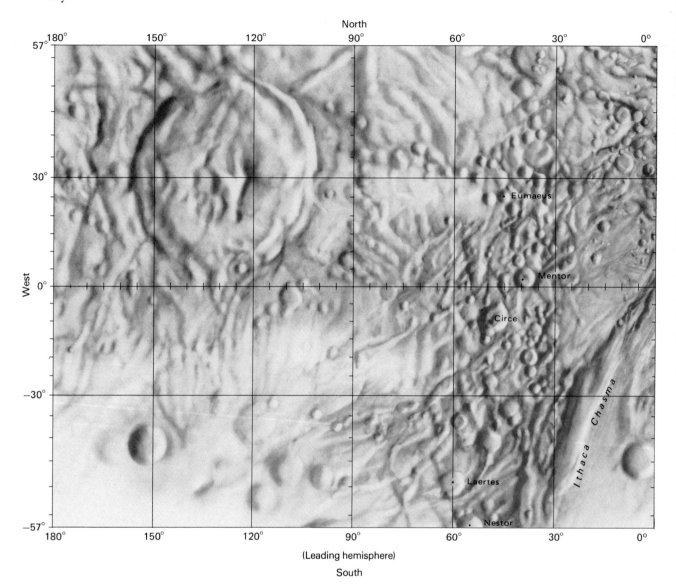

North

West

South

(Leading hemisphere)

Eumaeus

Mentor

Circe

Ithaca Chasma

Laertes

Nestor

North

0°　　　330°　　　300°　　　270°　　　240°　　　210°　　　180°

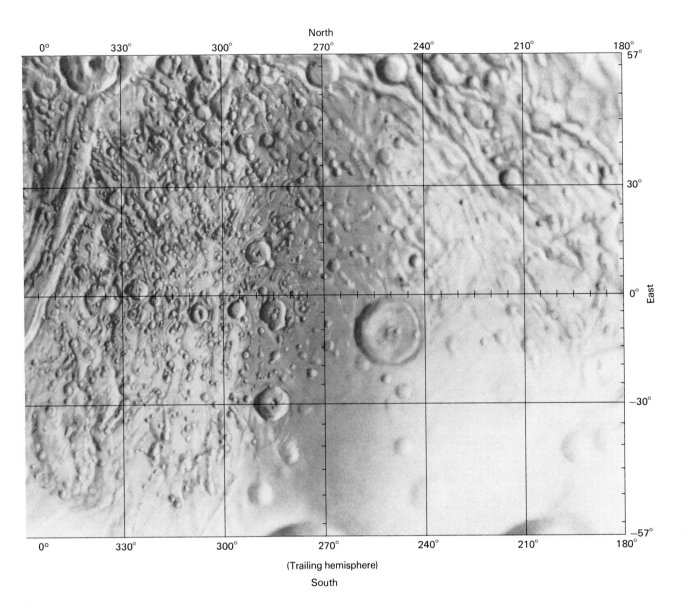

57°

30°

0°　East

−30°

−57°

0°　　　330°　　　300°　　　270°　　　240°　　　210°　　　180°

(Trailing hemisphere)

South

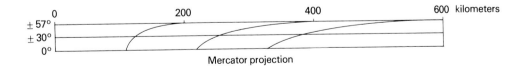

0　　　　200　　　　400　　　600　kilometers

±57°
±30°
0°

Mercator projection

203

Preliminary Pictorial Map of Dione

Atlas of the Saturnian Satellites
1:10,000,000 Topographic Series
Sd 10M 2AN, 1981

This map was compiled from Voyager 1 and 2 pictures of Dione. Map controls are based on the known position and orientation of the satellite with respect to the spacecraft at the time each picture was taken. A scaled grid, showing a perspective view of meridians and parallels, was superimposed over each picture. Map details were manually transferred, grid cell by grid cell, from the perspective view to Mercator and polar stereographic projections. Relative accuracy of feature placement is probably within 50 kilometers over 66 percent of the map area.

All landforms are shown as if illuminated from the west, regardless of their illumination on the photographic source material. Albedo markings visible on the Voyager pictures are also shown. It was not always possible to make distinctions between albedo and relief, either in interpretation or in portrayal. Extreme variation in image resolution precluded consistent interpretation of the pictures. Consistent portrayal was complicated by such phenomena as dark albedo deposits covering sunlit crater walls.

Names of features shown are provisional. The map projection is based on a sphere with a diameter of 1120 kilometers. The Mercator and polar stereographic projections have common scales at $\pm 56°$. Airbrush representation was made by Patricia M. Bridges. Grid, data preparation, and preliminary image processing were done by K. F. Mullins, Christopher Isbell, E. M. Lee, H. F. Morgan, and B. A. Skiff. The work was directed by R. M. Batson.

Sd 10M 2AN: Abbreviation for Saturn; satellite Dione; 1:10,000,000 series; second edition; A, shaded relief and markings; N, feature names.

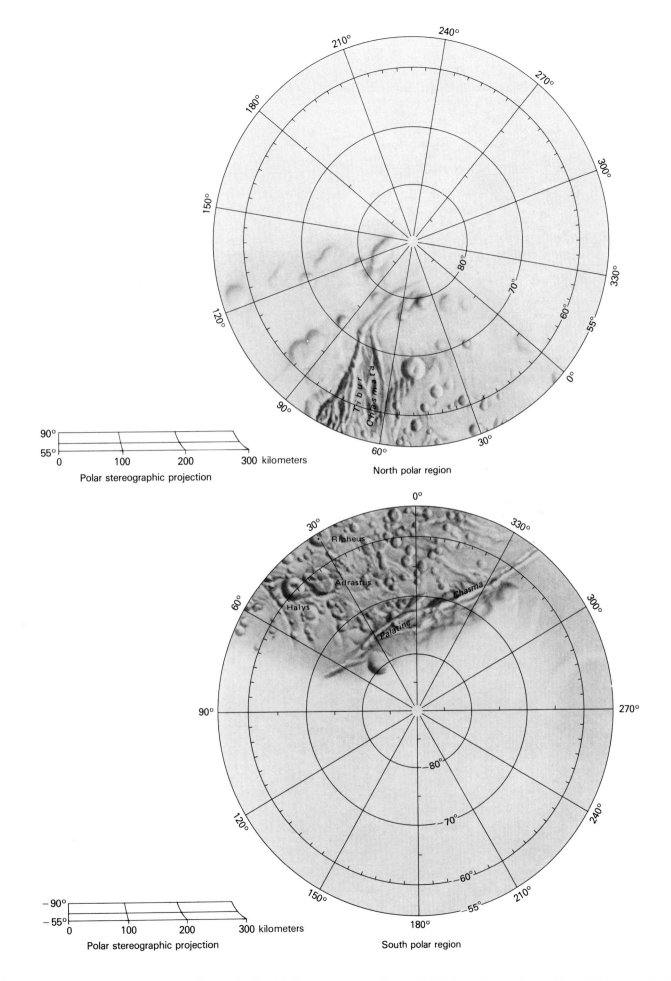

210° 240° 270°

180° 300°

150° 330°

80°
120° 70° 60° 55° 0°

Tibur Chasmata

90° 30°

60°

90°
55°
0 100 200 300 kilometers
Polar stereographic projection

North polar region

0°
30° 330°
Ripheus
Adrastus Chasma
60° 300°
Halys Palatine
90° 270°
80°
120° 70° 240°
60°
150° 55° 210°
180°

-90°
-55°
0 100 200 300 kilometers
Polar stereographic projection

South polar region

Dione

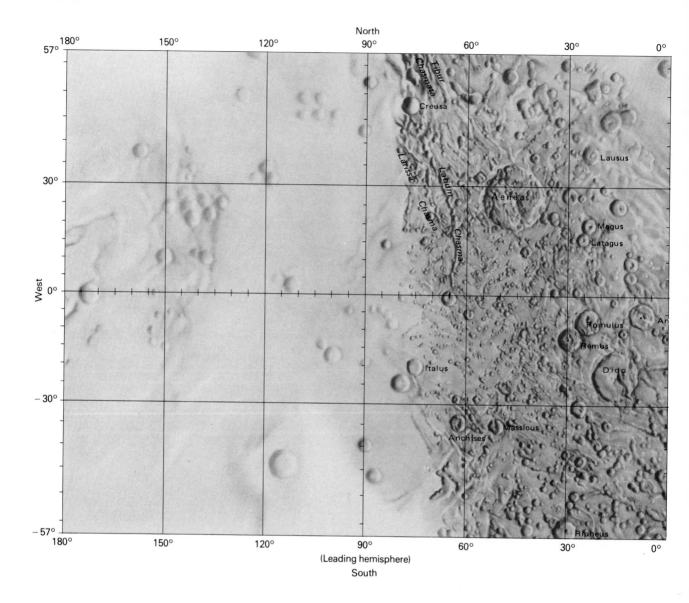

North

180°   150°   120°   90°   60°   30°   0°

Tibur
Chasmata

Creusa

Larissa

Latium

Chasma

Chasma

Lausus

Aeneas

Magus

Latagus

Romulus

An

Remus

Dido

Italus

Massicus

Anchises

Ripheus

West

57°
30°
0°
-30°
-57°

180°   150°   120°   90°   60°   30°   0°

(Leading hemisphere)

South

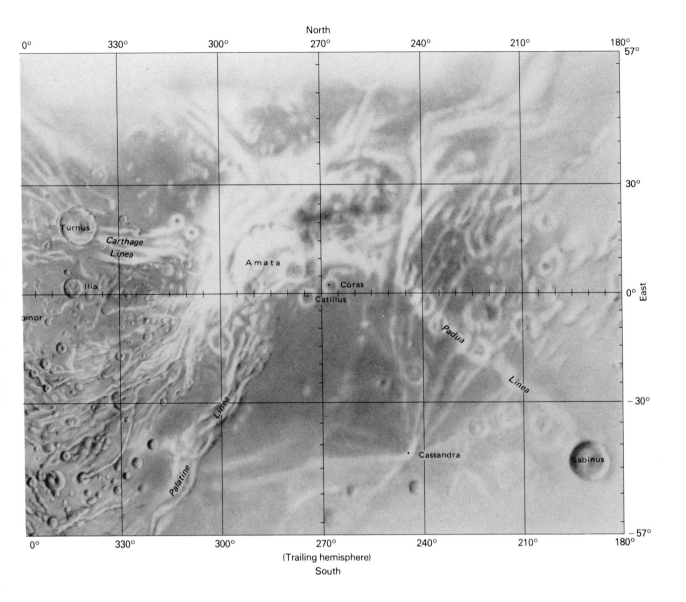

0°　　330°　　300°　　270°　　240°　　210°　　180°

57°

30°

Turnus

*Carthage
Linea*

Amata

Coras

Ilia

East

Catillus

0°

enor

Padua

Linea

−30°

Linea

Cassandra

Sabinus

Palatine

−57°

0°　　330°　　300°　　270°　　240°　　210°　　180°

(Trailing hemisphere)
South

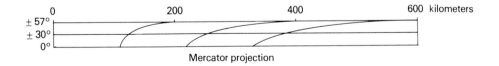

0　　　　200　　　　400　　　　600　kilometers

± 57°
± 30°
0°

Mercator projection

207

Preliminary Pictorial Map of Enceladus

Atlas of the Saturnian Satellites
1:5,000,000 Topographic Series
Se 5M 1A, 1981

This map was compiled from Voyager 1 and 2 pictures of Enceladus. Map controls are based on the known position and orientation of the satellite with respect to the spacecraft at the time each picture was taken. A scaled grid, showing a perspective view of meridians and parallels, was superimposed over each picture. Map details were manually transferred, grid cell by grid cell, from the perspective view to Mercator and polar stereographic projections. Relative accuracy of feature placement is probably within 20 kilometers over 66 percent of the map area.

All landforms are shown as if illuminated from the west, regardless of their illumination on the photographic source material. Albedo markings visible on the Voyager pictures are also shown. It was not always possible to make distinctions between albedo and relief, either in interpretation or in portrayal. Extreme variation in image resolution precluded consistent interpretation of the pictures. Consistent portrayal was complicated by such phenomena as dark albedo deposits covering sunlit crater walls.

The map projection is based on a sphere with a diameter of 500 kilometers. The Mercator and polar stereographic projections have common scales at 56°. Airbrush representation was made by Patricia M. Bridges. Grid, data preparation, and preliminary image processing were done by K. F. Mullins, Christopher Isbell, E. M. Lee, and B. A. Skiff. The work was directed by R. M. Batson.

Se 5M 1A: Abbreviation for Saturn; satellite Enceladus; 1:5,000,000 series; first edition; A, shaded relief and markings.

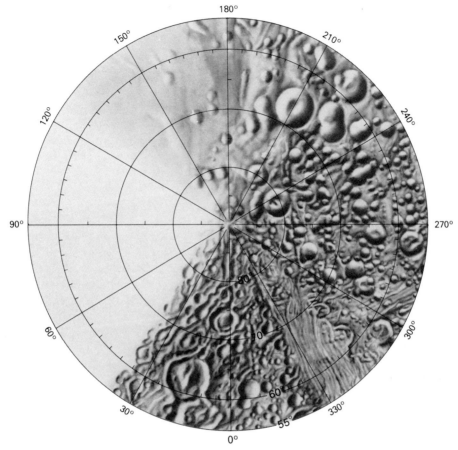

180°
210°
150°
240°
120°
90°
270°
80°
70°
60°
300°
60°
55°
30°
330°
0°

North polar region

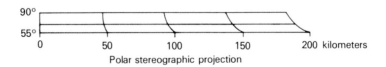

90°
55°
0   50   100   150   200 kilometers

Polar stereographic projection

Enceladus

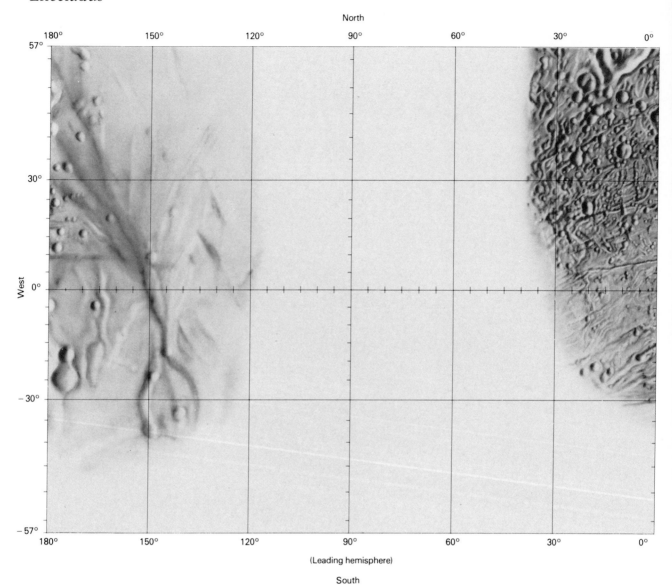

North

180°   150°   120°   90°   60°   30°   0°

(Leading hemisphere)

South

North

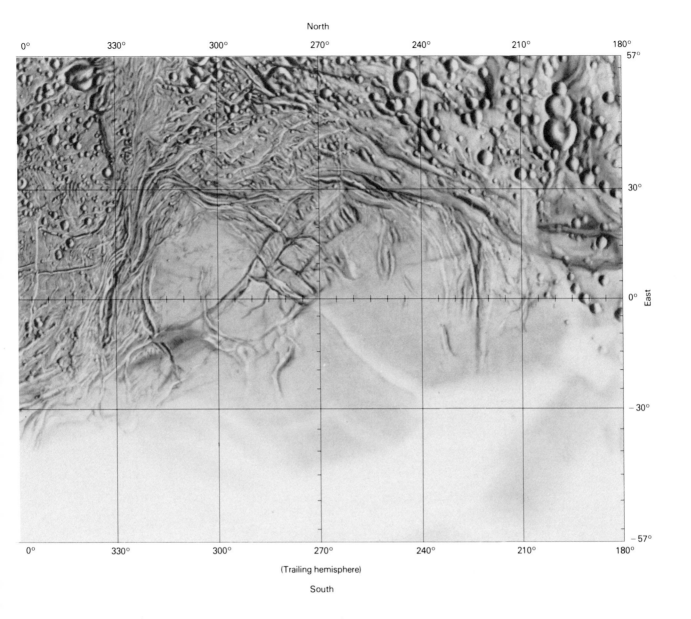

0°   330°   300°   270°   240°   210°   180°

57°

30°

0° East

−30°

−57°

0°   330°   300°   270°   240°   210°   180°

(Trailing hemisphere)

South

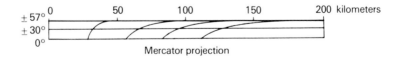

± 57°
± 30°
0°

0   50   100   150   200 kilometers

Mercator projection

211

Preliminary Pictorial Map of Iapetus

Atlas of the Saturnian Satellites
1:10,000,000 Topographic Series
Si 10M 1A, 1981

This map was compiled from Voyager 1 and 2 pictures of Iapetus. Map controls are based on the known position and orientation of the satellite with respect to the space-craft at the time each picture was taken. A scaled grid, showing a perspective view of meridians and parallels, was superimposed over each picture. Map details were manually transferred, grid cell by grid cell, from the perspective view to Mercator and polar stereo-graphic projections. Relative accuracy of feature placement is probably within 70 kilometers over 66 percent of the map area.

All landforms are shown as if illuminated from the west, regardless of their illumination on the photographic source material. Albedo markings visible on the Voyager pictures are also shown. It was not always possible to make distinctions between albedo and relief, either in interpretation or in portrayal. Extreme variation in image resolution precluded consistent interpretation of the pictures. Consistent portrayal was com-plicated by such phenomena as dark albedo deposits covering sunlit crater walls.

The map projection is based on a sphere with a diameter of 1460 kilometers. The Mer-cator and polar stereographic projections have common scales at 56°. Airbrush represen-tation was made by Jay L. Inge. Data preparation and preliminary image processing were done by K. F. Mullins, Christopher Isbell, E. M. Lee, and B. A. Skiff. The work was directed by R. M. Batson.

Si 10M 1A: Abbreviation for Saturn; satellite Iapetus; 1:10,000,000 series; first edi-tion; A, shaded relief and markings.

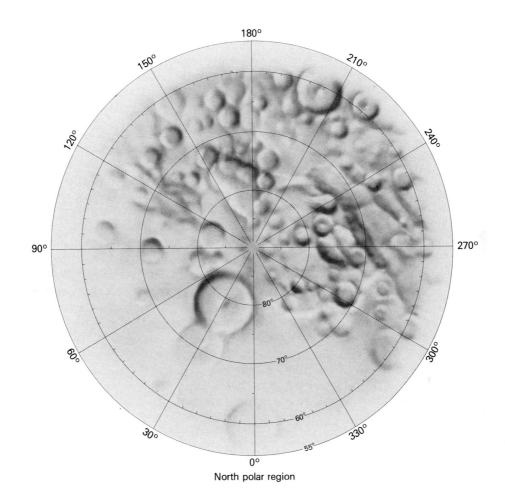

180°

150°   210°

120°   240°

90°   270°

      80°

   70°

60°   300°

      60°

30°   55°   330°

0°

North polar region

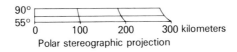

90°
55°
0   100   200   300 kilometers
Polar stereographic projection

Iapetus

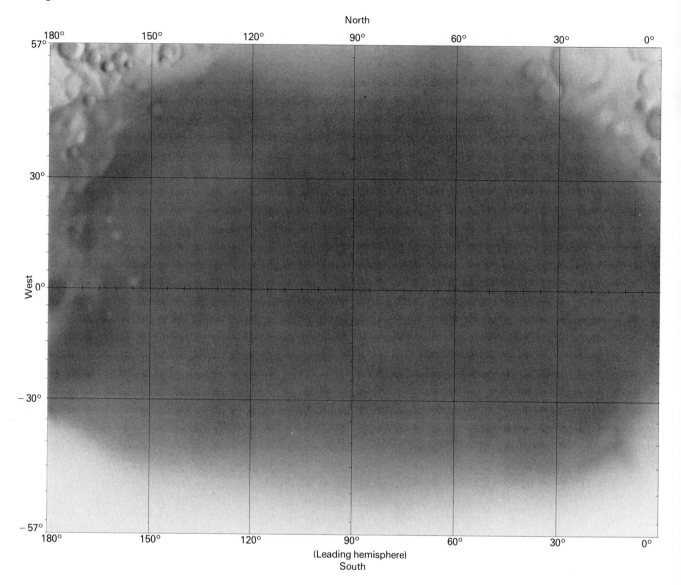

(Leading hemisphere)
South

North

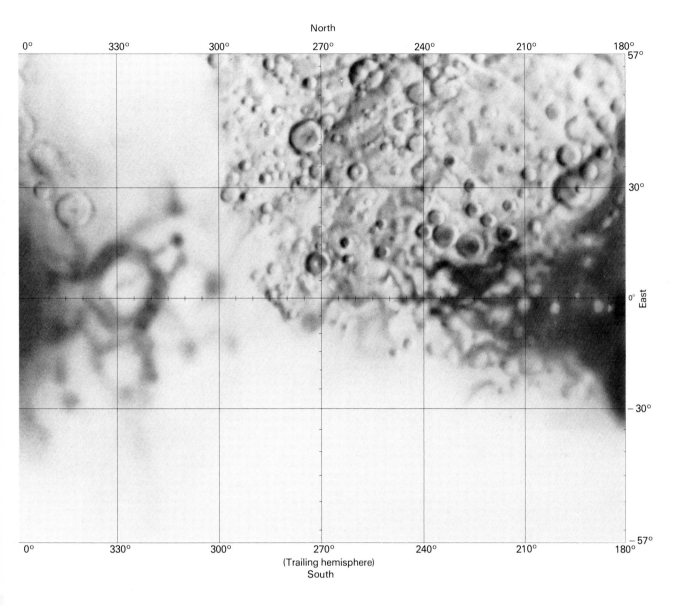

0° 330° 300° 270° 240° 210° 180°

57°

30°

0° East

−30°

−57°

0° 330° 300° 270° 240° 210° 180°

(Trailing hemisphere)
South

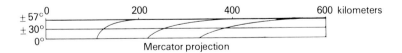

0   200   400   600 kilometers
±57°
±30°
0°
Mercator projection

Additional Reading

Technical

The Atmosphere of Titan, edited by D. M. Hunten, NASA SP–340, Washington (1973).

"The Rings of Saturn," by J. B. Pollack, *Space Science Reviews,* Volume 18, pp. 3-93 (1975).

"The Two Faces of Iapetus," by D. Morrison et al., *Icarus,* Volume 24, pp. 157-171 (1975).

Space Science Reviews, special Voyager instrumentation issues, Volume 21, No. 2, pp. 75-232 (November 1977); Volume 21, No. 3, pp. 234-376 (December 1977).

The Saturn System, edited by D. M. Hunten and D. Morrison, NASA Conference Publication 2068, Washington (1978).

"The Surfaces and Interiors of Saturn's Satellites," by D. P. Cruikshank, *Reviews of Geophysics and Space Physics,* Volume 17, pp. 165-176 (1979).

Science, special Pioneer Saturn issue, Volume 207, pp. 400-453 (25 January 1980).

Journal of Geophysical Research, special Pioneer Saturn issue, Volume 85, pp. 5651-5958 (1 November 1980).

"A First Voyager View of the Rings of Saturn," by S. A. Collins et al., *Nature,* Volume 288, pp. 439-442 (4 December 1980).

Science, special Voyager 1 issue, Volume 212, pp. 159-243 (10 April 1981).

Nature, special Voyager 1 issue, Volume 292, pp. 675-755 (20-26 August 1981).

"Planetary Rings," by P. Goldreich and S. Tremaine, *Annual Review of Astronomy and Astrophysics,* Volume 19 (1981).

Science, special Voyager 2 issue, Volume 215, (15 January 1982).

Nontechnical

The Planet Saturn, by A. F. O'D. Alexander, Faber and Faber (1962), Dover (1980).

Murmurs of Earth: The Voyager Interstellar Record, by C. Sagan et al., Random House, New York (1978).

Voyage to Jupiter, by D. Morrison and J. Samz, NASA SP–439, Washington (1980).

Pioneer—First to Jupiter, Saturn, and Beyond, by R. O. Fimmel, J. Van Allen, and E. Burgess, NASA SP–446, Washington (1980).

The New Solar System, edited by K. Beatty, B. O'Leary, and A. Chaikin, Sky Publishing Corporation, Cambridge (1981).

Voyager: Story of a Space Mission, by M. Poynter and A. L. Lane, Atheneum, New York (1981).

"Rendezvous with a Ringed Giant," by J. K. Beatty, *Sky and Telescope,* Volume 61, pp. 7-18 (January 1981).

"Voyager: Science at Saturn," by R. Beery, *Astronomy,* Volume 9, No. 2, pp. 6-22 (February 1981).

"Voyager 1 at Saturn," by R. Gore, *National Geographic,* Volume 160, No. 1, pp. 3-31 (July 1981).

"A Reporter at Large: Saturn," by H. S. Cooper, Jr., *New Yorker,* pp. 39-81 (24 August 1981).

"Saturn's Surprises," by A. P. Ingersoll, *Natural History,* Volume 90, No. 9, pp. 44-51 (September 1981).

"Secrets of Saturn," by J. Eberhart, *Science News,* Volume 120, No. 10, pp. 148-158 (5 September 1981).

"The Puzzle That Is Saturn," by M. M. Waldrop, *Science,* Volume 213, pp. 1347-1351 (18 September 1981).

"No Small Rapture — Satellite Observation of Saturn, Rings, and Satellites," by J. K. Beatty, *Science 81,* Volume 2, pp. 26-31 (January-February 1981).

"Saturn's Secrets Revealed — A Special Report," by C. Sutton, *New Scientist,* Volume 88, pp. 491-495 (20 November 1980).

Glossary

Albedo
Reflectivity; the ratio of reflected light to incident light.

Anticyclonic
Description of the sense of rotation of an atmospheric spot or storm; anticyclonic motion is clockwise in the northern hemisphere and counterclockwise in the southern hemisphere; it suggests a high pressure region.

AU
Unit of distance, equal to the distance of the Earth from the Sun, about 150 million kilometers.

Azimuth
Back-and-forth motion around a vertical axis; for instance, a measure of position around the horizon.

Backscattering
Reflecting light back in the direction of the source.

Bar
Unit of pressure (short for atmosphere), equal to the sea-level pressure of Earth's atmosphere.

Bow Shock
Outermost part of a planetary magnetosphere; the place where the supersonic flow of the solar wind is slowed to subsonic speed by the planetary magnetic field.

Co-rotating
Sharing the rotation of a planetary magnetic field, as in a co-rotating plasma.

Density Wave
A kind of wave induced in a flat plane of a resisting medium (such as the rings of Saturn) by gravitational forces, often assuming the form of a tightly wound spiral.

Eccentric
Noncircular; elliptical (applied to an orbit).

Elevation
Up-and-down motion around a horizontal axis; opposite to azimuth.

Forward Scattering
Reflecting light approximately away from the source.

Imbedded Satellite
A postulated class of satellites orbiting inside the rings, searched for but not found.

Ion
An atom or molecular fragment that has a positive electrical charge due to the loss of one or more electrons. The simplest ion is the hydrogen nucleus, a single proton.

IRIS
The Infrared Interferometer Spectrometer, one of the Voyager instruments.

Lagrangian Point
One of the solutions to the three-body problem discovered by the eighteenth century French mathematician Lagrange. The two stable Lagrangian points, L-4 and L-5, lie in the orbit of the primary body, leading and trailing it by a 60-degree arc.

Leading Side
For a satellite that keeps the same face toward the planet, the hemisphere that faces forward, into the direction of motion.

Magnetopause
The boundary of the magnetosphere, lying inside the bow shock.

Magnetosphere
The region surrounding a planet within which the planetary magnetic field dominates and charged particles can be trapped.

Plasma
A low-density gas in which the individual atoms are charged, even though the total number of positive and negative charges is equal, maintaining an overall electrical neutrality.

Plasma Wave
An oscillation or wave in a plasma that falls in the audio range of frequency.

Primitive
Used in a chemical sense, indicating an unmodified material representative of the original composition of the solar nebula.

R_S
Unit of distance equal to the radius of Saturn, 60 300 kilometers.

Radiation Belts
A common misnomer for regions of charged particles in a magnetosphere; the belts contain particles, not radiation.

Resolution
Ability to distinguish visual detail, usually expressed in terms of the size (in kilometers) of the smallest features that can be distinguished. (Here resolution is given in kilometers per line pair.)

Resonance
    A relationship in which the orbital period of one body is related to that of another by a simple integer fraction, such as 1/2, 2/3, 3/5. (see Box, page 5).

Retrograde
    Backwards; as applied to an orbit, moving in the opposite sense from the great majority of solar system bodies.

Scan Platform
    The part of the Voyager spacecraft that carries the imaging, IRIS, ultraviolet, and photopolarimeter instruments. It can be pointed to any part of the sky by rotating around two axes (azimuth and elevation).

Sequence
    A series of commands stored in the Voyager computers containing instructions for operation of the scan platform and the scientific instruments; also, the resulting observations themselves.

Shepherd
    Informal name applied to a satellite orbiting very close to a ring and thought to cause a gravitational focusing that keeps the ring particles from drifting in the direction of the shepherd satellite.

Solar Nebula
    The large cloud of gas and dust from which the Sun and planets condensed 4.6 billion years ago.

Solar Wind
    The charged particles (plasma), primarily protons and electrons, that are emitted from the Sun and stream outward throughout the solar system at speeds of hundreds of kilometers per second.

Spokes
    Informal name given to the transitory radial features in the B Ring, appearing dark when seen in backscattered light and bright in forward scattered light.

Stratosphere
    The cold region of a planetary atmosphere above the convecting regions (the troposphere), usually without vertical motions but sometimes exhibiting strong horizontal jet streams.

Telemetry
    Radio signals from a spacecraft used to encode and transmit data to a ground station.

Torus
    Solid geometrical figure with the shape of a doughnut or innertube, as in the toroidal hydrogen cloud surrounding Saturn near the orbit of Titan.

Trailing Side
    For a satellite that keeps the same face toward the planet, the hemisphere that faces backwards, away from the direction of motion.

Troposphere
    The lower regions of a planetary atmosphere where convection (rising warm air and falling cool air) keeps the gas mixed and maintains a steady increase of temperature with depth. Most clouds are in the troposphere.

Index

About
the
Author

Professor of astronomy at the University of Hawaii, David Morrison specializes in planetary science. His research has involved observational studies of the planets and their satellites as well as smaller solar-system bodies such as asteroids and comets, performed primarily with the optical and infrared telescopes at the Mauna Kea Observatory in Hawaii. He has published more than 80 journal papers, and edited books on asteroids, the Saturn system, and the Jovian satellites. He has also written numerous magazine articles on astro-nomical subjects and, with Jane Samz, was the co-author of *Voyage to Jupiter* (NASA SP–439).

Currently a member of the Imaging Team for Voyager, Dr. Morrison has been part of several prior NASA missions, beginning with the Mariner 10 mission to Venus and Mercury. He has also served two tours of duty at NASA Head-quarters, most recently as Acting Deputy Associate Administrator for the Office of Space Science. He's 41, energetic, and lives in Honolulu with his wife Janet.